MULTI-LEVEL LEVEL MARKETING

*The Definitive Guide to America's
Top MLM Companies*

MULTI-LEVEL MARKETING

The Definitive Guide to America's Top MLM Companies

THE SUMMIT GROUP

1227 West Magnolia, Suite 500, Fort Worth, Texas 76104

99 98 97 96 95   5 4 3 2

Library of Congress Cataloging-in-Publication Data

Multi-level marketing: the definitive guide to America's top MLM companies.
     p.cm.
    ISBN 1-56530-059-9: $24.95
     1. Multilevel marketing—United States—Directories. 2. Direct selling—United States—Directories. I. Summit Group. II. Title: Multilevel marketing.
HF5415.126.M86 1994
381'.1—dc20
                                     94-2220
                                        CIP

TABLE OF CONTENTS

INTRODUCTION

BY DIRK JOHNSON

DIRK JOHNSON IS EXECUTIVE VICE PRESIDENT OF UPLINE FINANCIAL PRESS

Are you completely satisfied with your job? Do you have all of the money you will ever want or need? Are the hours you work the ideal hours for you? Is your lifestyle the lifestyle you would choose if you had a free wish?

If you answered "yes" to all of the above questions, this book probably can't do much for you. But, if you answered "no" to even one of them, this book could be the best investment you ever made.

It's a book about business—*your* business. But more than that, it's a book about *you*—how *you* can become an entrepreneur, an independent business person, regardless of your current financial and personal situation.

This book opens the doors to the world of MLM (multi-level marketing) also known as network marketing. Network marketing is a low-investment, high-return strategy for making money and achieving dreams.

You've probably heard of MLM, because it's a booming industry. Chances are that you've even looked at an MLM opportunity. But the chances are even better that you have never been given the opportunity to look over the industry as a whole, because information about this potentially very lucrative industry is difficult to come by.

Very simply, MLM, or network marketing, is a distribution system, or form of marketing, which moves goods and/or services from the manufacturer to the consumer through a "network" of independent contractors. It's a system that cuts out the "middle-men."

We are all familiar with retail stores. In fact, many people think of the retail store, or the point-of-purchase store as the only form of product distribution. We are also familiar with direct mail (also called by many "junk mail") and direct mail catalogs. And we all know about the door-to-door salesperson, although this person is rapidly disappearing. The door-to-door salesperson engages in "direct selling."

All three of these—point-of-purchase, direct mail, and direct selling—are means of bringing a product or service from the manufacturer to the consumer—and in this respect none of them differs from MLM.

But, multi-level marketing differs as much from direct sales as it does from point-of-purchase, or retail store, sales. And the difference lies not in what is sold, but in how it is sold.

MLM began as a means to move personal care items, nutritional products, and household care products. But during the past thirty or forty years, MLM has undergone tremendous changes. It is now possible to purchase a wide range of goods and services through MLM—you can buy a Cadillac, a Magnavox computer, a Xerox machine, a Seiko watch, a Botany 500 suit, a ticket on American Airlines, or food for your dog and litter for your cat through MLM; you can even acquire your long-distance telephone service through network marketing.

MLM has stood the test. People used to laugh at Ray Kroc's offer of a McDonalds franchise. In those days, franchising was considered a fringe form of marketing. Today, franchising is one of the most successful forms of point-of-purchase marketing in the world. In fact, the success rates of franchises outstrip all other forms of point-of-purchase sales ventures.

At this very moment, MLM is making the same breakthroughs that franchising made two decades ago. Major American and Japanese corporations are entering the MLM distribution system at breakneck speed, some by supplying products to the system, others by subsidizing or starting new network marketing companies, and still others by purchasing existing MLM companies.

The time is ripe for an MLM revolution.

This book will introduce you to nearly fifty MLMs which have been in business for more than five years, as well as thirteen which have been in business for fewer than five years.

In this book, the former executive editor of the Washington Post and the San Francisco Examiner, whose staff won a Pulitzer prize in investigative journalism, gives you an extended overview of the network marketing industry.

And, you will find many in-depth articles, written by MLM professionals, to help you get started, and to help you succeed, in your own network marketing business.

Here's to your success! ∎

THE TIME IS RIGHT FOR AN MLM REVOLUTION

BY LARRY KRAMER

PART 1: OYSTERS OR PEARLS

LARRY KRAMER IS THE FORMER EXECUTIVE EDITOR OF THE SAN FRANCISCO EXAMINER, AND THE WASHINGTON POST. HIS STAFF AT THE EXAMINER WON A PULITZER PRIZE IN JOURNALISM, AND THE SELDON RING INVESTIGATIVE REPORTING AWARD, AMONG OTHERS. HE HOLDS AN MBA FROM HARVARD AND IS CURRENTLY PRESIDENT OF HIS OWN COMPANY DATASPORT, INC.

The stories never stop. From the tales of legendary Amway distributors who made millions for themselves and others, to the horror stories of couples who gave up well-paying jobs only to lose everything when they went in business together as Meadow Fresh Farms distributors.

And guess what, they are both true. Just as in all walks of life, there are successes and failures in multi-level marketing.

Just as in life, your own experience, if you choose to take a chance at MLM, will likely fall somewhere in between.

One thing is certain, the economic climate today is very conducive to network marketing. It is a time when low-cost opportunities to make extra cash are needed like they have never been needed before.

People are hurting. Layoffs are running at record rates for people at all levels of the economic strata. Many are looking not only for new jobs, but for ways to supplement income in order to build up some savings in case they are next to lose their jobs.

"MLM is available to everybody," says Sandy Elsberg, who is by any measure a smashing success as one of the top ten performers in Omnitrition, a health/skin/hair care company in the network marketing business. "All you need is the hunger and willingness to change. There's no franchise fee, but there are people willing to show you the way to succeed, if you want to work for it."

Still Elsberg and most people in the business agree that success doesn't come to everyone in the world of MLM. "The success rate is the same as in all walks of life," she says. "There are three pearls in every one hundred oysters. Most people would rather sit in front of a TV."

According to several people in the networking business, around ten percent of those who enter the world of MLM wind up successful at it. Even the brashest of firms rarely boast of success rates higher than ten percent. "We are seeing a ten percent success rate," says Linda Marshall, president of Elysee, "and that is much higher than average."

In fact, according to *Kiplingers Personal Finance Magazine*, the percentage of MLM distributors who drop out, "is high, at many companies hitting eighty to ninety percent annually."

Combined Goods and Services Moved Through This Book's MLM's

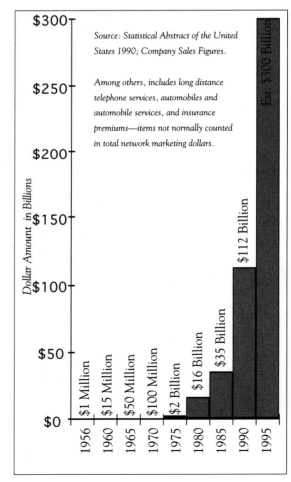

Source: Statistical Abstract of the United States 1990; Company Sales Figures.

Among others, includes long distance telephone services, automobiles and automobile services, and insurance premiums—items not normally counted in total network marketing dollars.

Joe Hair, dean of the marketing department at Louisiana State University, says that turnover rate is at least 70 percent. He also told the *Baton Rouge Business Report* in a recent interview that only 1 or 2 percent of all multi-level marketing distributors ever earn significant income.

Hair did say that many successful converts to direct sales are frequently people who already have some standing in their communities. People who have been in politics or highly respected professions like medicine can do well. "Esteemed members of the community have high visibility and high credibility and can sell more easily," he said.

But why would a doctor or other professional get into network marketing? Like everyone else, professionals suffer during a recession.

"The thing that's attractive to professionals is with two to ten hours a week of discretionary time, you can accrue income of two to five thousand dollars a month," said Dr. Allan Allbritton, a veterinarian in Gonzales, Louisiana, who moonlights as an Amway distributor. "This would attract anyone."

Joe Grisaffe, who had to close his realty company during tough times, echoed Allbritton's comments. Grisaffe said he was surprised to see so many professionals in multi-level marketing when he joined NSA, a large network marketing company that sells water and air treatment systems.

"Keep in mind that when a doctor is not at his practice, he's not generating any income. He's out of business," he told the *Business Report*. "If a dentist is not in somebody's mouth, he's not producing any income. With this, all they've got to do is pass along a video. "

Besides, the price of finding out that you aren't right for MLM doesn't have to be very high. Usually the cost of getting started is minimal — from twenty to five hundred dollars for most firms — and one can figure out quickly if they are comfortable putting in the time and energy needed to do direct selling and recruiting.

Is Your Job Secure?

During the past year alone, 375,000 jobs have been lost from U.S. companies. And, according to the chairman of a leading Chicago-based out placement firm quoted in *Time Magazine* recently, fewer than twenty-five percent of those firms have completed the painful job of downsizing.

And that's not the worst of it. Those jobs will likely never come back. As companies trim staffs and approach former levels of profitability, they are not returning to previous staffing levels —preferring instead to run leaner and meaner as a cushion during bad economic times.

So the time-honored search for the American dream of long-term security for those who work

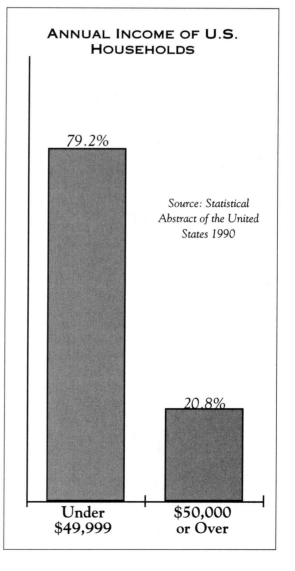

ANNUAL INCOME OF U.S. HOUSEHOLDS

79.2%

Source: Statistical Abstract of the United States 1990

20.8%

Under $49,999 $50,000 or Over

As companies trim staffs and approach former profitability, they are preferring to run leaner and meaner.

hard has become increasingly elusive. The foundation that has held so many American families together - the job security of the breadwinner - is quickly becoming a memory.

Layoffs are not limited to aging rust-belt dinosaurs, either. Go-go companies like Apple Computer, Inc. with its groundbreaking programs that put the employee first with everything from daycare centers to generous benefits plans, have had to eat crow and close domestic plants and lay off staff, even as sales approached record levels.

The damage cuts across industry lines. In a one year period ending in June, 1992, the number of jobs dropped in just about every industry you can think of: Electronics jobs down 3 percent (fifty thousand jobs lost); Construction down 2 percent (1.1 million jobs lost); Food down 0.5 percent (nine thousand jobs); Retailing down 1 percent (one hundred and fifty thousand jobs).

**MAKING LESS
AND ENJOYING IT LESS**

For those lucky enough to keep jobs, there has been an accelerating trend toward cuts in benefits and wage increases. After inflation, the average U.S. worker is making 14 percent less than he or she did in 1979.

During the past two years alone, The median family income has actually dropped from $37,579 to $35,939, according to the Census Bureau.

Traditional perks are also falling by the wayside one by one, again increasing the need of the employee to dig deeper into his or her own pocket to maintain a certain lifestyle. From company cars and club memberships to free employee parking and even personal use of frequent flyer miles (witness the recent first-ever prosecution of a former employee for "stealing" frequent flyer miles from his company) the advantages and rewards of working as a long-time employee of one company are gradually dwindling.

All of this has led to an unprecedented level of dissatisfaction by employees with their work situation. And if you don't think people are unhappy with their jobs, check out this stat from a twelve-year study done by the Bureau of Labor Statistics: By age twenty-nine, the average worker has held nearly eight jobs and worked an average of thirty-six weeks a year since the age of eighteen.

And, naturally, with people moving more and more from one job to another, fewer of the traditional long-term benefits, like retirement plans, will be secured by those people.

CAN YOU RETIRE?

To make matters worse, companies are continuing the trend of relieving themselves of the burden of providing a future nestegg for their employees. For example, virtually all new companies and many established ones are leaving pensions out of their benefits packages and demanding at least some employee contribution to increasingly expensive health plans—leaving the door open to shift more of that burden to the employee in the future. Where they do have 401K and other retirement-related plans, employers' programs generally include or depend upon employee contributions as their foundation.

All of this comes against the backdrop of what the increasing cost of retirement will be for today's workers.

Many of those facing retirement are staring yet another new reality in the face: The decline in interest rates and investment revenue has already

HOW WELL WILL PEOPLE BE PREPARED TO RETIRE? THAT QUESTION IS FUELING THE MLM REVOLUTION.			
ASSUMPTION FOR CURRENT ANNUAL INCOME	**$20,000**	**$35,000**	**$60,000**
Current Age: 25			
Retirement Income Needed To Stay Par:	$141,000	$246,000	$422,000
Income Producing Assets @ 10% ROI			
Needed to Produce Equivalent Retirement Income:	$1.4 Mil	$2.46 Mil	$4.22 Mil
Necessary To Save Per Year To Get There:	$35,000	$62,000	$106,000
Current Age: 35			
Retirement Income Needed To Stay Par:	$86,000	$151,000	$259,000
Income Producing Assets @ 10% ROI			
Needed to Produce Equivalent Retirement Income:	$860,000	$1.51 Mil	$2.59 Mil
Necessary To Save Per Year To Get There:	$29,000	$50,000	$86,000
Current Age: 45			
Retirement Income Needed To Stay Par:	$53,000	$93,000	$159,000
Income Producing Assets @ 10% ROI			
Needed to Produce Equivalent Retirement Income:	$530,000	$930,000	$1.59 Mil
Necessary To Save Per Year To Get There:	$27,000	$47,000	$80,000

begun to squeeze people who thought they had enough squirreled away for a comfortable retirement.

"I'll be retiring soon and I don't think retirement will be enough," said Melissa Anderson of Columbus, Ohio. She and her husband James were interviewed by a Business-First of Columbus while they were going up and down the aisles at the "Own Your Own Business Expo" there last year.

"We're here because we know there are things that we could be taking advantage of but we're not."

There is evidence that the Andersons' concern is real. The large stock market runup of the 1980's left many pension funds fat and happy. In 1987, according to Buck Consultants Inc. in *Business Week*, 93 percent of all pension funds were fully funded, and the pension fund assets of major corporations equaled 170 percent of their obligations. Now, those numbers have dropped to 79 percent and 129 percent respectively. And with interest rates down, pension plans can no longer rely on inflation to lessen the burden of those future obligations.

WHERE DID ALL OUR TIME GO?

Recent studies have also shown a dramatic reversal in what had been a trend to more leisure time. For years unions fought for shorter hours in the working day and even for fewer days in the work week. But a few studies released over the past couple of years revealed that people are working longer hours than ever. "The twin indicators of how long and hard people work . . . reached record levels in recent months," said *Time* last July.

Even though not all of those additional hours are spent in the office, the traditional employee is taking more and more work home. The pressure to work hard to keep one's job or to get ahead in companies with fewer and fewer advancement opportunities has been enormous.

Fear of economic trouble runs deeper than just the traditional full-time workforce. One of the side effects of prolonged tough times is that even our children begin to believe that it takes a

second job or special effort to be able to get the things you want.

A recent *Newsweek* article pointed out that 47 percent of male and 36 percent of female high school seniors with part-time jobs are putting in more than 20 hours a week in those jobs.

"After-school jobs have become a major force in teen life. More than five million kids between twelve and seventeen now work, according to Simmons Market Research Bureau," *Newsweek* reports. "Teens are twice as likely to work as they were in 1950."

In many ways the recession is creating a huge potential workforce for multilevel marketing firms.

The overall message is a clear one: We have come to a point in America where virtually everyone has to worry about his or her future. There is no more security. If you are going to have to work long hours into the night, why not work for yourself?

Long-time employees, especially those who thought they had paid their dues and were owed a secure future by their employers, are traditionally risk-averse and loathe to take the kind of chances associated with going into business for themselves. And the disaster stories of those who do strike out on their own are legion.

A recent *Wall Street Journal* front page article chronicled the enormous frustration and failure levels that confronted a dozen Crown Zellerbach Corp. executives who took buyouts and invested in opening up AlphaGraphics Inc. quick-printing franchises. Finding life out from under the corporate umbrella more difficult than they imagined, many spent most or all of their large severance bonuses in failed attempts to launch their new businesses. Only one of the twelve still maintains his franchise.

Against that backdrop, we are seeing a growing number of people turning to the world of multilevel marketing, where the cost of trying something new is relatively low, but the potential rewards are high. Seeking the opportunity to increase or supplement income through openings in the growing field of network marketing often can be done in conjunction with another job. In

We have come to the point where everybody has to worry about his or her future. There is no more security.

fact, many MLM companies encourage their distributors to start out doing it part-time.

Jeffrey Babener, a partner in a Portland law firm who specializes in MLM issues, predicts it will always be a predominantly part-time industry. He estimates that the average MLMer should be able to make $300-$500 a month on a part-time basis.

Leonard Clements, an industry observer and publisher of *MarketWave*, a newsletter that focuses on the MLM industry, told *New Business Opportunities Magazine* that a survey of one hundred of his readers revealed that the vast majority of them were looking to supplement incomes, not replace them.

PART 2: MARKETING DYNAMICS

The business of merchandising has experienced nothing less than a double-barreled earthquake: 1) the drop in spending power of the American consumers and 2) the startling dismantling of the traditional retailing giants.

The dramatic changes in retailing came because of several factors, including the high cost of leveraged buyouts, the failure of the consuming public to finance those buyouts, and the growth of competitors who have redirected the huge amounts of money traditional retailers spent on advertising and promotion.

A survey of the various types of merchandising over the past few years shows that each has its

Americans spent an average of four hours a month in malls in 1990, down from twelve hours a decade earlier.

ups and downs, but that there is a pattern to the successes: Those who get closest to the customer get the best shot at that customer.

THE DECLINE AND FALL OF THE DEPARTMENT STORE

One by one great metropolitan retailers have disappeared or fallen on hard times: Gimbels, Bambergers, Liberty House, Federated Stores, Sears, Macy's, etc.

In addition, many of the great discounters like East Coast behemoths E.J. Korvettes and Alexanders have collapsed.

Of the fifteen largest U.S. retailing companies, at least half are having serious problems. And, according to *The Economist*, more than 17,000 stores went bankrupt in the United States in 1991 alone.

The largest of them all, Sears Roebuck, is desperately trying to remake itself and shedding large parts of its business in a desperate attempt to refocus on the retail market that has begun to slip through its fingers.

In early 1992, Sears announced that it was cutting 7,000 jobs. Others, like Macy's and Carter Hawley Hale, which operate many of the biggest department stores in the country—household names for decades—have had to go through gut-wrenching bankruptcy proceedings.

Macy's has announced a five-year recovery plan that will involve huge cuts in advertising budgets and several other cost-cutting actions to offset dropping volume.

People who do go to department stores are spending less. The average credit card transaction at U.S. department stores dropped 4 percent between 1990 and 1991 according to a survey by *Chain Store Age* magazine.

In an article for *Business Horizons* magazine, author Richard Rauch detailed a series of changes that have led to the worsening plight of the traditional department stores and supermarkets, both of which he said "are slowly slipping into extinction."

"Changes in the demographic, economic, physical, technological, political, and cultural environments have rendered these institutions obsolete as the American shopper's lifestyle has changed," said Rauch.

He said most department stores were misusing or neglecting current technologies and available expertise.

"They are exacerbating the situation by utilizing poorly trained and motivated personnel who adversely affect their merchandising presentations, human interactions, and product logistics," he added.

On top of that, it's just a bigger hassle to go to a store these days. Traffic and parking problems have begun to push consumers to try direct marketing alternatives.

But the big stores have contributed to their own spiral.

"The store atmosphere created by management decisions reducing the number of slower-moving specialty items available to the shopper, lowering the amount of personnel serving the customer, and the resultant longer lines at the checkouts are enticing shoppers to investigate systems like Videotex with interactive cable TV and personal computers," Rausch observed. "The new opportunities offered by direct marketers' toll-free numbers available for conveniently ordering merchandise at night or on Sunday are adding to the shopper's dilemma of a trade-off of 'high touch' for 'high tech.'"

The problems with decreasing department store sales have also led to problems in another great American institution: the mall.

According to *The Wall Street Journal*, Americans spent an average of four hours a month in malls in 1990, down from twelve hours a decade earlier. Worse yet, 25 percent of those who do go to the mall only stop in one of the anchor department stores, making things even worse for the smaller stores in those malls.

Average vacancy rates in malls have risen to 12 percent, and sales per square foot have dropped 17 percent since their peak in 1978.

BUYING THROUGH THE MAIL BOX

The pattern repeats for many catalog and direct response houses, though certainly not all. The $165 million consumer electronics catalog firm DAK is in bankruptcy protection. Other legendary catalog houses like 47th Street Photo in New York, Haverhills, Joan Cook, and The Company Store are in some form of reorganization. Sears has dicontinued its mail order catalog.

The Sharper Image, the bible of the Yuppie Culture, has also seen some hard times. With earnings off considerably in the past few years, the San Francisco-based catalog and specialty store chain has begun to totally rethink its concept.

Gone are the scores of high-priced electric gadgets. In their place on The Sharper Image shelves across the county are ties, leather jackets and Sandy Koufax autographed baseballs. Perhaps the customers will come. But it's still too soon to tell.

The catalog business in general is rapidly becoming saturated. And catalogs now run the gamut from the cheap and tacky to extremely elegant. Among the recent entries are the very top museums from around the country who have extended the sale of exclusive items based on their collections into a booming catalog business.

Retailers, like home merchandise companies Williams-Sonoma and Hold Everything, are building complimentary catalog businesses to reach customers who don't come to the store.

The catalog business is becoming saturated. Catalogs run from cheap and tacky to extremely elegant.

Catalogs appeal to certain types of people, many of whom are also potential MLM customers. There are people who don't live near stores that carry the items in the catalog. There are others who have been turned off by the crowds and deteriorating service at stores. There are people who can't easily get around, or just don't feel like it.

But as you can tell by just looking in your own mail box, the catalog business has become highly competitive. Maine outdoors retailer and mail order legend L.L. Bean, for example, has seen aggressive competition from upstarts like Eddie Bauer and Lands End.

Those three are all high-quality retailers who know that there are significant sales to be made right in the home.

In boom industries where new products come on line daily, like computer software or peripherals, mail order catalogs are the fastest and most successful way to reach customers with news of the latest offerings.

The MacWarehouse is a good example of a catalog operation that made its name and reputation by selling only Mac-related products at the lowest possible price and promising next day delivery. Its value to customers is obvious - they don't have to see all the products made for PC's to find what's available to MAC and they know the price is right and the products are the latest available.

The MacWarehouse catalog is as eagerly anticipated as any other monthly magazine in some households.

Now, of course, there are several imitators coming along with similar offerings and many of the same attributes of the MacWarehouse.

WHO NEEDS ADVERTISING ANYWAY?

There is substantial growth in non-advertising supported sales. Even in retailing itself, huge chunks of business have shifted to discount "clubs" like Costco and Price Club, which do no advertising and project a no-frills image, giving the customer the feeling that he or she is not paying for huge ad budgets or fancy store interiors.

The Price Club, often cited as the pacesetter in the $23 billion membership warehouse business, had 1991 sales of $6.6 billion, up 25 percent over the year before.

Even the so-called warehouse store industry is seeing some cooling off. Competition is on the upswing, and the major growth now appears only in new markets where there were no such stores before.

And, many of these stores have had to increase their product lines to include everything from high-priced office equipment, computers, and even pianos to meats and baked goods to fuel growth in total sales.

Many traditional stores are going into the discounting business with new lines of stores, in much the same way Filenes, the noted New England Retailer, launched Filenes' Basement years ago. They used to use such outlets to move merchandise that stayed on the shelves of the main store too long. But increasingly such outlets, like The Nordstrom Rack, are selling lower priced merchandise sold only at that outlet. They found they had to stock some lines in order to insure the fact that anyone coming to these outlet stores would find something in his/her size.

THE INFOMERCIAL

At the opposite end of the spectrum is the Infomercial. Instead of no advertising, the consumer gets nothing but advertising for thirty-minute shots. Here the merchandiser can be saving money by cutting out the retail outlet completely.

The half-hour infomercial can now be found at almost any time of the day, on almost any kind of television station. An infomerical is really nothing more than a very long commercial, often made to appear like traditional programming as part of the "sell."

Ross Perot elevated the infomercial to new heights during his presidential campaign. In fact, Perot's half-hour paid segments drew huge ratings and were credited with giving his view maximum exposure in a very short period of time.

Of the estimated $200 million in infomercials that will air on television this year, according to *Western Advertising News*, most will be the work of entrepreneurs and will be low cost efforts that dominate late-night television.

Major corporations are beginning to see the value in infomercials. In February 1992, Volvo North America aired a 30-minute safety infomercial in Los Angeles. And high-end exercise equipment makers of NordicTrak and Soloflex are heavily into infomercial marketing.

General Motors used a "documercial" - an infomercial by another name - to unveil its long-awaited Saturn line of cars last year. Time-Warner regularly uses slick infomercials to sell its historical music collections.

Western Advertising News reported earlier this year that AT&T and GTE are looking into infomercials to sell some of their more complex products, like electronic answering services, caller ID's, and the "smart phone."

Infomercials generated an estimated $500 million worth of sales in 1990, according to Jeffrey Knowles, general counsel for the National Infomercial Marketing Association. He told *Marketing News* that the volume of sales through infomercials has "doubled every year since 1984."

The entire infomercial industry was born that year when the Justice Department ruled that the television industry's self-imposed limit on the number of commercial minutes per broadcast hour was in violation of the antitrust laws. That ruling opened the floodgates to commercials to run longer than the minute or two to which they had been restricted.

Following a stampede of dubious ads, often disguised to look like legitimate programming, the infomercial industry still has some work to do to clean up its image. In a business loaded with "how-to-make-a-fortune-in-real-estate-overnight" hucksters and all kinds of 900-number advice lines, there are still credibility problems to overcome.

"Infomercials haven't started out very well," said Barry J. Cutler, director of the Federal Trade Commission's Bureau of Consumer Protection in an interview in the *Philadelphia Business Journal.* "But they may become the electronic mail-order industry of the future."

LET'S TALK SHOPPING

Also booming is home shopping over computer lines or phone lines. The Home Shopping Network now reaches 62 million households 24 hours a day on television. It claims annual sales of more than $1 billion and profits of $66 million. The customer sees something on TV that he or she wants and all that is needed is a quick phone call to have the goods on the way.

Another method of shopping at home is growing along with the number of home computers entering the market. Interactive networks, like Compuserve and Prodigy, offer electronic catalogs. More than 50,000 products and services are available through Prodigy, along with electronic bulletin boards and classified advertising.

With the number of home computers growing again, Prodigy's market continues to grow, too. The base charge is only about ten dollars a month, so the cost of browsing through the many shopping alternatives on the network is practically nothing.

Once again, many mainline retailers are jumping into Prodigy and other on-line services to try to protect themselves from the erosion of their customer base. J.C. Penney, Sears, and literally hundreds of different specialty retailers offer products on Prodigy, along with the ability to order them right from the computer.

BRING ON THE ENTREPRENEURS

Franchising and direct marketing often boom during periods of corporate downsizing. As more and more middle or high level managers get put out onto the street, they begin to look for something they can own, in part to make sure no one can ever lay them off again and in part because it may be difficult or impossible to find the kind of position they left.

This recession is no exception. With the real estate market depressed, many prime locations for franchise stores are available, and with interest rates so low, financing–if you can get it–is a bargain.

In fact, today the franchisee can often borrow startup capital from the franchiser. The Small Business Administration is working with many

Shopping at home is growing with the number of home computers. More than 50,000 products are available through interactive networks.

franchisers to help them help their new franchisees put together SBA loan applications. Some franchisers go as far as to guarantee the loans of their franchisees.

"Franchising is one bright spot in a lagging economy," says Gregg Reynolds, chairman of the International Franchise Association in Washington, D.C. in a recent interview in *Nation's Business* magazine. "Last year, more than 18,500 new businesses were created, adding approximately 108,000 new jobs to the economy."

Franchising is attractive in a down economy for many of the same reasons network marketing is. The successful franchises during a recession are the ones that respond quickly to the changing marketplace, have a relatively narrow focus, deliver products directly to the home, and are reasonably priced.

"If there is a recession-proof mechanism within this economy, it is entrepreneurship, said Joseph Simone, executive vice president of Mamma Ilardo's, an Italian-pizza franchise in Baltimore, to *Nation's Business*. Entrepreneurs "embrace the philosophy of customer service, high quality, and fair price."

NETWORK MARKETING TAKES OFF

What many of these successful strategies have in common is the fact that they put the buying decision in the home, where a growing number of people would rather have it. And network marketing has one significant advantage over the other avenues: it doesn't cost very much to get started and try it out. There are no franchise fees, no leases, no loans.

With a reputation for bringing products to the customer, MLM "has been experiencing a mini-boom," according to a story in the August 1992 *Home Office Computing Magazine*.

The headline on that story calls network marketing and direct selling "New Age Capitalism." MLM is actually growing at a rate of 30 percent a year, according to Babener.

The Direct Selling Association in New York reports that 5.1 million people are now in some form of direct selling activity. They are said to deal with $12.96 billion in sales around the world.

Nearly three hundred MLM companies account for more than half of those sales, and that number is growing, according to *New Business Opportunities Magazine*.

"Markets are becoming so fragmented that it's difficult to reach them through mass advertising," says Bryan Barbieri, a marketing professor at Montreal's Concordia University. Barbieri told Canada's *Financial Post* that "word-of-mouth is one of the best ways to promote a product."

As to criticism of multilevel marketing, Barbieri counters, "If the product is a good one, then I see no essential difference from any other form of distribution . . . distributors have to feel they can sell the products. If they think they'll simply make money from recruiting, then I fear they'll have trouble sleeping at night."

It appears that an increasing number of U.S. corporations agree with that assessment.

Many traditional firms are branching out into multiple forms of marketing to preserve or enhance market share.

According to a piece in *The Harvard Business Review*, more and more companies are putting together hybrid marketing systems. More than half of the firms they surveyed at the end of 1990 said they were building hybrid systems involving everything from telemarketing to catalogs to direct mail.

Several traditional corporations have begun to use forms of network marketing to move their products.

"MCI's Friends & Family program is a network marketing program. Relatives and friends refer each other to MCI, which gives better long-distance rates when referrals sign up," said Gregg Stewart, a partner in Network Productions Inc., which produces and markets books, tapes, and videos explaining how multi-level marketing programs work and how people can be successful at them. "Certainly no one would call MCI a disreputable company."

Stewart and his partner Randy Stoltz, profiled by the *Business Journal* in Phoenix, said there are some cultural reasons that Americans have been a bit slower to embrace network marketing than others. Americans like to think of themselves as independent thinkers, as opposed to the Japanese and Europeans who tend to place more weight on the personal recommendations of products by friends.

MCI competitor U.S. Sprint has started its own network marketing operation to sell long distance services. Sprint contracted with a company called Network 2000 Marketing to supply an estimated 36,000 part-time, home based sales reps who can earn a minimum of 0.5 percent of their customers' long distance bills.

"You're selling a service, not a product, and that means no money changes hands," said Bill Plikaitis of Sprint to *Minneapolis-St. Paul Business* magazine. "There are no quotas. You can work however much you want and just sell enough to meet your needs."

Plikaitis, who is in charge of the Network 2000 Marketing program for Sprint, said there were three kinds of sellers in the system:

"Some want to make only thirty to fifty dollars a month. We can show them how to get it. It's a recurring income through the continuing long-distance charges of their customers.

"Some who want to make as much as one to three thousand dollars a month have to build an organization."

The third category includes those out for the big bucks. According to Plikaitis they make as much as three to four thousand dollars a month.

There is another category says Clements. He points to large numbers of people getting into MLM not as a first job, but as a way to buy the products they sell at wholesale prices.

Many other traditional firms have turned to successful network marketing firms to move product. MCI had a relationship with Amway long before the Friends & Family program that helped it grow from a startup to a powerhouse competitor to AT&T, which also wound up subcontracting to MLM firms. Amway has now sold many traditional products, like Firestone tires and Ford automobiles.

PART 3: WHAT'S NEXT

The growing costs of everything from educa-

tion to home ownership have increased the need for supplemental income.

We are deeper in debt and have saved less to protect ourselves from rainy days. Household debt grew from 66.6 percent of personal income in 1979 to 86.7 percent in 1991, according to the Economic Policy Institute.

The American public seems unwilling or unable to save money. According to *Business Week*, Americans save 5.4 percent of their income. That number compares to 14.1 percent in Japan, 13.7 percent in Germany, and 12.7 percent in France.

That is just one of the many reasons there is a new emphasis on "value" and "no frills." The fact is people still want to look beautiful, but the need to wear a designer dress or brand name makeup is rapidly being overtaken by a willingness to spend as little as possible while maintaining the same appearance.

Those trends play into network marketing's high value/low price strategies.

In a story entitled "How to Prosper in the Value Decade," *Fortune Magazine* called this trend "a global change that is transforming markets for industrial and consumer products alike."

The magazine reports that a "profound change that won't end when economies revive is the novel ideal that quality can and should be affordable...Today's buyers know what they want and how much they're willing to pay for it."

Shopping patterns and lifestyles are changing, too. One-parent households now make up 27 percent of all "families with related children" - up from 22 percent ten years ago. In a one-parent household the parent doesn't have much time to do anything he or she wants to do. That means he or she is looking for ways to shop while at home.

Fifty-seven percent of all children under age fifteen, or about thirty million kids, had working mothers in 1988, according to the Census Bureau. Ten percent of them had stay-at-home dads.

It seems like almost everyone is out making money or trying to, one way or another. According to the Labor Department, dual-income families are now the norm in America, jumping

People still want to look beautiful, but the need to wear a designer dress or brand name makeup is being overtaken by the willingness to spend as little as possible with the same appearance.

from 20 percent of all households in 1950 to 42 percent today.

The move to dual-income households hasn't been fueled just by the need to support kids. The number of married couples without children–27.8 million in 1991–now exceeds the 24.4 million couples with children, according to a recent *Business Week*.

THE NEW DIVERSITY

On top of that, the population of the United States has become far more ethnically diverse. Approximately 20 percent of our population is Black, Hispanic, or Asian, compared to half that in 1950.

Ethnic markets are natural for direct marketing and the most difficult for mass marketing. In fact, the new cultural diversity has led to a fundamental change in America that plays into the hand of network marketing. As a society, we are de-centralizing. We now tend to stress our differences as opposed to our similarities. Our television networks are going the way of *Life and Look Magazine* a generation ago: They are victims of a society that no longer wants to have a common culture.

Hundreds of cable channels have joined thousands of specialty magazines in trying to appeal to the various and growing segments of our society.

Today people are watching and reading only what they want to and when they want to. The consumer can control his or her consumption of information just like the consumption of food. As in choosing an ethnic restaurant, they can choose on a moment-to-moment basis to read about or watch political news, international news, local news, news of their industry, news of their company, news of their religion, or even commercials. They can see stock prices, sports scores, or even what's on sale at department stores on Prodigy, Compuserve or other on-line services. They can even call up news, sports, weather, or their own mail on dozens of new hand-held devices that receive data over the airwaves.

This is not a function of laziness but more a reaction to the fact that people just have less time for everything and are victims of another aspect of

what has happened in the new "Information Age." We are now bombarded with so much information that our toughest task has become figuring out how to dissect it. Much of today's entrepreneurism is designed to make it easier for people to get the kind of information they want, and only that information, when they want it.

Likewise, it seems that more and more people don't have the time or patience to shop. One stop or no stop (someone comes to you, either in person or through the mail) shopping continues to grow. Supermarkets continue to expand product lines, as do the drug store chains. The big discount clubs stock wide ranges of products, from toilet paper to pianos. Even Apple Computer, Inc. decided for the first time late in 1992 to sell by mail order.

All kinds of service-related businesses are cropping up. Some have as their only charter helping people to find a product or service as quickly and cheaply as possible.

There are scores of new auto buying services, for example, who generally are in business to do what many people have come to hate at any price: deal with a car salesman to get to an agreeable price. That buying service will work for you and get you the car in the colors you want with the features you want. It can probably even get you the best possible price.

WE'RE GETTING OLDER AND LONELIER

During this decade, the number of people aged forty-five and older will grow by more than eighteen million, while the number of eighteen to thirty-four year olds may decline, according to *American Demographics* magazine. The magazine further speculates that the graying of the population contributed to the recession by reducing demand for youth-oriented products, which have dominated our marketplace.

The older, more affluent consumer is generally one who looks for quality. They generally spend more on goods, but buy fewer of them.

There is a huge jump foreseen in the number of older, single people living alone. In the category of people from thirty-five to fifty-four years of age, the Census Bureau projects a 30 percent increase in people living alone during the 1990's. For people fifty-five and over, another 13 percent increase in those living alone is due by the end of the century.

Older women living alone will be the largest growth group during the next decade. Two out of three women who live alone will be fifty-five or older.

More singles means more movement between jobs, less security, and more individual freedom for people in that category to spend one's time unburdened by family ties. Since one of the drawbacks of MLM's is that they take time away from the family, this would leave a larger pool of people, particularly women, who would be free of family ties during the next ten years.

IN THE 1990'S, SMALLER IS BIGGER

For the past decade, there has been a trend away from the corporate world and toward small entrepreneurial enterprises, even among the best educated members of the workforce.

"More people realize that nobody in corporate life has any security anymore. They are beginning to think they had better create their own security, their own career," said Bud Dimmitt, director of entrepreneurial services at the out placement firm Lee Hecht Harrison, in a recent *Fortune* story.

As industries consolidate into fewer large companies, the opportunities abound for smaller companies to pop up and fill niche markets.

During the two-year period from 1988 to 1990, large corporations lost more than 500,000 jobs. But during that same period, companies with fewer than five hundred people added more than 3 million jobs.

In *Megatrends 2000*, the sequel to their first book a decade earlier, John Naisbitt and Patricia Aburdene devote a chapter to a celebration of "The Triumph of the Individual."

"It is an individual who creates a work of art, embraces a political philosophy, bets a life savings on a new business," they wrote. They deduced that new technologies have changed the world to allow individual entrepreneurs to prosper.

Every new business gadget, from the fax machine and cellular phone to desk and portable computer, has helped give entrepreneurs and new businesses enormous reach, even if they are one-person operations working out of their home.

With the rise of the individual entrepreneur, there is a concurrent empowerment of the individual consumer. When the corporations ruled, the individual customer got whatever those corporations made. "No more," says "Megatrends 1990." "With the rise of the individual has come the primacy of the consumer. It has been said for many years: The customer is king. Now it is true."

SERVICE, BUT WITH A SMILE?

A growing number of people are employed in information and service-related positions. In 1960, The Labor Department reports there were 16.8 million manufacturing jobs and 33.7 million service jobs in the United States. By 1992, there were 18.2 million manufacturing jobs and 85.1 million service jobs. Government employment grew from 8.4 million to 18.6 million during that period.

Indeed, most Americans are now in the business of information. They move it, process it, or in some cases even create it. Even people who work for manufacturing companies are holding information-related jobs in those companies.

With the rise of the entrepreneur, there is an empowerment of the individual consumer.

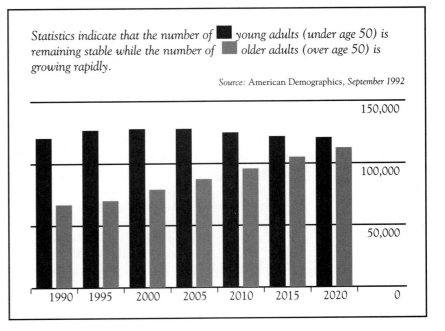

Statistics indicate that the number of ■ young adults (under age 50) is remaining stable while the number of ▨ older adults (over age 50) is growing rapidly.

Source: American Demographics, September 1992

150,000

100,000

50,000

1990 1995 2000 2005 2010 2015 2020 0

Information and service-related jobs, with the proper equipment, can often lend themselves to being done at home. Eighteen million of America's ninety-two million households now have some form of income-producing home office according to research firm BIS CAP International, cited in the book *Working At Home* by Paul and Sarah Edwards.

The Edwards' have discovered some new trends in the type of people entering into entrepreneurial ventures. During the 1980's, most were young, brash, and hungry to make a big financial score. Now the Edwards' have discovered a new category of "propreneurs," who are "not in love with business enterprise per se."

Many of these people are older, more risk-averse, and are trying to preserve a certain lifestyle rather than drive only for growth.

Link Resources' 1990 National Work-at-

get on a home computer at night. This group is growing at a rate of 20 percent.

Why shouldn't we work at home? Our highways are overcrowded and falling apart; traffic congestion is approaching constant gridlock in many of our cities even as gas prices continue to rise; our air quality is a disaster because of all those traffic jams, and with more two-adult working families the need for someone to be around the house to deal with children from time to time has increased dramatically.

Besides, the rise of the computer and satellite technology has revolutionized the movement of information. For most secretarial or clerk jobs, the work can just as easily be done at home and transmitted back and forth to and from the office.

One has only to visit a modern office, in which the employees are linked by computers and electronic mail systems, to understand why it

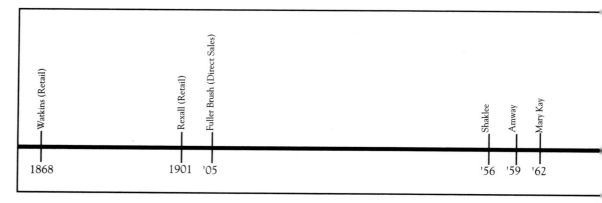

Home survey reported 34.8 million people doing work at home in the United States. That number should swell to almost 45 million in 1993. Link Resources divides the work-at-home population into 4 groups:

• Primary self-employed home workers (10.8 million people). The people in this group depend upon the income they make from their home business as their sole or largest income.
• Part-time self-employed home workers (9.5 million). This group holds at least one other job.
• Telecommuters (3.6 million). These are employees for companies based outside the home who spend some or all of their official workweek on a computer at home.
• High-tech corporate after-hour home worker (10.4 million). This is the group of people who

probably wouldn't matter if many of the people there were elsewhere. Just watch how those people communicate with each other. Often across the room from the person they are communicating with, someone will send a computer message instead of getting up and talking to them.

For many of those who already do work at home, MLM offers the best way to become an entrepreneur and make some extra money. One out of three new businesses today starts out of the home.

"MLM reduces the individual's risk," says direct marketing legend Joe Sugarman. "It's a form of direct marketing that allows some to get in for practically no investment and at the same time have camaraderie, support, encouragement, guidance, and a safety net from the network."

PART 4: NETWORKING EXPLOSION.

The question remains, is it networking that's right for you?

"MLM is the last bastion of the free enterprise system," says Omnitrition's Elsberg, "and it takes people from all walks of life. . . the school teacher, the corporate president, the cab driver. . . all personality types."

Network marketing is appearing in many new forms. The following companies are reported to be either part of a MLM network or establishing their own: MCI, Sprint, Coca-Cola, Colgate, Palmolive, Gillette, GM, Ford, Visa International, Lipton, Scotts, Johnson & Murphy, Canon, Magnavox, Sharp, Del Monte, Smith Corona, and Xerox.

"It's a billion dollar industry that hasn't been

before anyone can make big money," she says.

"This isn't a free lunch industry," agrees Portland MLM lawyer Babener. In a *New Business Opportunities* interview in the fall of 1992, he added, "The people who succeed at this business work hard at it."

Still, says Elsberg, even without huge payouts MLM is more attractive than going into other forms of business because it doesn't require much capital. "I know lots of people who worked very hard and borrowed and begged to start new businesses but didn't succeed because of dollars. The good thing about networking is that you're in business for yourself but not by yourself. This business is built on relationships."

ARE YOU HUNGRY ENOUGH?

So who does succeed? And how many millionaires really made their fortunes in MLM?

MLM is the last bastion of the free enterprise system and it takes people from all walks of life.

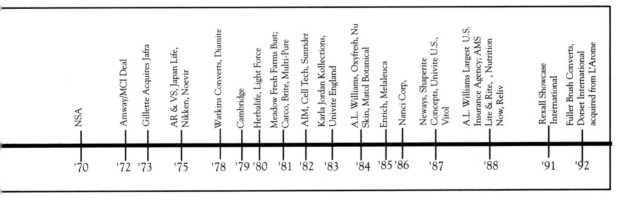

| '70 | '72 | '73 | '75 | '78 | '79 | '80 | '81 | '82 | '83 | '84 | '85 | '86 | '87 | '88 | '91 | '92 |

NSA — Amway/MCI Deal — Gillette Acquires Jafra — AR & VS, Japan Life, Nikken, Noevir — Watkins Converts, Diamite — Cambridge — Herbalife, Light Force — Meadow Fresh Farms Bust; Carco, Brite, Multi-Pure — AIM, Cell Tech, Sunrider — Karla Jordan Kollections, Univite England — A.L. Williams, Oxyfresh, Nu Skin, Matol Botanical — Enrich, Melaleuca — Nanci Corp. — Neways, Shaperite Concepts, Univite U.S., Vitol — A.L. Williams Largest U.S. Insurance Agency; AMS Lite & Rite, , Nutrition Now, Reliv — Rexall Showcase International — Fuller Brush Converts, Dorset International acquired from L'Arome

viewed strategically by industry as a whole," says Sprint's Plikaitis. "Little by little, big companies are finding out they can harness it. It will generate results."

Several experts interviewed agreed that MLM can work for many people but shouldn't be seen as a get-rich-quick scheme. "For most people in America, five hundred dollars a month would save their life," says Elsberg. "It's not a get-rich-quick type of business. It takes nine months to get a baby born. Starting a business is no different."

"Just two hundred dollars a month would prevent 80 percent of all personal bankruptcies," claims Linda Marshall of Elysee. She agrees people shouldn't jump in with expectations of making lots of money in a hurry. "It's probably two years...

"There are three kinds of people," says Elsberg. "People who watch it happen, people who hear about it happening, and people who make it happen."

"It's a question of hunger, passion, and a sense of change," she added. "I look for people who can break the self-esteem barrier and rejection barrier."

Not surprisingly, MLM is like most business opportunities. It takes hard work to do well, both before you start and when you start. Says industry-watcher Clements, "If you want to make a comfortable living out of MLM, you must go to school. Read MLM books, listen to tapes, go to training meetings, read as many MLM publications as you can, and learn everything there is to know about your product line or service."

But it is clear that many people do get what they want from a network marketing opportunity.

One success story is Kim Brecheen, a thirty-four-year-old legal secretary profiled this year in the *Baton Rouge Business Report*. Invited by a friend to a F.U.N. (For Us Now) party two years ago, she could hardly keep herself from snickering at the product line of lingerie, lotions, novelties, and bedroom accessories called "marital aids."

But she was surprised. "It was really tastefully done," she said. "It was the type of party you could take your mother to and not be embarrassed."

Not only wasn't Brecheen embarrassed, she decided to become a part-time distributor for the California-based company.

In 1991, she sold $98,000 worth of goods. She estimates $200,000 in sales for 1992. She said she averages 50 percent commission on her products. Her family has now been able to move into a four-bedroom home with a swimming pool.

Of course, one full bedroom and several closets are filled to the brim with product she must warehouse for herself and thirty-five distributors she has recruited. No matter, she is one happy hostess.

"Where else can you go, meet a lot of new women, talk about sex, and go home with their money?" she asks.

AN INDUSTRY GOES STRAIGHT

The network marketing industry is working hard to shed the image of hucksterism that grew out of some unfortunate problems of the past, including well-publicized pyramid schemes, investigations, and a long line of late-night television infomercials that tout get-rich-quick schemes.

"Nowadays, MLM is an industry hellbent on cleaning up both its act and its image. And so far, it's been fairly successful," writes Stephanie Barlow in *New Business Opportunities* magazine. "What with the debacle of the pyramid schemes of the 70's, which brought the industry under federal scrutiny and culminated in legal proceedings against some of the biggest names in MLM, the industry has encountered its share of legal entanglements."

Several big players in the MLM industry have had to weather federal probes. After four years in the 1970's fighting Federal Trade Commission charges that it was a pyramid scheme, Amway ultimately won that critical case.

There are thousands of stories about what the MLM experience has done for and to people.

There have been scores of published horror stories, like the couple that gave up jobs to go full

SAMPLING OF U.S. FIRMS THAT PROVIDE GOODS/SERVICES THROUGH AN MLM ORGANIZATION AND/OR OPERATE AN MLM

FIRM	PROVIDES	OPERATES
AT&T	✔	
Avon	✔	
Bausch & Lomb	✔	
Bell Atlantic	✔	
Bell South	✔	
Campbell Soup	✔	
Chrysler Corp.	✔	
Coca-Cola	✔	
Colgate/Palmolive	✔	✔
Corning	✔	
Fieldcrest Canon	✔	
Ford Motor Co.	✔	
Fruit of The Loom	✔	
GTE	✔	
General Electric	✔	
General Mills	✔	
General Motors	✔	
Gillette	✔	✔
H.J. Heinz Co	✔	
IBM	✔	
Litton Industries	✔	
MCI	✔	✔
Motorola	✔	
NCR	✔	
Quaker Oats Co.	✔	
Sharp Electronics	✔	
Sprint	✔	✔
Texas Instruments	✔	
Whirlpool Corp	✔	✔
Xerox Corp	✔	
Zenith Electronics	✔	

This listing is not comprehensive and is provided for the purpose of demonstrating that America's leading corporations take MLM very seriously.

speed into an MLM and lost everything they had.

It's still fair to say that anyone looking to get into network marketing should take many of the blind claims with a grain of salt.

One of those myths that is oft-repeated is that MLM is taught at the Harvard Business School.

"We do not teach such methods at the Harvard Business School," wrote HBS professor Thomas Bonoma in *Marketing News* in February 1991. "—they are not part of our curriculum; to my knowledge, they are not taught at this or any other reputable business school in the country."

Bonoma went on to warn of the evils of many multi-level marketing schemes, though acknowledging that there are some successful and ethical examples as well.

He encouraged anyone seeking to enter MLM to investigate the opportunity with the local Better Business Bureau or other watchdog organizations.

THE DARK SIDE

"I think you have to sell your soul a lot," says a former top performer at two different MLM's, who asked not to be identified. "The positive side is that you can make a lot of money, set your own hours within a certain framework, even be your own person," she adds. "But multi-level companies can be pimps, and the people who work for them prostitutes. Many of the women-only organizations feed on people who become dependent. They are maternalistic and authoritarian organizations who force you to do things their way if you want to get recognized."

MLM's aren't the only firms that demand certain behavior from their employees. The road to the top of most large corporations is lined with personal sacrifice and compromise.

Still, many network marketing firms concentrate so heavily on motivational skills that they are clearly concerned about the psychological impact of heavy, motivational pressures on certain kinds of people.

"I know some good people who backed out of MLM's who had become recognition junkies," says the disenchanted MLMer. "These are people who came from families where the room was never clean enough, the boyfriend was never good enough. They went to an organization that rewarded them, that put them on magazine covers, that made them feel like they were good enough. . . and then, fed on them. But then, when it started to wear off, and those same women let up a bit because they saw that their lives at home were being shortchanged, their new 'family' discarded them pretty quick. If your numbers weren't there, you just weren't that important anymore."

This unnamed woman added that there are many success stories, too. "The people who make it probably would have made it working for Colgate or Bechtel, too. These are largely savvy business women who have paid their dues. There are a lot of divorcees. Lots of single mothers and single women are attracted to many MLM opportunities because they can become stars."

Once again, these failures and success stories are not dissimilar to those you might read about in many other professions. Success often carries a high price. In some ways, that is her message: MLM is not necessarily a way to escape many of the pressures that come with success in the corporate and business world.

Even though she made a six-figure income and was "drowned in furs and diamonds," she said, "I paid a high price . . . I spent a lot of nights away from my kids. I gave up a lot."

EVENTUALLY YOU RUN OUT OF FRIENDS

Don Griffin tasted success in network marketing, but now has nothing but regrets. In telling his story to the *Baton Rouge Business Report* earlier this year, Griffin said he understood the temptations that attracted him to not one, but four different network marketing companies.

It was his search for the hot product and big money that led him from one dream to the next. Each time he was drawn in with rapt enthusiasm. It's not a flattering self-portrait and in many ways he paints himself as someone with weaknesses that he ignored time and time again.

"It really can be a form of addiction. The tendency to have tunnel vision, not being able to turn it off," he said.

Lots of single mothers and single women are attracted to MLM opportunities because they can become stars.

In each case, Shaklee (vitamins), Herbalife (vitamin and diet products), United Sciences of America (vitamin and diet products), and A.L. Williams (life insurance), he found himself burning out.

Each time his world revolved around the company and the people he worked with, to the exclusion of everything else. "It's linear living," he said. After "every multi-level I've gotten involved with and gotten out of, I noticed a whole new world out there that was going on without me."

He also told the *Report* that he alienated friends, family, and others by always being on the prowl for new distributors. He said he was living by the three foot rule he was taught, "Anyone within three feet of you can help your business."

"There's always this ulterior motive festering inside of you," he said.

In response, MLMers are quick to point out that most good "Network Marketing" firms try to steer their distributors away from depending upon selling to friends. They are encouraged to seek out new contacts for their businesses.

Griffin didn't deny he made some good money during some of his time in network marketing. He was making $15,000 a month at Herbalife until the Food and Drug Administration raised questions about the safety and quality of the products - plunging his income to $1,000 a month almost instantly.

Toronto retailing and marketing consultant Len Kubas says that the simplicity of network marketing is appealing, but he told *The Financial Post*, "my feeling is that sometimes these schemes are presented as being a bit too easy."

"Eventually," Kubas says, "you run out of friends and contacts to bring into the system."

In the same article, Robert Appel of the Marshall McLuhan Center on Global Communications in San Francisco labeled MLM a system that "strip-mines human enthusiasm."

"I think multi-level marketing will make a huge dent in the way things are marketed in the future, but it's a numbers game," he adds. "You get one hundred people into a room, knowing that eighty-five won't be interested. Fifteen will sign up, and maybe two will stick with it. They strip-mine human enthusiasm by getting people worked up, but they don't think about what they're doing with the eighty-five people they've ticked off."

Again, one can make similar comments about the road to the top of many corporations, which promote a small fraction of their employees up to the higher rungs on the ladder.

As is the case in many of those companies, both Kubas and Appel agree, much of the chance for long-term success of "Network Marketing" firms really rests with the product—it has to be good.

THE UP-SIDE

There are, to be sure, successful network marketers who still like what they do and do it very well. Dexter Yager of Charlotte is a celebrated example.

According to *Forbes* magazine, Yager runs a network of more than 100,000 Amway distributors and nets in excess of $10 million a year.

While few reach the level of a Yager, many do reap various rewards. Though an estimated half of the almost two million distributors in the Amway world-wide network will drop out each year, there are as many new recruits to take up the slack.

According to *Forbes*, the average Amway distributor in the U.S. will net around $780 a year from the actual sale of about $1,700 worth of goods. But that same average distributor will also use $1,068 worth of Amway goods himself or herself. So the big money is in building large, stable networks like Amway Diamond Jim Dornan.

So it is important for a potential MLMer to assess his or her feelings about recruiting as well as selling.

"I hate selling," writes newsletter publisher and MLM advocate Clements in his publication. "Loath it. Like most people I can't stand the rejection." Even more remarkably, a study he did for MarketWave revealed he wasn't alone. They asked 136 current and ex-distributors what they disliked the most about MLM. An astounding 83 percent mentioned "selling" in their top three answers, making it the most common answer.

That may be why so many network marketing companies advertise their products to potential distributors as the products "that sell themselves."

Hogwash, says Clements. "To this day, I've never seen a bar of soap call up one of my neighbors and invite itself over for a swim. Not once."

But the ability to make it work is clearly there, if one realizes that it's just like any other job: if you work hard, you can succeed.

BE PATIENT

Clements advises people thinking of going into MLM not to be discouraged if "you feel you are one of those who . . . dislikes selling. MLM can still work for you."

"Take some time to build your confidence," he says. "Acquiring selling skills can come naturally, in time. Taking a comfortable, slower, more passive approach to your opportunity will delay your success, surely, but better to succeed slowly than fail fast."

Len Clements offers good advice for an aspiring MLMer before taking the dive. He tells them to get a product they like that prices fairly and competitively from a company that's been around a while. He also warns you to choose your sponsor carefully, avoid any attempts to force you to buy a lot of inventory up front, or pay the company much at the outset.

He says calculate what your high end profit can grow to by looking at the compensation structure. Check how often you are paid and in what form. Don't believe companies that offer instant wealth.

Everyone interviewed says you mainly have to really want it.

"I haven't seen any pattern to what kind of person succeeds in this business," says Elysee's Linda Marshall.

"Some people I thought would be phenomenal have bombed; others we thought had no real chance have done well."

"All I can say is that the people who do make it," Marshall added, "are motivated in a big way to take control over their own lives."

"What I look for are people who are passionate enough to change," says Omnitritian's Elsberg. "They have to have that hunger, for whatever reason, to succeed."

FACTORS CONTRIBUTING TO MLMs CONTINUED SUCCESS

LEVERAGE POINTS	ASPECT FUELING GROWTH
Compensation	Generally, MLMs circulate a large percentage of profits back to distributors, rather than spending it on middlemen, advertising, and promotion.
Products	*Not available in stores* — this is a major hallmark of MLM. Some succeed with quality alternatives to major-brand consumables; others with items requiring a too-large "carried inventory" to be profitable in retail stores: MLM makes it possible to target geographically non-uniform market segments efficiently and effectively.
Service	Due to their structure, MLMs can provide personalized service to a vast number of customers almost simultaneously. Responsive, high quality service is a critical element in MLM success stories.
Lifestyle	Men and Women suffering from "burn-out" in large corporate structures and small businesses alike are increasingly seeing the MLM opportunity as "a way out" for themselves, their families, and their friends — a way that allows them a wide selection of lifestyle options.

Even if you feel you are one of those who dislikes selling, MLM can still work for you.

Do advocates of multi-level marketing have more passion for their companies than the average American worker? It would seem so. The following account about Linda Cole of O'Fallon, Illinois was taken from the monthly magazine distributed by Mary Kay to their Beauty Consultants.

When interviewed, she admitted she came to Mary Kay Cosmetics because she coveted a pink Cadillac. She stayed because she developed a real knack for selling the product and sharing the opportunity.

Linda said she continues to find "a career of life-enriching, life-changing proportions. I would do this career for free if the opportunity came along again!" Linda had pursued a career in speech and hearing therapy as a means of helping others, but she never could have touched as many lives as she's been able to since joining Mary Kay in 1976. "I tell every woman joining this company her life will be enriched. And I'm not talking about money."

When the grim news arrived that her son had a brain tumor and needed surgery, cards and flowers and prayers poured into his hospital room from Consultants throughout the nation. She told the hospital personnel, no, her son wasn't a celebrity, just a member of the Mary Kay family. "How many people actually think of their company as family?"

When describing her success, the company says, "She is great at selling others on this career. She makes the career so exciting that others want to do what she does."

Linda earned her first career-car in 1978, the same year she became a Director. Now she can't imagine being without her pink car. "You talk about spoiled," she laughs.

When talking with women who have jobs they like, Linda stresses that a part-time career with Mary Kay "will be the most fun you'll ever earn until you see the big picture of what this opportunity offers to those willing to pursue it."

Linda concluded, "Where else could the rewards and benefits have been so great and yet be so totally overshadowed by the priceless spirit and attitude of the company?" And she wondered aloud, "How does everyone else get through life without all the positive people of Mary Kay Cosmetics?"

Mary Kay is not the only company to have such a following. Tola Newman with Elysee Cosmetics is seventy-eight and one of the original skin care consultants to be trained by Dr. Elizabeth Blumenthal in 1945. Tola's story becomes even more interesting when you know that she is blind. "I can give a skin evaluation just by feel," says Tola. "My husband handles the phone calls and paperwork, and we make a good team. Where else could a seventy-eight-year-old woman in retirement and blind earn more than $40,000 per year?"

Where else indeed. ■

ALL OF THE PRODUCTS WHICH WON'T BE AVAILABLE THROUGH NETWORK MARKETING IN THE YEAR 2,000

Do You Have The Right Stuff?

By Mike Cooper and John Milton Fogg

John Milton Fogg is the editor of Upline™, the journal for network marketing leaders and author of The Greatest Networker in the World. He conducts seminars for networking professionals and produces The Upline™ Masters Seminar Tapes.

Mike Cooper is the president of The Network Institute, Inc. which provides training and development programs, and productivity tools such as Management Action Planner, and The One Minute Networker. There is no connection between Upline™ and this publication.

The more we know about what it's like to be a network marketing leader, the more clues we have for developing those qualities in ourselves and our people.

Our new research study was developed to determine who are network marketing leaders and what makes them tick.

This joint research project is called "The Definitive Profile of a Network Marketing Leader." Undertaken by the Drake P³, The Network Institute, Inc., and UPLINE™, the research effort revolved around a carefully designed questionnaire conducted with a cross section of selected individual network marketing leaders throughout North America.

Our intention for this research project was to provide people with a standard by which to judge their own qualities as network marketing leaders. As you read this summary of the "Definitive Profile", notice those traits you have which are common among networking leaders.

Most importantly, we want you to look and see what's different about you compared with this profile. Look closely at yourself and see what's missing–what characteristics and life skills could you develop which, when you did, would put you right on track to becoming a high-performance top producer and high-income earner in network marketing.

What Is A Network Marketing Leader?

A networking leader is a dominant and controlling person, outgoing–an extrovert. He or she balances that outward expression of power with a degree of patience well above that possessed by the average man or woman.

An NML (network marketing leader) is *absolutely* a non-conformist. Structure and too many regulations make them uncomfortable, yet they are at home with and relatively good at analysis and organization.

Network marketing leaders are risk takers. They are adventurous, enjoy challenges, and have a competitive streak. These are forceful folks–bold, powerful, persistent, and persuasive. The word "quit" is not in their vocabulary.

Tenacious in pursuit of a goal, convincing in conversation, their key word is "influencing." NML's are adept at getting things done *through* other people. They easily delegate detailed assignments, responsibility, and authority to others. They are perceptive in their assessment of people, empathetic and sensitive to others' concerns, yet clearly *they* are the ones in control. This makes them excellent team-builders.

Network marketing leaders are clearly people-people. They have a large circle of friends and acquaintances and a much higher than average level of congeniality. They are outgoing and optimistic, very friendly, eager to please, and enthusiastic. It is important for them to be liked.

They are good communicators who find it fairly easy to see another person's point of view. They show a lot of confidence in the character and abilities of other people, and sometimes this good-natured trust is taken advantage of.

NML's *like* being leaders and are good at it.

A Networking Leader's Motivation

In order to be motivated and productive, a network marketing leader requires lots of interaction with people. They crave new contacts, meeting new people, and making new friends.

They are clearly team players, and their business-building efforts are fueled by their desire to create and be part of a growing, successful organization. The prestige and public image of their organizations (and their company affiliations) are very important to them.

Acceptance, belonging, and recognition are high up on the value chart of networking leaders. If they feel they are not part of the team (not invited to meetings or not included in decision-making) and if they are not encouraged to grow in power and status and supported by their company and upline sponsors, then they will go elsewhere. Considering their proactive bias, if they are unrecognized and/or under-appreciated for too long, they will either get what they want–or move on very quickly.

To keep an NML happy and productive, give them: daily challenges, opportunities for innovation, results-oriented projects, direct and to-the-point communication, and, above all, freedom from rules, regulations, details, and anything that smacks of the conventional, status-quo, or "business as usual."

Networking leaders *require* opportunities to improve their lot in life, and this means making more money. With their drive for recognition and reward, perhaps money is one of their ways of keeping score.

THE RATIONAL NETWORKER

Decision-making styles encompass a range of abilities: logic, intellect, an analytical mind, perception, feelings, and intuition. Network marketing leaders will use all of these and more—but when it comes down to making choices, they lead with their gut and heart.

Networking leaders are intuitive decision-makers. They rely on their subjective skills. This same style is also typified by the salesperson, the counselor, and others involved in predominantly people-oriented professions.

As decision-makers, our leaders are true to their network marketing roots. The sharing and caring orientation of this business is well evidenced in their open-minded, empathetic, intuitive *feeling* approach to making important choices and decisions in their life and work.

HIGH ENERGY FUELS NETWORK MARKETING LEADERS

One's energy level measures the degree of one's wellness, awareness, and responsiveness. Simply put, anything that's alive—which has energy—responds to a stimulus. The more energy one has, the more responsive one is.

Here is the range, the "Definitive Profile" used for measuring energy levels: Below Average, Average, Above Average, High, and Very High. Where do NML's fall in this range? "Very High!" And what does having a "Very High" energy level mean?

Network marketing leaders are high achievers. The payoff for this mega-energy is that they can accomplish almost any goal or task. People with lower energy levels will frustrate them. Network marketing leaders will tend to describe them as lazy and will not act with their characteristic patience.

These fast-lane, fast-trackers must be kept busy. They are always-on-the-go types, easily bored if they aren't "where the action is." If their business-building efforts don't provide adequate stimulation, they will seek additional activities outside their daily routines. In short, NML's are active, productive, high-performance people.

The cost? Stress – mild or strong. Networking leaders are susceptible to becoming over-stressed. Burn-out prevention should be well up there on these people's list of "things to do" – it's critically important for them to take care of their health and well-being. If their batteries are not recharged with rest, relaxation, good diets, proper sleep, *and FUN* – NML's will fall victim to ill health, susceptibility to accidents, mental errors, and a lack of focus and concentration. Then they'll lapse into showing up as a reactive-type personality, rather than their more-true-to form proactivity.

The key is balance. Balance of what? Of movement and rest, of work and play, of business and family.

SUMMARY

What have we learned here? Well, not surprisingly, the network marketing leader's character is not unlike other leaders in any field of endeavor. He or she is a take-charge individual, an extrovert, a non-conformist, and a risk taker intent on achievement and being well rewarded and recognized for his or her accomplishments.

What is unique about networking leaders is their talent and passion for being among and working with people. The "Definitive Profile" found that NML's show well above average rankings in these areas: friendliness, empathy, communication skills, being team players, desire to be part of a successful, well-respected organization, listening, perception, congeniality, and meeting and making new friends.

No matter what other skills or demands are put forth as criteria for leadership in the network marketing industry, this fact above all is where the rubber meets the road: network marketing is a people business.

A successful network marketing leader is very simply a person who genuinely cares about having his or her people become network marketing leaders too. ■

Readers may receive a personalized Drake P³ Definitive Profile of a Network Marketing Leader by request. Use the Reader Service card and order the Books, Tapes, Videos and Organizations list for further information.

The more energy one has, the more responsive one is.

NETWORK MARKETING IS LIKE A SLEEPING GIANT

BY BOB WALLER

BOB WALLER IS A NATIONAL MARKETING DIRECTOR WITH NSA. DURING HIS SIXTEEN YEAR CAREER IN BANKING, HE REACHED THE CEO LEVEL . HE IS FEATURED IN A GENERIC NETWORKING VIDEO, THE GIANT AWAKENS.

A fairly new marketing technology known as network marketing is getting ready to stand up and be recognized for the business force that it really is. Like a giant waking up, it stirs slowly at first, but once awake it makes the ground shake as it begins to move.

While my academic training as an undergraduate student was in marketing, I was never exposed to either the terminology or ideology of network marketing. Marketing education was, and still is, directed at "traditional marketing" with the typical "manufacturer to wholesaler to retailer to consumer" flow chart. What the educators are not recognizing (or admitting) is that the traditional marketing of goods and services, while very successful in the Sixties and Seventies, was the primary culprit of inflation during this period and led to the demise of many businesses in the Eighties. Inflation in its simplest terms means rising prices, and the primary cause of rising prices is the continual increase of business overhead expense. All the levels in the traditional marketing chain require a minimum profit margin. In order to maintain this margin at an acceptable level, increases in overhead expense must either be absorbed, which reduces the profit margin, or must be passed down the marketing chain to the consumer. In order to maintain the "status quo" profit margin at each level in the marketing chain, the consumer ends up paying for the entire increase in overhead expense.

Due to increased competition for traditional businesses from "Discount" stores during the past several years, the simple answer of increasing the price of the product at the retail level is no longer acceptable. If you cannot continue to pass all expense increases to the consumer, you must eventually look at reducing overhead expenses and becoming more efficient.

NEW METHODS OF DISTRIBUTION NECESSARY

There is an "exodus" taking place to the "new kid" on the block, network marketing. It is simply defined as the movement of quality products from the manufacturer to the ultimate consumer at a fair price. The technology and application of network marketing has been around for many years and has created such successful companies as Amway, Avon, Mary Kay, and NSA, just to mention a few.

Through the use of network marketing, companies can eliminate most of the costly overhead expenses of traditional marketing such as advertising, wholesale/retail sales forces, maintenance of retail outlets, and local and regional warehouses. By eliminating or substantially reducing these expenses, the manufacturer is able to offer substantial commissions to its distributors. These commissions are earned from direct (personal) sales and/or rebates and bonuses based on the wholesale volume of the organizations the distributors have developed. This concept has allowed many of the large network marketing companies to operate without high leverage from debt and to achieve strong capital (net worth) and liquidity (cash) positions.

While the advantages to the manufacturers that use network marketing are substantial, the opportunity it creates for their distributors is even greater. The majority of working age people in this country work for someone else and only have dreams of ever working for themselves and becoming financially independent. Even the people who start their own traditional businesses are confronted with the unavoidable traditional overhead expenses. Most people think that in order to have a "legitimate" business you must invest a substantial amount of your own money, borrow from the bank, sign lease obligations or purchase real estate, buy or lease equipment, carry inventory, and hire people. What people do not understand is that this is not necessarily the creation of a legitimate business, but the creation of a legitimate risk.

Network marketing allows you to start your own business on either a part-time basis or on a full-time career basis without the overhead expenses of a traditional business. If you become a distributor with a quality company, your potential for income can be many times greater than working for someone else or owning your own traditional business. ■

No Help Wanted

By John Milton Fogg

JOHN MILTON FOGG IS
THE EDITOR OF
UPLINE™, THE
JOURNAL FOR
NETWORK MARKETING
LEADERS AND AUTHOR
OF THE GREATEST
NETWORKER IN THE
WORLD. HE CONDUCTS
SEMINARS FOR NETWORK-
ING PROFESSIONALS AND
PRODUCES THE
UPLINE™ MASTERS
SEMINARS TAPES.
THERE IS NO
CONNECTION
BETWEEN UPLINE™
AND THIS PUBLICATION

For almost fifty years, network marketing has been held as "alternative employment." Like "alternative" medicine and "alternative" agriculture, our industry has been a possibility for only those few adventurous men and women willing to risk the stormy entrepreneurial seas outside the safe harbor of conventional business.

Now that's changing–in large part because of the dramatic transformation of the American workplace.

The Employment Side

Current unemployment is at 7.4 percent (October 1992), way up from the 5.2 percent of two years ago. You know the litany–nearly two million jobs cut in non-farm sectors in the past two years, and hundreds of thousands cut from electronics, construction, managerial/supervisory–it's hitting collars of all colors.

A decade ago we wrestled with a 10 percent jobless figure, so that's no big deal. Or is it?

Yes, it is. What's different about this recession/recovery is that this time an alarming percentage of the jobs lost are gone forever. Some economic experts (such as author Paul Zane Pilzer) predict 20 percent unemployment by the year 2000. Why?

Because the changes we are witnessing in the American workplace are not just a series of seasonal or even cyclical alterations, but a dynamic transformation to a new and better way of working. The focus of business in the 90's is "leaner, cleaner, and meaner."

The Corporate Side

Business cannot afford to pay the going human being wage rate if the same work can be done by a computer or a machine. An American auto worker earns $65,000 in pay and benefits. A middle manager makes $50,000. If a robot or computer can do their jobs, without need for day care, life insurance, sick leave, or paid vacations, there is no dollar-sense in keeping them on. And that's what's happening in both blue and white-collar professions.

Where will this cost-for-performance trend show up next? In marketing. Marketing (meaning promotion, advertising, sales, and distribution) is 80 percent of a product's cost. If a corporation can invent a way to pay less for its marketing efforts, increase sales results in current and new markets, and pay only for sales results after those sales are made, they'll do it. Wouldn't you?

Both Sides Now

As jobs are cut (but not forgotten by the people who once had and still need them) and as corporations become more bottom line-oriented, network marketing will become the beneficiary of both business megatrends.

People will turn to network marketing to augment their incomes, as a hedge against unemployment, and ultimately as a positive, full-fledged career choice.

Corporations will turn to network marketing as a way to increase sales, enter new markets, and pay for both only after the results are in. In both cases and for both reasons the network marketing industry stands to benefit greatly.

The Wave of the Future

Network marketing is an answer to the employment dilemma for the disenfranchised American worker and workers around the world as the networking explosions in Poland, Brazil, South Korea, and Austria attest.

Network marketing is one of the solutions to the cost versus productivity problem faced by business around the world. ■

INCOME CLAIMS

BY KEITH B. LAGGOS

LAGGOS IS PRESIDENT AND PUBLISHER OF MONEY MAKER'S MONTHLY, THE INTERNATIONAL JOURNAL FOR DIRECT SALES AND NETWORK MARKETING. THIS ARTICLE WAS REPRINTED FROM THE MARCH, 1992 ISSUE.

Sometimes, it seems, an individual earning $1,200 per month won't try an income opportunity unless they have been told that the opportunity offers an earning potential of $100,000 per month—even if the chances of achieving it are less than one in a million. One wonders if people stop and think when they hear these high potential income claims.

One piece of literature, for a company now about nine months old, claims to have an income potential of about $540,000. When you do the calculations to determine how many sales and distributors you need in your organization to accomplish this potential, you will realize that this is unrealistic.

In fact, this company claims to have paid out two million dollars in commissions and currently has about twenty-four thousand distributors. If you divide two million dollars by twenty-four thousand, you will note that the average total commission paid out to date is about eighty-three dollars per distributor over a nine month period. Even the top distributors of this company, with thousands of distributors in their downlines, are making a small fraction of the $540,000 potential.

FACT NOT POTENTIAL

Another new company claims that you can earn over eight thousand dollars with eighty-nine sales. In fact, in the first two months there were several dozen distributors who indeed earned over eight thousand dollars. It would be proper for that company to say, "We had x number of distributors who have earned in excess of eight thousand dollars in the first two months." This is stating a fact. Although it is a fact, it is less proper to insinuate that you too can earn eight thousand dollars.

Some programs are prone to income claims. One such example would be deep level matrix programs. In this type of program, it is very easy to calculate the number of sales needed to fill a sales organization and the income a filled sales organization would produce. For example, in a 2 x 12 matrix, to have a filled matrix would require 8,190 distributors actively purchasing or selling the product/service without any holes in the sales organization.

Although there have been larger sales organizations than this in certain types of programs, as far as I know, no one—not even the company itself—has ever perfectly filled a 2 x 12 matrix.

Because these claims are not illegal, you may encounter several examples of income claims during your search for an appropriate MLM. Be advised that as a consumer you must be aware and use good business sense and logic.

Canada will not allow income claims that can not be substantiated. You may only state, as a matter of fact, the income you have personally earned or the average income that 90 percent of the distributors have made in the company.

This is a wise policy. Distributor income claims should be restricted to actual achieved income or to a statement of another individual's achieved income. In addition, it would be proper to be able to state the income potential from each individual large volume sale.

All income claims should be based on verifiable history. In other words, statements such as, "I have personally made two thousand dollars in the first two weeks," ought to be allowed if payments for the claimed earnings can be verified. If something is true, it always should be allowed to be stated without legal consequences.

Even when statements are made based on actual income earnings, there is still room for misrepresentation. Over the years, I have seen many large misleading checks flashed; in some cases the checks had not been earned, but were written for marketing purposes; in other cases, the checks represented several commissions combined into one large check.

However, if income claims were restricted to actual amounts earned, it would give a prospect a realistic idea of what is at least possible. The information would be based on fact rather than projection. ∎

Upline Financial Press Reader Service

The companies and authors listed below are making additional information available. Just circle the corresponding provider number on the adjacent card, affix postage and mail. You will be sent the requested information as soon as possible. If your card is missing, just write the provider numbers on a plain postcard, making sure to include return address, and mail it to UFP Reader Service, 8 Church Street, Ste. 109 , Montclair, NJ 07042.

Upline Financial Press acts as an information clearing house on your behalf. We want to know that the information you have received is useful to you. Please send comments or suggestions to the above address.

TO RECEIVE INFORMATION ABOUT BOOKS AND NEWSLETTERS BY CONTRIBUTORS TO THIS BOOK (CHOOSE AS MANY AS YOU LIKE):

01) Larry Kramer
02) Keith B. Laggos
03) E. Kearney & M. Bandley
04) John Kalench
05) Debbi A. Ballard
06) Greg Stewart
07) Leonard Clements
08) Jeffrey A. Babener
09) D. Jack Smith
10) Dirk Johnson
11) Doris Wood
12) J.Micheal Palka
13) John M. Fogg
14) Gini Graham Scott
15) Tom Williams
16) Jack M. Zufelt
17) Kathy Mathews
18) James B. Lawrence
19) Henry W. Marks
20) Resource List for Books, Tapes, and Organizations

TO RECEIVE INFORMATION ABOUT MULTI-LEVEL MARKETING COMPANIES FEATURED IN THIS BOOK, CIRCLE ONE OR MORE OF THE FOLLOWING (PLEASE ALLOW AMPLE TIME FOR DELIVERY OF INFORMATION, DUE TO THE FACT THAT IT WILL BE COMING FROM VARIOUS SOURCES):

100) A•Dora
101) AIM International
102) AMS, Inc.
103) Amway Corporation
104) Body Wise International
105) Brite International
106) Cambridge
107) Carco International
108) Cell Tech
109) Diamite
110) Discover Toys
111) E. Excel International
112) ElySee Cosmetics
113) Enhanced Living
114) Enrich International
115) Envirotech International
116) First Fitness International, Inc.
117) The Fuller Brush Company
118) Herbalife International
119) Jafra Cosmetics, Inc.
120) Japan Life International
121) Karla Jordan Internatonal
122) Light Force
123) Lite & Rite
124) MXM Living
125) Mary Kay Cosmetics, Inc.
126) Matol Botanical
127) Melaleuca, Inc.
128) Multi-Pure Corporation
129) The Nanci Corporation
130) Natural World Incorporated
131) Natus Corporation
132) Neways
133) Nikken USA, Inc.
134) Noevir, Inc.
135) NonScents
136) NSA
137) NuSkin International, Inc.
138) Nutrition Express Corporation
139) Nutrition For Life
140) Omnition
141) Oriflame International
142) Our Secret Creation
143) Oxyfresh USA, Inc.
144) Quorum International
145) Reliv
146) Rexall Showcase International
147) Shaklee U.S., Inc.
148) Shaperite Concepts, Ltd.
149) Sunrider International
150) Uni-Vite U.S.A., Inc.
151) Vitol International
152) Watkins
153) Younger Living, Inc.

TO RECEIVE INFORMATION ABOUT BEING CONSIDERED FOR INCLUSION IN THE NEXT EDITION OF THIS BOOK:

1000) MLM Company
2000) Awards for Excellence
3000) Spotlight on Success
4000) Article Contributor

Everyone's your Customer

By Michale Bandley & Elizabeth Kearney

Michale Bandley and Elizabeth Kearney are the authors of Network Marketing: Another Form of Direct Selling, and the principals of Kearney/Bandley Enterprises, creators of the Prospect Quotient Checklist.

You have only four minutes to make an impression on another person. What they see, how you speak, and what you do will have far more impact upon them than the actual words you use.

A well-known UCLA study showed that in virtually any presentation: 7 percent of the impact comes from the words said, 38 percent of the impact relates to body language, and 55 percent of the impact is related to the way you say the words.

This information is important to remember whenever you are dealing with a customer or prospect.

For example, there is a story that came out of WWI about a meeting held by a young sergeant who was asking his men to enroll in a life insurance program set up by the army. He told them that by doing so they would be providing for their families in case of death.

The men showed no interest in it even though he pointed out that their money would vest and that the rates were exceptional. After several tries, he gave up.

A young officer saw his disappointment and asked if he could talk. "Now, look here men—here's the deal. The army is offering us ten thousand dollar life insurance policies before we get to the front. If we die, it costs them money. Who are they going to put on the front lines? The man who is going to cost them ten thousand dollars or a man who doesn't cost them a cent?"

After a shocked silence, every man in the room signed up. Why? The approach had impact.

When you gear your information to the values and behavioral styles of the customers addressed, you increase its impact and its likelihood of acceptance.

Customer Relations

Good customer relations require that you understand the other person. Strong relationships are more likely to develop when we are friendly, but not overly so, when we are at ease and comfortable with the other person, and when we are assertive, but not aggressive. Pay attention to your own nonverbal signals. They may have more impact than you realize.

All of us can spot the signals that signify rejection: the person looks away, rolls his/her eyes, begins to squint. When we see these signals, we get the message.

Eye Contact

How often do you look away? Where do you look—up, off to the side, or directly at the person? By using your powers of observation, you can pick up signals from your client.

You can control eye contact by consciously following three simple steps:
1. observe
2. synchronize
3. lead

Pay attention to your customer's eye movements. If you find that they are frequently focused away from you, don't try to force contact. Look away as often as the customer does. Gradually increase the contact by looking at the customer for longer periods of time.

We have been taught that those who look at us are more concerned, interested, and honest than others. Use this past information to your advantage and build the rapport you need.

Gestures

Gestures are another important way to convey our information and personalize our communication. Open hands with palms up seem to say "trust me," whereas fists and fidgeting fingers often make the client or customer feel uncomfortable and ill at ease. When people put their hands on their hips, they assume a power position.

Even though body language is important, don't read too much into it. For example, arms crossed across the chest are often thought to indicate hostility or doubt. The person could just be cold.

A study done by Dr. Edward Hall produced interesting anthropological information regarding our communication in ways that most of us don't consider.

ENVELOPES OF SPACE

We have envelopes of space (a personal space that is not to be invaded except by invitation). The space you maintain and the space that your customers or clients prefer to have maintained between them and others makes a marked difference in the effectiveness of any communication. For example:

Distance	Type of Communication
18 inches	Intimate
1 to 2 feet	Personal
2 to 4 feet	General Contact
4 to 7 feet	Social
7 to 12 feet	Formal
over 12 feet	Public

When this distance is violated, the interchange is often short-circuited. We have all seen someone backing away from another who is moving forward, talking, and unaware that little, if any, real communication is occurring.

The space envelope is less developed to the side and back. If you aren't sure that this is right, try this experiment. Get in a crowded elevator and face the group. Watch the reaction.

VOICE

People form a lasting impression of you from hearing you speak. Make certain that the impression is a good one. The variation of pitch can create different moods and reactions, so you can control the impact you make by controlling the pitch of your voice.

Accents and language patterns can help or hurt communication. If your pattern is the same as the customer's, you are on firm ground. However, some patterns are irritating to those from other geographical areas.

Remember this and avoid the most pronounced patterns or colloquialisms. Enunciate clearly. Blurred words can be annoying and confusing.

Your voice resonates differently in your head from how it comes across to others. Try taping yourself and play the tape back with the intent of improving your voice pattern and tone.

Remember to pause when you are searching for words or ideas. Don't fill in the pauses with "you knows" or "uhhs."

Usually, the most pleasant voice to listen to is low in pitch. Your prospects and clients will listen longer if your voice is soothing and not penetrating, so work on keeping it pitched low, even when irritation or frustration rises. Most people associate a high pitch with hysteria.

Working on your voice can be fun. Try it. ∎

MORE TIPS ON SELLING
by John Kalench

- *Add variety to your presentations by using visual aids. Flip charts, photographs, products, and videos help drive your point home.*

- *Ask open-ended questions to keep your prospect engaged. An open-ended question is one that can't be answered with a "yes" or "no." The average adult has a short attention span, so it's important to keep them interested in what you're saying. For example:*
  If you had an extra five hundred dollars per month income, what would you do with it?
  Why would you like to have your own business?
  What are your personal and financial goals for the next six months?
  How do you plan to achieve these goals?

- *Product demonstrations are especially effective if there is an immediate result that your prospect can see. Skin care classes, facials, air and water filters, and heat-resistant insulators can easily create the kind of drama that adds to the user's commitment.*

- *Humor can be used as an ice-breaker, a rapport builder, and an attention getter. But avoid using jokes or quips which could be offensive to your audience.*

John Kalench is President of Millionaires In Motion (MIM), an educational company for the network marketing industry, and the author or two best-selling books, Being the Best You Can Be in MLM, and The Greatest Oppportunity in the History of the World..

THE STREET SMART DISTRIBUTOR

BY ROBERT BUTWIN

ROBERT BUTWIN IS ONE OF THE CONTRIBUTING EDITORS OF UPLINE, THE JOURNAL FOR NETWORK MARKETING LEADERS AND THE AUTHOR OF THE BOOK THE STREET SMART DISTRIBUTOR THERE IS NO CONNECTION BETWEEN UPLINE ™AND THIS PUBLICATION

Getting immediate results is vital in our business. How long can you or your people continue to devote the time, energy, and effort required to build an MLM business without seeing tangible results? The answer is: not very long. One key to success in network marketing is setting it up so people get immediate results. As Dave Klaybor, president and founder of Powerline Systems, says, "First, you want to become a good student, then a great student. Next, become a good teacher, and then a great teacher."

The first step to creating fast results is learning how to talk to people when you first begin and which people to talk to.

WHO YOU GONNA CALL?

When you set out to build a network, you have a choice: do you want to start with your friends or with people you don't know? A lot of people, for whatever reason, don't want to approach their friends at first. It's "too risky." I use the image of a gold mine to help put this in perspective.

Let's say you've just stumbled on to a gold mine. I mean a real one with millions of dollars worth of honest-to-goodness gold nuggets, right in your backyard. There's more gold in here than you could ever mine in a dozen lifetimes. Obviously, there's enough to go around. So, with whom do you want to share it? With your friends or people you don't know?

If you really know the mine is rich, you probably want your family and friends to have first crack at sharing the wealth. It seems only natural. If you're not sure whether that's really gold in them thar hills and doubt how rich it really is, you might want to try sharing it with people you don't know first, just so it can prove itself before you "risk" turning your friends on to it. You wouldn't want to get your friends' hopes up, right? Besides, you don't want to look foolish to them.

LOOKING GOOD

It's a fact of human nature: we absolutely hate to look bad in other people's eyes. Especially those people whose opinions we value most highly.

Naturally, most of us place a higher value on the opinions of our family and close friends than we do on those of strangers we may never see again.

What do you do? Network marketers have an expression, "Let the tools do the work." What that really means is, "Let the tools do their work" and you just be responsible for doing yours.

What's the tools' work? Their work is to look good, to be the "experts," to make a positive impression, and to provide the information you need to share. Your work is to be the friend who shows them the tools; your work is to nurture the relationship.

Use your upline and the tools. A professional video will do wonders for how people respond to the opportunity being presented. A three-way call with your sponsor may do even more, especially if he or she says something about how committed he or she is to helping you and your prospect change your pattern of success for the better.

GIVE YOUR FRIENDS A BREAK

When new distributors don't approach people they already know with their networking opportunity, I say it's because they don't believe it's a gold mine. They're playing it safe by talking to strangers first. If a few dozen strangers sign up and start to do the business successfully right away, then it must be okay. Then, they'll share the opportunity with their friends. I say, approaching it that way is doing your friends a disservice. If you're convinced that this business you're in really can lead to a better life, give the people you know first shot at it. Let the tools do their work. Your job in the beginning is to set it up so your friends will take a look at the tools so their interest can be qualified. That's all you have to do.

From then on, it's a sorting process. If they get the big picture of what network marketing offers, they'll want to know more.

Many network marketers condition themselves to think a person is only saying no for now. That's all it is, for now. Check back with them next week, next month, in three months. Everything in our world is constantly changing, even people's opinions and perceptions of your MLM business opportunity.

Let Them Take a Look

There's an old salesman's adage that goes: "twenty, twelve, two." Out of twenty sales calls, you'll get about twelve appointments (people taking a look) and make an average of two sales. The more people you talk to, the more who'll take a look, and the more who'll get involved.

If you were to call up strangers from your local telephone book and ask them to take a look at your opportunity, how many would do that? If you were to call up family and friends and ask them to take a look at your opportunity, how many would do that? For immediate results, first contact people you already know just for a look. One effective way I've found to approach people goes something like this: "Tim, you know I've been looking for ways to diversify my income. I want to have a richer, more rewarding life. I want more freedom, more time to do what I want, and more money. From all the research I've done, I think network marketing is the best opportunity for me. You know what, Tim? The biggest problem I've found in getting started in this business is other people's perceptions. Everybody seems to have a strong opinion about what this business is really about. I've seen how it can work for me. I think it can work for you, too. Would you be willing to check out some information about network marketing if I sent it to you?"

The goal at this point is to have people agree to take a look. That's your only job. Your job is not to "get them into the business." That's their job. Yours is to have them take a look. Then the attractiveness of your opportunity, the value of your products, your enthusiasm, and their ability to see themselves reaching the goals they want through your opportunity takes over. You can help that process along by letting them have the best tools and sharing your own excitement and passion, but it's their choice.

What If They Say No?

Here's how I handle that: They say, "Robert, thanks for sending me the information (tape, samples, whatever), but I'm not interested." I say, "You're welcome. I appreciate your taking time to look at it. One key to my business is referrals. Is there anyone you know, somebody who is ambitious, wants a little extra income, or maybe in a dead-end job, who'd be interested in taking a look at my business?"

Let's use psychology for a minute. This person, probably a friend of yours, has just said no to you. Nobody likes to disappoint people, especially a friend. You just gave them an opportunity to make it all better. Nine times out of ten, they'll jump at the chance to help out with a couple of names. That takes the heat off them and enables them to support you.

Now, I add some spice to the game with, "Network marketing is about rewarding people fairly for their efforts. Frank, if you give me the name of someone who joins me in the business, I'll treat you with a gift certificate for dinner."

That costs me fifty dollars only when the referral comes into the business. It allows me to make a juicy offer to Frank right now, and I'm going beyond my normal network of acquaintances, which is a major plus. By the way, through this whole process, do you think Frank may be taking another look at how this business actually works? Maybe he's even thinking about how simple it is, even fun? Not all the "Franks" you talk to are doing that, but you'd be surprised how many are.

Frank said no, then he gave me a couple of referrals. Great. Then I ask, "Frank, I've learned that people's circumstances change. Is it okay to keep in touch with you? You know, send you some additional information, copies of articles, newsletter reprints, anything I come across about network marketing and let you know how my business is going?"

Most people say yes, and now you've got a chance to keep your success in front of them. It's amazing how people who weren't interested in April get very interested in October, when they see how you've gone from zero dollars to a couple of thousand dollars income or more in such a short time. Just drop them a short note sharing your success attached to an article or flyer. Success is a very contagious condition. ■

HANDLING DISAPPOINTMENT

BY HENRY W. MARKS

HENRY W. MARKS, A WELL-KNOWN PUBLISHING VETERAN, HAS HELD SENIOR MANAGEMENT POSITIONS AT PSYCHOLOGY TODAY, THE WALL STREET JOURNAL, PLAYBOY, AND TRAVEL & LEISURE.

Disappointment is a thief! Disappointment steals our ability to act on our plans. Disappointment steals our ability to act with courage. Disappointment steals our peace of mind, leaving only heartache. Disappointment steals our freedom, our health, our dignity, and our dreams.

And disappointment patiently waits for us all. It waits to wreck havoc on us when we are unprepared and when we are most vulnerable.

Disappointment is a sneak-thief .

HAVE A HEART

When the thief strikes, we become discouraged. We search for strength, we "feel sick." The phrase: "The heart's gone out of him," seems to describe all too well how we are feeling.

The French word for "heart" is *coeur*, and *coeur* is the root of "courage." To deal with disappointment we need renewed courage with which to act in a positive and forward manner. Renewed courage must spring from the heart. As the song goes: "Ya gotta have heart. Lots and lots of heart!" "Faint heart never won fair lady" is a time-honored phrase, though not currently politically correct. Let's say, "Faint heart does not big bucks make."

How do we get our courage back?

With Action.

Action imprisons disappointment. The thief is banished from the present and sentenced to silence in the past, behind us, where we want it.

Courage doesn't come from whistling in the dark like a schoolboy passing a graveyard on a dark, cold night. Courage comes from taking action.

How to act is the most important issue to address when ridding ourselves of disappointment. And rid ourselves we must. If we try to "deal" with disappointment, we keep it alive. We keep it in the present. We get all tangled up with the emotional and mental problems that disappointment uses to immobilize us.

So, we don't want to "deal" with disappointment. We want to have the strength, the heart—the courage—to act in the most appropriate manner, to replace disappointment with satisfaction.

RETARGET THE GOAL

The most important action we can take is to determine our present position. Where are we as opposed to where we want to be? Where do we need to be? How much of a detour from our most direct route to the objective are we on?

It is the size and direction of this "direct line gap" that we have to determine in order to plan the actions that we have to take in order to get back "on target." In computing the detour (the nature of our unwelcome position), it is necessary to answer basic questions about the factors we must bring into play to get us back to where we want to be.

Stay away from dwelling on questions like "What went wrong?"

Get on with: How do I get to where I want to be? What are prospects saying my solutions should be? Do I need fresh cash to re-direct the business? What training do I have to get done? What adjustments do I have to make in my business plan? What are my new time frames? How will I audit my progress?

MAKE A MAP

As we determine the answers to how we get back on target, it's necessary to create a picture of what we have to do with some sense of priorities that point toward the timing we need to take into consideration.

Rather than write a narrative, try to make a grid, a map. Going down the left hand side of the page list the various topics that call for action. Across the top put the specifics of the timing (when), quantities, options, name and phone numbers, sources to be researched, and other topics that come off our investigation of what it is we have to do in order to get to where we want to be.

The first time I saw this done was on a sheet of brown butcher's paper about 8 feet long and 3 feet wide. The manager in charge had marked it up with crayons and had laid out the main areas of information and activity that required action.

If required for investment purposes or internal communications, an Action Plan or "Revision of Business Plan" can now be written, with ease from our grid.

In the meantime, refine the "Action Map." Keep it in sight, visible. Find ways to signal accomplishments: green stickers, check-marks, high-lighters. Get the audit of action going, immediately.

GET EXTRA POWER

We all have professional and informal "counselors." Whether they are accountants, lawyers, colleagues, or friends who are in related or other businesses, we all have access to "counselors" who are interested in our well-being. It is vital that we use these resources.

It is our ability to unburden ourselves, to share, and to start listening to ourselves talk about what we are going to act on that helps us to jumpstart our action plan.

We have the power to start talking our way into the actions we need to consider and take in order to get to where we want to be. To harness that power we have to do some thinking, and then some talking. If we get more than a head-nod in response, we begin to achieve insights. Our "consultative sounding board" begins to play back to us the perspectives and assistance we need to round out our thinking and our plans.

One of the most successful "turn arounds" I have ever met told me, "I start to talk about solutions even before I know what I'm talking about for a simple reason. I can't stand to feel isolated, and talking to people who are interested in my business gives me a sense of strength and support. Then I can act. It's the original talking cure."

A LEARNING EXPERIENCE

As we stay away from "dealing with disappointment," the question comes up: "If I don't spend time dealing with my disappointment won't I make the same mistake over again?"

The answer is: If you follow a good plan to get you off your detour, you'll be just fine.

There is a principle to consider and to take into account that will help assist us in learning how to avoid a repetition of past errors that underlie disappointment.

The principle is: People do what they can, with what they think they have, as they see the given situation.

We have to be able to apply this principle to ourselves, as well as those we work with. For in order to get a new result, we have to foster a new consciousness from which we are able to create new planning and actions that succeed.

To change our behavior and actions and to minimize repetition of unrewarding actions, we have two variables with which to work: "what we think we have" and "how we see the given situation."

The first variable is a matter of taking inventory. We have to be able to take a realistic inventory of what we have in order to figure out what we have either overlooked or what we need to get in order to accomplish our plan. Writing down this "inventory" and going over it with business associates or "counselors" will quickly give us direction and assistance in knowing what changes we have to make, now.

The second variable is a matter of perception. "How we see the given situation" is what we have to change. It is our initial perception that has led us to our disappointment. The actions that we have taken from this misperception have led us to being disappointed. Now we examine, we scrutinize, the situation. Where has our perception been proven realistic and where has it been tested and found to be unrealistic? Again, we urge ourselves to write down our observations, so that we can look at them and discuss them with others. We find out what we have overlooked, where we can bring new views of our situation, and what new ways to look for options with which to gain our objectives.

When working with associates it is vital that we bear this behavioral principle in mind. If we wish to change the behavior of our associates, then we have to help them to either change their perceptions, which means re-orientation, or what they think they have, which demands new plans and training from us. And when we find that we are getting feed-back indicating shifts in realizing the presence of either new or unutilized resources, plus a new view of the situation, then we are well on our way to helping re-direct behavior, and to obtaining new results.

JAIL THAT THIEF

I've never agreed with what I was told as a boy, that we grow from pain. I have found that we can grow as much, if not more, and with less effort, if we grow from the nourishing experience of satisfaction. Winning breeds winning.

Knowing that Newton's Law applies in matters of success, that "Success will continue unless we screw up," we court the experience of success. We move toward productive thinking and action. We never, never attempt to deal with disappointment.

It's a waste of time. ■

Saturation: Myth or Reality

By Greg Stewart

Greg Stewart and Randy Stoltz co-founded Network Productions, Inc., producers of the videos Turning Dreams into Reality and The Blinding Paradigm.

You may have been told that saturation will not occur within an MLM company. I would like to present two opposing views for you to think about.

With approximately 250 million people in the United States alone, it's easy to show that a company that has as many as 50,000 to 100,000 distributors has a long way to go.

It appears obvious there are many new people available to approach and sponsor into your downline to achieve your financial freedom. After all, hasn't Amway been around for approximately thirty years? Everybody is not an Amway distributor, right?

Here are some things to think about. What do 50,000 to 100,000 distributors represent? The total number of distributors that have been entered into the company computer or just the active distributors? There can be a vast difference.

Please understand that the majority of distributors do not see the financial success they expected with their opportunity then quit or become inactive with the company. And, of course, they are never to blame; it is always someone else's, typically their sponsor's or the company's, fault. People don't like to admit to any type of failure.

The attrition rate of distributors can be over 90 percent with any MLM company. Many companies find it beneficial to cleanse their computers of inactive distributors, usually by requiring an annual renewal fee.

A company that has 50,000 to 100,000 currently active distributors may have had well over one million people that have been distributors in the past. And, for each distributor that was sponsored, many more had been presented or approached with the opportunity that did not become distributors. Millions of people may have been approached.

Public awareness of a company's opportunity may be a detriment to your downline's growth or, more accurately stated, to your percentage of distributor growth. This happens when people have an awareness of an opportunity or have been approached many times with the opportunity of a specific company and know of friends and family who participated and have since quit. Prospects or potential distributors may prejudge such a business opportunity. They may think they know all about it, even though they don't have all the necessary information to make a valid decision. This is what I call the "perception of saturation."

Here are two different arguments. If a company's opportunity had a 33 percent level of awareness with our population, you might think 67 percent of the population have never heard of the company's opportunity or products. Therefore, they are not going to prejudge it, as it has a long way to go in terms of potential growth and income for you as a new distributor. Another way of looking at the same percentages is that one out of three people is aware of the company and its opportunity.

You may be told that now is the best time to get involved with a company because it is seasoned or going through a momentum phase of growth. If there is no saturation and the opportunity is the same now as it was earlier, why do top distributors rush to new countries as they open up? Why do distributor incomes grow at a much slower rate for those getting involved at a later growth cycle of a company compared to those distributors who started before its momentum phase of growth?

Large incomes earned in MLM are developed by the creation of large downlines, and large downlines are developed by the process of duplication. You may have great communication skills and sponsor many people under the most difficult circumstances. Will your new distributor be able to do the same?

Mathematically, the market never really saturates; sometimes it just seems that way. Is perception reality? ■

Ground Floor or Momentum?

By Leonard W. Clements

Leonard Clements is the publisher of MarketWave, an opportunity analysis newsletter focusing on the MLM industry. MarketWave features in-depth reviews of popular programs, as well as exposés on the latest schemes, scams and money-games. As a speaker and trainer, Mr. Clements conducts his Facts & Myths of Multi-level Marketing seminars throughout California.

When's the best time to get in? One of the many controversies surrounding MLM theory is determining the optimum time to get involved with an opportunity. Pre-launch, ground floor, right before or just after the momentum phase begins, or after the company growth stabilizes or matures. Who knows for sure?

Ground Floor

There are pros and cons to each argument. The major problem with getting involved with a pre-launch or "ground floor" opportunity is that they are usually no more than one story high. Most start-up MLM's are long gone before the ink on their brochures dry. This failure rate seems to be dropping slightly, but even if it matches that of conventional start-up businesses, it'll still be a staggering 85 percent in the first two years.

Another drawback to start-up operations is the lack of a sophisticated support base. When you try to go upline to get advice and support from those already successful in the business, you may hit the president of the company just two levels above you.

The flip-side, of course, is that eventually you could end up at the tippy-top of a huge organization if your company happens to become one of the handful that survives the long haul.

But even if it does make it through those treacherous first two years, you still may have to wait one, two, three, four, or more years before any substantial growth occurs.

Momentum

The "momentum" phase is when name recognition starts to kick in and the geometric expansion of the organization starts to explode. Some say the best time to get in would be right before this momentum stage hits. But, alas, that would require a crystal ball. The time when a company is about to go into momentum is totally speculative.

How about right after momentum hits? Some will say that's too late. It may appear to be true since a good indicator of when a company is in momentum is when everybody seems to be doing it.

The saturation myth starts to take over. If this logic were correct, then momentum would cease. Yet, for some MLM opportunities, momentum phases last years. Some momentum phases, though, are short-lived and weak, while others never really occur at all. This stage of an MLM company's growth cycle can also be crippling or even fatal. Many times a company is not ready for the momentum and can't keep up. Those that anticipate it may have to go into heavy debt since revenues are not there yet.

This stage is actually a normal part of the growth cycle of any kind of business, except the upward growth tends to be much more acute and the increase in sales more dramatic in an MLM operation due to the geometric expansion of the sales force and product movement.

I firmly believe that the whole MLM industry is about to go into a momentum stage. With more and more people wanting to work at home or not working at all, this "alternative" form of income will become more intriguing.

Not only do companies go into momentum, but individual downlines do as well. Eventually, if you stay with it long enough, this geometric progression will kick in for your specific downline.

The real question you should ask is: what's best for you?

All phases of a company's growth have their advantages and disadvantages. Your risk factor increases the earlier you get in, but sometimes so does your income potential.

You could label multi-level marketers the same way you label investors. Conservative? Then find a well established company past the scrutiny stage. Aggressive? Go for pre-launch. Or are you somewhere in between?

Only you have the answer. ∎

THE ABC TECHNIQUE

BY LEONARD W. CLEMENTS

Would you ever try to pour hot coffee into a thermos with the lid still on? Could you put a video cassette into your VCR if it already had a cartridge in it?

Of course not. Unfortunately, the way that most people prospect for MLM partners makes about as much sense.

For many years, you've all been taught to call up your friends and try to get them to come to an opportunity meeting, at least read some information, or watch a video about your MLM opportunity. To do anything different would be going against the number one commandment of your industry—duplicate what works. In other words, "Thou shalt not try to reinvent the wheel."

I'm certainly not about to suggest otherwise. However, I do believe there are very effective ways of making the wheel roll a little smoother and a little faster.

First, you must remember that when you propose your opportunity, you are offering a business opportunity. It is a chance at being a true entrepreneur. Secondly, you are proposing that your prospect get involved with multi-level marketing. In other words, you have at least one, probably two, major challenges here—challenges you must overcome before you can even think about proposing your specific opportunity. These challenges, nine times out of ten, are the reasons why your prospect won't even look at your opportunity.

Surveys indicate that about 85 percent of all working Americans would like to own their own businesses if they could. In other words, if all obstacles were removed, they would prefer to be their own boss rather than work for someone else.

This amounts to approximately 160 million people. These are your MLM prospects. Now, when 160 million people want to do something and don't do it, there must be a good reason.

When asked why they don't go into business for themselves, people usually come up with one or more of the following four reasons:

1. It takes too much money. I don't have thousands of dollars to invest in a business.

2. It takes too much time. I don't want to work eighty hours a week, seven days a week to get my business going.

3. It is too risky. Over 80 percent of all businesses fail in the first two years.

4. I don't know how. I've never taken any business courses. I don't know anything about taxes, accounting, or marketing.

I can assure you, if your prospects are not currently operating their own business, they have considered the possibility at some time in their lives. They have also determined the reasons why they can't (probably all four reasons). Therefore, before you even start to offer your MLM opportunity, you might want to dispel, as much as possible, these beliefs about why they can't go into business for themselves.

Let's say you are having lunch with your friends and you casually mention the fact that you are thinking about starting your own business. Then you ask if they have ever considered it.

Sure, they have considered it at some time or another.

You ask, "Well, why didn't you?"

They will inevitably respond with one or more of the previous four reasons.

Now comes the fun part. You ask them if they would ever consider going into business for themselves if:

• The total start-up costs were under five hundred dollars and the income potential were higher than the earnings of some CEO's of *Fortune 500* companies.

• The total time investment could be as little as ten to twenty hours a week.

• They could continue to work in their present job until the income from their business was sufficient to earn them at least an equal income, so there is little risk.

• There were numerous consultants available to them who are experts at running this business—who would train and advise them personally—for an unlimited number of hours, for the life of their business, absolutely free.

Not only that, you say, but there is another company that will take care of all your research and development, shipping, payroll, sales and payroll taxes, and legal problems. And, this company will do this for them every month for the life of their business for around twenty dollars a year.

Of course, your friend won't believe any of this. Ask them if they would consider it if all this were true.

Most likely they'll say something like, "Well, sure. But there's got to be a catch."

Is there? Isn't this an exact description of your basic MLM business opportunity? Is any of this an exaggeration?

No. You've just completed step "A" of the "ABC" technique.

Now, for the first time during this conversation, you will suggest that this type of business involves "network" or "multi-level" marketing. But don't get into your specific opportunity yet. There still may be a major hurdle to overcome. You still have step "B" to take care of.

There are basically three types of people you are going to come across during your recruiting efforts.

First, the cynics or skeptics. They believe MLM's are all scams, get-rich-quick schemes, illegal pyramids, and involve door-to-door and home party sales. One person I know even referred to them as "cults." For whatever reason, these people have a low opinion of MLM in general.

The second type are those who don't know anything about MLM. Perhaps they only think that it's something like a pyramid or that Amway is one.

The third, unfortunately smallest, group are those who are naturally intrigued by the concept. Usually these are people who were originally in the second group who heard about someone who made a lot of money in MLM. (By the way, if you find someone in this group, skip step "B". This step is presenting the MLM concept as a viable, honest form of business, which usually involves explaining what MLM is not, not what it is.)

Basically, you may want to mention that there are well over five million people in the U.S. who are pursuing this form of business. Also, throw out names like Rexall, MCI, and U.S. Sprint, which all involve MLM as a means of obtaining new customers. Briefly explain the obvious difference between an illegal pyramid and a legitimate MLM company. It would be helpful to share a sampling of favorable articles about the MLM industry in general. You may want to lead in with a generic video or audio cassette, that's scripted to legitimize the industry, not promote any particular opportunity. Whatever you can do to give the industry more credibility, do it.

Once these first two "preparation" steps are completed, you should then hand your prospect the video or literature about your opportunity. Challenge them to find the catch. Tell them you can't, even though you thought it was too good to be true, too. Instead of trying to get them to find out all the good things about your program, encourage them to find all the bad things. Challenge them to debunk it. Let's face it, someone would be much more likely to watch a video if it were for the purpose of justifying their negative beliefs than to contradict them. It's human nature.

The bottom line is this. The real trick to successful recruiting in any MLM organization is not convincing persons who have looked at your opportunity to get involved with you, it's getting them to just look at the opportunity.

Once someone seriously looks at a good MLM opportunity, it's pretty hard not to be at least a little intrigued. Unfortunately, nine out of ten won't look seriously. Actually, I'd guess five out of ten won't look at all. You've got to get them to just look. If you've got a good opportunity, the rest will take care of itself.

Two good analogies here would be the thermos and the VCR. Like the thermos, you must open your prospect's mind before you can pour anything into it. And like the VCR, there may already be something in there that you might have to remove first.

To borrow an analogy from Anthony Robbins (Robbins Research), it's as if your beliefs have legs like a chair. Only these legs are usually solid steel instead of wood. Believe me, people's beliefs as to why they can't go into business for themselves and what they believe MLM to be are solid beliefs. If you don't do something to at least weaken those legs before you come in with your new belief, forget it. It will bounce right off.

I'm certainly not suggesting that this "ABC" technique is going to knock down those legs, although it could. But if you can at least instill some doubt in the mind of your prospect, some spark of interest, or at least pessimistic curiosity, you've made a major gain. ∎

Legal Issues: MLM Vs. Pyramid Schemes

By Jeffrey A. Babener

Jeffrey Babener is a partner in the law firm of Babener & Associates, a graduate of USC Law School, and a member of both the California and Oregon State Bars. He is editor of the publication, Direct Sales Legaline, and author of many books, including The MLM Corporate Handbook. Reprinted with permission. @ copyright Jeffrey A. Babener, 1992.

Although not without its challenges today, as a general matter, legitimate network marketing companies are well received throughout the U.S. With increasing frequency, federal and state governments offer assistance and guidance to the network marketing industry. The IRS releases special publications and videos and has adopted specific regulations recognizing it as a legitimate profession. As in the franchising industry, several states have also adopted specific legislation for multi-level distribution companies which set forth objective standards for those companies to follow. Differentiating a legitimate network marketing opportunity from a pyramid scheme should not be a difficult task for the entrepreneur when some basic and objective indicators are observed.

Any industry that offers such dramatic rewards and carries with it such a low dollar cost of entry obviously will tend to attract some of the best and some of the worst entrepreneurs. The industry has not always thrived. Over the years, it has come perilously close to extinction as a result of prosecution by regulators who claimed the industry promoted pyramid schemes under the guise of legitimate marketing. And, in many cases, the prosecutors were correctly chasing and eradicating such pyramid schemes.

Other programs which were in fact legitimate have survived, however. In a classic legal decision in 1979, the Amway Corporation prevailed in such a prosecution; and, in fact, effectively received a stamp of approval of its marketing program by the Federal Trade Commission. This particular decision opened the door to many other legitimate multi-level marketing companies.

Because of the abuses of the "rotten apples" of the industry, multi-level marketing has become a closely scrutinized and regulated industry. Regulations regarding multi-level marketing companies in the United States are a constantly changing patchwork of overlapping laws, which lack uniformity and vary from state to state.

The basic thrust of these statutes is that marketing plans are prohibited when they require an investment or purchase by sales representatives for the right to recruit others for economic gain.

Under these statutes, multi-level marketing companies must be bona fide retail organizations which market bona fide products to the ultimate consumer. Inventory loading and "headhunting" (remuneration for the mere act of recruiting others) are prohibited. Sales kits should be sold at actual company cost to sales representatives.

In the leading legal decisions, a variety of abuses have been targeted as potential elements of illegal marketing plans:

1. Products which have "no real world" marketplace, i.e. the marketing program is a facade for a scam.

2. Products which are sold at inflated prices.

3. Plans which result in inventory loading or "buy-in" qualification by distributors.

4. Substantial cash investment requirements.

5. Mandatory purchases of peripheral or accessory products or services.

6. Plans in which distributors are left with substantial unsold inventory upon cancellation of participation.

7. Plans in which fees are paid to distributors for headhunting and emphasis is on recruitment rather than sale of product.

8. Earnings misrepresentations or inflated earnings representations.

In determining whether or not a program is a legitimate multi-level marketing opportunity, the would-be participant should consider several important points:

Product or Service: The company should offer a high quality product or service in which consumer satisfaction is guaranteed. It must have a "real" demand in the marketplace. If the product is consumed by distributors themselves, it must be one that distributors would want to buy on its own merits, irrespective of participation in the marketing plan.

Price: The price of the product or service must be fair and competitive in the marketplace. Distributors should be able to purchase the company product at wholesale or at a substantial discount from prices found in retail stores.

Investment Requirement: There should be no investment requirement at all, except a sales kit or demonstration material sold at company cost.

Purchase and Inventory Requirement: A legitimate marketing program should have no minimum purchase requirement, nor any inventory requirement, for one to become a distributor or sales representative. Once in the business, however, ongoing activity or qualification requirements are typical of network marketing companies.

Use of Product: Products should be used by consumers and not end up in a garage or basement.

Sales Commissions: Sales commissions should not be paid for the mere act of sponsoring other distributors.

Buy-back Policy: A legitimate multi-level marketing company will agree for some reasonable period of time to buy back inventory and sales kit materials in resalable condition from distributors who cancel participation in the program.

Retail Sales: The focus of the marketing program should be to promote retail sales to non-participants. Many states and programs recognize that purchases for personal or family use in reasonable amounts by distributors are also retail sales.

Distributor Activity: Many of the new statutes regarding multi-level distribution companies require that distributors perform a bona fide, supervisory, distributive selling or soliciting function in moving the product to the consumer, i.e. that they have meaningful contact and communication with their downline sales organization.

Earnings Representations: The basic rule is that a legitimate marketing program should not make any earnings representations unless those representations are based on a track record. Testimonials by individuals of their own experiences are not uncommon, however.

Training: A good network marketing program should offer solid training in sales and recruitment to its distributors.

The future of the network marketing industry will require cooperation by companies, distributors, and those governmental agencies charged with regulating the industry to assure that legitimate practices prevail and pyramiding schemes are stamped out. Every network marketer should apply the above principles in evaluating a new program or working within his/her existing program. ■

MLM Sensitive States

By D. Jack Smith

D. Jack Smith represents direct selling, franchising, and multi-level marketing companies, and is author of 50 State Multi-Level Compendium. He is a current member of the board of directors for the MLMIA, and member of the Lawyer's Council and Government Relations Committee for the DSA.

Multi-level marketing law is perhaps our nation's newest and most rapidly developing body of law.

Most of our traditional laws came to us from old England and are approximately nine hundred to one thousand years old. Our better known areas of law such as those pertaining to contracts, negligence, accidents, commercial transactions, and crime derive from English common law as influenced by an even older body of law coming from the Roman Empire.

Both of these areas and others are taught in law schools. At least a working knowledge of them must be possessed by every aspiring lawyer in order to pass each state's bar examination.

This is not the case with Multi-level Marketing law.

Multi-level Marketing law began in this country in the early 1940's. For all practical purposes, it is only as old as, perhaps its prime example, Amway Corporation.

Multi-level Marketing law is not taught in any law school in the United States. For one to have a national overview or grasp of this new body of law and its rapid development, an attorney must be uniquely situated or have had a lucky break which took him or her to many, many state capitols either in negotiations or litigation.

Most states don't have any specific Multi-level Marketing law statute. They have only an old "pyramid" law, which in many cases was passed prior to the founding of even the first multi-level marketing company.

The case law is scanty, sporadic, random, and often inconsistent. Even the judges have been afforded no opportunity to have any organized overview of the development of this rapidly emerging body of law.

In my practice it is not uncommon to see a young assistant attorney general right out of law school who believes that every time he sees a downline he has caught a pyramid scheme.

On some of these unhappy occasions, harmful and mistaken litigation results because the suit was filed through ignorance and through a lack of understanding of the social usefulness and benefit of the multi-level marketing method to the company's management, staff, sales force, and especially to its customers and consumers of its products and services.

The job of this new regulator is made even more difficult by the creativity of many entrepreneurs in our industry. Enforcement personnel can understand, now, the marketing of vitamins, health products, and tangible goods and services such as telephone services, but anything that is new or departs from the traditional unfortunately raises the suspicion level of the inexperienced agency. Some of the new coin merchandising plans in our industry furnish a good example of this.

Fortunately, however, our government agencies are 99 percent staffed by upright, sincere, and prudent people who do their best to obtain the facts before acting precipitously.

This means that each year, in my experience, only three to five states could be what I term "sensitive" to our industry. Interestingly, these states are not the same each year. For many reasons approximately one will drop off the sensitive list as another is added.

All states are vigorous in their pursuit of scams, frauds, and the empty pyramid schemes which offer no legitimate product and are merely money changing, geometrically growing recruitment schemes which are without any social benefit or utility whatsoever.

More important to us, though, are those states where through ignorance, inexperience, hostile attitudes, emotionalism, or politics, companies that have manifested a genuine intent to be marketers are being unfairly subjected to scrutiny, hassled, or even in some instances unfairly sued.

From my personal experience, I would urge the industry to be careful in the states of Missouri, Iowa, Wisconsin, and Idaho. Missouri is in a class by itself.

Because of the hostility towards our industry on the part of one young assistant attorney general in Missouri and, rumor has it, because of some political considerations in the state, the atmosphere for new and emerging MLM companies has been made very dangerous.

The Direct Selling Association and other MLM leaders are currently active in attempting to change this atmosphere and have lobbied to pass legislation to improve our industry's position in that state. Nevertheless, at this writing Missouri should be approached with the utmost caution.

To a lesser degree, these cautions apply in Iowa. Until a recent election for Attorney General in Iowa, some regulatory personnel seem to have been allowed to run loose and vent their hostile emotions. Hopefully, now, a more dispassionate and mature leadership may be in place; it is too early to tell.

I've always found Wisconsin to be tough but fair. The industry should know, however, that one of the decision makers in that state has no love lost for multi-level marketing. The most conservative approach should be taken in structuring marketing plans when doing business in that state.

It has always been a genuine professional pleasure to deal with the Attorney General's office in Idaho. They are fair and very sincere. The Better Business Bureau in Boise, Idaho, through a radio station is very vocal and has, perhaps, an undue influence on government there. The commentators do not know Multi-level Marketing law and are apt to loosely take on any "cause," especially one that has a downline. Consequently, Idaho has recently become more active in litigating new or pioneering marketing plans.

Having no more negatives to say about any governmental agency in the United States in 1991 means, obviously, that the good news is overwhelming and far outweighs the above minor "bad news."

As our industry becomes more well known and its legal principles are further developed, refined, and understood by all governmental agencies, our future grows brighter and more secure with each passing year. ∎

State	Referral Sales Law?	Registration Law for MLMs?	Laws re: Bus. Opportunities?	Anti-Pyramid Laws?	State	Referral Sales Law?	Registration Law for MLMs?	Laws re: Bus. Opportunities?	Anti-Pyramid Laws?
Alabama	✔			✔	Nebraska	✔		✔	✔
Alaska				✔	Nevada				✔
Arizona	✔			✔	New Hampshire				✔
Arkansas				✔	New Jersey	✔			✔
California			✔	✔	New Mexico	✔			✔
Colorado				✔	New York	✔			✔
Connecticut	✔		✔	✔	N. Carolina	✔		✔	✔
Delaware				✔	N. Dakota	✔			✔
Florida	✔		✔	✔	Ohio	✔		✔	✔
Georgia		✔		✔	Oklahoma			✔	✔
Hawaii	✔			✔	Oregon	✔			✔
Idaho				✔	Pennsylvania				✔
Illinois				✔	Rhode Island	✔			✔
Indiana	✔		✔	✔	S. Carolina	✔		✔	✔
Iowa	✔		✔	✔	S. Dakota	✔		✔	✔
Kansas	✔			✔	Tennessee	✔			✔
Kentucky	✔		✔	✔	Texas	✔		✔	✔
Louisiana	✔	✔	✔	✔	Utah	✔		✔	✔
Maine			✔	✔	Vermont				
Maryland	✔	✔	✔	✔	Virginia	✔		✔	✔
Massachusetts	✔		✔		Washington			✔	✔
Michigan				✔	Washington DC	✔			
Minnesota	✔			✔	West Virginia	✔			✔
Mississippi				✔	Wisconsin	✔			
Missouri				✔	Wyoming	✔	✔		✔
Montana				✔					

THE CORPORATE PYRAMID

BY DIRK JOHNSON

DIRK JOHNSON IS EXECUTIVE VICE PRESIDENT OF UPLINE FINANCIAL PRESS.

For centuries, the pyramid structure was the way we organized and managed ourselves. From the Roman army to the Catholic Church to the organization charts of General Motors and IBM, power and communication have flowed in an orderly manner from the pyramid's top, down to its base; from the high priest, the general, the CEO perched at the very tip, down through wider ranks of lieutenants and department managers clustered in the middle, to the workers, foot soldiers, and true believers at the bottom."

So opens the chapter "From Hierarchies to Networking" in John Naisbitt's *Megatrends*—the chapter which is most likely responsible for the misquotation prevalent in some circles that *Megatrends* predicts that network marketing will be the dominant business practice of the 21st Century.

Although Megatrends makes no such prediction, the chapter is yet an appropriate starting-point for discussions of pyramids, traditional corporate organizations, and network marketing.

But it isn't necessary to turn to a book of predictions for an authoritative statement about traditional business organization. A writer highly regarded and well respected in virtually any circle is Peter Drucker. In *Management–Tasks, Responsibilities, Practice*, Drucker says:

Traditional organization theory knows only one kind of structure, applicable alike to building blocks and whole buildings: the so-called scalar organization, that is, the hierarchical pyramid of superior and subordinates. Traditional organization theory considers this structure suitable for all tasks.

Anyone who has initiated a discussion about network, or multi-level, or dual, marketing has come into contact with the theory that network marketing is a pyramid. The reason for this perception is that network marketing is a revolutionary approach to sales management, and the primary method of describing it is by drawing the organizational chart.

If you or I were to apply for a job in a traditional corporation, someone in personnel would ask us for detailed information about our past lives. They would want to know whether we would fit into the "corporate culture" before they would even be willing to discuss the opportunity with us at all. They would want to know whether we had completed the requisite obstacle course prior to taking up their precious time with our search for economic security. The primary question, the underlying question, though never asked, is in reality one regarding wether we are sufficiently institutionalized.

We wouldn't dream of challenging the organizational structure of a typical company, of calling it a pyramid, of saying that "the guys on the top make all the money." (After all, most of us are sufficiently institutionalized.)

Most of us have heard the charge levelled against multi-level marketing companies that they are made up of fanatics, of "true believers"—they have even been described as cults—and that network marketers are "addicted" to their activities, to their companies, and to their opportunities.

Rather than counter these aspersions, let's examine an average week of a typical worker in a traditional corporation. I'll call her Debbie.

When the alarm goes off, it's still dark. Debbie gets a small jolt of adrenaline from the momentary fear at a sudden loud sound. But it isn't enough to get her up. She hits the snooze button a few times before the fear of the boss motivates her to drag herself into the shower. This is the rite of the forced early rising.

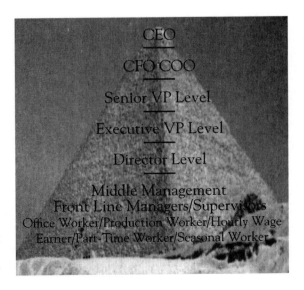

CEO

CFO COO

Senior VP Level

Executive VP Level

Director Level

Middle Management
Front Line Managers/Supervisors
Office Worker/Production Worker/Hourly Wage
Earner/Part-Time Worker/Seasonal Worker

After hastily pulling on nylons (somehow today they didn't run) and a smart business suit, she wobbles out the front door in heels she only wears to work, climbs behind the wheel of her Japanese import, and while backing out of her driveway nearly has a rear-end collision with her neighbor Bob, who is also backing out of his driveway.

Finally, she gets to the freedom of the highway—where stalled traffic gives her time to apply make-up and lipstick while listening to news reports of unemployment and skyrocketing prices. This is the rite of the morning rush hour.

After picking up a muffin and some coffee, she finds herself at a desk flooded with low-intensity fluorescent light and stacks of file folders containing items which have no value to her at all save that by manipulating them she can pay for her car and her abode. Though interrupted several times from her work during the morning by frivolous and unreasonable requests from her superiors, and by imbecile questions from overcautious subordinates, she finally gets some peace: lunch.

She gathers a small clique of barely tolerable associates to stand in line with her at a nearby coffee shop, and finally dines on the establishment's carefully prepared egg-salad and white toast with a vintage diet beverage among chatter of superficial personal details. This is living, but she has to cut it short to stand in line at the bank.

After another four hours of alienation at the office, she is looking forward to being stuck in traffic with a hundred-thousand frantic drivers so she can get home, pay the bills, drive the baby-sitter home, and maybe, just maybe, vegetate awhile in front of a television set before mixing and boiling the family's pre-packaged dinner.

She even manages to squeeze in a couple of minutes with her husband and children before dropping off to a fitful sleep thinking about what didn't get done today, and what needs to be done tomorrow.

Yet, few would say that Debbie is a fanatic, a "true believer," that she belongs to a cult, or that she is "addicted" to her way of life. But it is at least as objectively true of her situation as of that of any network marketer we've ever heard of.

The differences between traditional corporate structure and network marketing are mainly differences of flexibility and choice.

Traditionally structured organizations are "hierarchical pyramids of superiors and subordinates." Frequently, promotion up the levels of the pyramid are made according to performance. But,

just as frequently, these promotions are made for other reasons. Even within organizations where performance is the bell-weather of success, there are fewer and fewer positions available as the performer becomes more and more accomplished. Even when there are open positions, promotions are usually slower than performance. In some instances, performance actually hinders promotion, because in those cases promotion means a loss to the company of the particular productive work accomplished by the performer. It is also customary in traditional corporate structures to limit the income of subordinates to a figure below that of superiors, regardless of performance. They can't allow a new salesperson to make more than a sales manager, no matter what he does. This is a true pyramid.

Although the organizational structure of a network marketing organization looks like a pyramid on paper, the number of top positions available is nearly unlimited. In contradistinction to closed traditional structures, network marketing organizations are open. Within any given line of sponsorship, both uplines and downlines are independent business people sharing a common interest in getting the job done. One's upline is one's business associate at a different level of accomplishment, not one's boss. Perhaps most importantly, advancement is never hindered by performance. Performance is rewarded very quickly. Although not easily done, in most networking organizations a newcomer who outperforms his or her upline will make more money. Even in those organizations where it is not possible to be passed in level by a downline, it remains possible for the downline to make more money. This is a horizontal organizational structure.

Traditional corporations are static structures in which the working relationships among workers change only very slowly if at all, and in which competition among workers in a company can easily result in reduced effectiveness of the work force. Network marketing organizations are dynamic groupings in which people are rewarded for assisting in the success of others. Networkers share the resources of a providing manufacturer or distribution center in pursuit of very individual dreams and goals, all of which are achievable through the mechanism of mutual success.

According to John Naisbett, "...networks are people talking to each other, sharing ideas, information, and resources... The important part is not the network, the finished product, but the process of getting there..." ∎

Selecting an MLM Opportunity

By Doris Wood

Doris Wood is President and CEO of the Multi-Level Marketing International Association (MLMIA). She has over 30 years in the industry as a distributor, field manager, corporate staff member, company founder, and consultant. She is author of Here's Doris..."No Hype, Just How!"

The multi-level marketing industry is experiencing a period of unprecedented growth. Many new companies are starting. People who never considered MLM are looking for advice on how to choose one from the many available.

Others, who may have had a bad experience with a company that "died before its time," but want to remain in MLM are searching for their ideal match.

The following advice is based on my personal experience obtained over almost thirty years as a distributor, field manager, corporate staff member, company founder, and consultant to the industry. Also included is input from product manufacturers, attorneys, and authors in this business.

You need to look at several areas that I will call the product, the company, your sponsor, making money, and industry scuttlebutt.

THE PRODUCT

First, last, and always, find a product or service you can love. Use it until you are a convert. You must believe in your product or you will have trouble selling it or getting others to do so.

Then, make sure your product or service:

1) **Has a real world marketplace demand.** It is easier to sell a product that is "ahead of its time" or "better than what is available in stores" than it is to educate a consuming public regarding an entirely new product category.

2) **Is sold at a reasonable, uninflated price.** The price must represent a good value, not necessarily a bargain, and be competitive with what is readily available in stores.

3) **Can be purchased at wholesale or at substantial discount from prices of similar products found retail.** Your initial earnings will be made from the profit margin between cost and sale price. Make sure it's worth your time.

4) **Is of high quality.** This goes without saying, but you should verify claims of quality with signs of federal approval, conformity to state standards, or private laboratory testing. Awards and testimonials are good if they can be validated.

5) **Customer satisfaction must be guaranteed.** The company should have a liberal return or exchange policy.

Ask yourself the following questions:

Would I buy this product if I were not considering it as a business opportunity?

Is the product consumable? Will I have contented repeat customers and be able to attract other salespeople who will have repeat customers?

THE COMPANY

Don't sign anything. Read all the materials given to you twice. If it is a good opportunity now, it will be one tomorrow. Before signing up with any company try to find out the following details:

1) How long has the company been in business? Two to five or more years is very good, although there have been companies that were successful right from the beginning.

2) The company's success depends very heavily on the management team. Check out the owners or top executives. How long have they been in MLM? What other companies have they worked for? What happened to those companies?

3) Does the company have adequate capitalization? Can they pay their bills? Do commission checks go out on time? Do distributors get product as soon as ordered or is there a long back-order period? Does the sales volume quoted to you work out on paper? (Dollars sold divided by number of distributors divided by months should give a rough dollar per distributor per month amount.)

4) Has the company grown at an impressive rate? Remember network marketing grows in a geometric proportion. The growth curve should rise sharply.

5) A good MLM company will have a buy-back policy of at least 90 percent for all unsold inventory and aids in salable condition.

6) The company probably has posted its policies and ethics in a statement somewhere on the support material. Read it and make sure you can agree wholeheartedly with its values.

YOUR SPONSOR

The person sponsoring you into a business is very important to you. You are essentially becoming business partners. Take a good look at the person and ask yourself:

Will this person train me, learn with me, inspire me, and continue to support me?

Does this person share my values and goals? Do we have anything in common?

Is this person successful?

Don't accept the person that tries to recruit you if you can't answer yes to the first question. Don't accept stories about how easy it is to succeed or how much money someone makes. Ask to see proof if someone mentions their title (level name) or income.

What is the structure for learning set up by your sponsor? There should be weekly and monthly meetings for new distributors.

Again, years in the MLM industry count and time with one company is good. Don't join just because you like the sponsor. And don't jump to another company because your sponsor wants you to.

Don't ever let anyone pressure you to join. That decision should be an informed one that you feel good about.

MAKING MONEY MATTERS

Watch out for claims of enormous overnight success. Average earnings are usually modest, especially for the first year or two. It takes time and commitment to be a "big" financial success.

Be prepared to put in the effort, time, and work that it takes. In the right company, the opportunity is there. You can make it big by grasping the true principals of MLM, which will bring the large income and make a solid business. Each distributor should:

1) Sell product weekly
2) Sponsor at least one person monthly
3) Train those they sponsor to sell, sponsor, and train.

MLM SCUTTLEBUTT

Remember these things when looking at any MLM opportunity:

•The focus of the marketing program would be to promote retail sales to nonparticipants.

•No legitimate program will make earning representations in a start-up situation.

•Legally, a company cannot make a profit on a sign–up fee. A sales kit or demonstration materials should be the only investment required.

•Watch out for plans where headhunting fees are paid, or emphasis is on recruitment rather than sales. Distributors cannot be paid for recruiting.

•A legitimate MLM program has no minimum purchase or inventory requirement to become a distributor.

•Front or inventory-loading is illegal. Mandatory purchases of accessory products or services is illegal. ■

Glossary of MLM Terms Used

Buy-Back Policy: *The manufacturer's rules concerning the return of unsold products for a full or partial refund.*

Benefits: *All types of compensation including markups, commissions, bonuses, overrides, and perks such as insurance, travel, and vehicles.*

Consultant/Distributor: *An adult who completes an agreement, pays an enrollment fee if required, and is eligible to represent the manufacturer's products as an independent salesperson and recruiter.*

Direct Sales/Direct Selling: *A method of selling in which manufacturers or marketers of merchandise reach consumers with their products through a personal sales contact. All MLM business opportunities employ direct selling, but not all direct sales firms employ multi-level marketing.*

Downline: *The line of sponsorship between a particular distributor and all sponsorship levels below.*

Dual Marketing: *Used by Mary Kay Cosmetics to refer to the fact that the corporation itself does no recruiting for their opportunity.*

Front Loading/Front-end Loading: *An illegal practice that pressures new distributors to purchase products in order to take advantage of an opportunity. While most professionals agree that it is a good idea for newcomers to purchase enough products to become familiar with the company's product line, no reputable firm will require or pressure new distributors to invest hundreds or thousands of dollars in products to get started.*

Generation: *All distributors in a leg after reaching a certain level; usually refers to breakaway legs (see Stairstep/Breakaway).*

Leg: *A line of distributors which begins with someone you personally sponsor and continues below that distributor.*

Level: *Generally refers to who sponsors whom within a distributor's network. Someone personally sponsored by a distributor is referred to as first level. Someone sponsored by the first level distributor becomes second level to the original sponsor.*

Matrix: *A type of compensation plan which creates an organization of a pre-determined size and structure. For instance, a distributor might be allowed to sponsor no more than a set number of individuals and each of those distributors would be allowed*

to do the same. Any person sponsored above that number would automatically fill an open space in the downline.*

MLM/Multi-Level Marketing: *A method of selling in which customers have the option of becoming distributors, who in turn develop downlines, and in which all levels share in the profits of the level or levels below them.*

Network Marketing: *A synonym for multi-level marketing.*

Overrides: *Money paid on the production of breakaway legs.*

Pyramid or Ponzi Scheme: *Illegal businesses superficially resembling legitimate network marketing companies which generate income solely from recruiting new members and charging them fees, with no actual product or service being moved.*

PV, BV: *Point Volume or Business Volume. Used by many MLMs to calculate commissions and overrides instead of using dollar amounts.*

Renewals: *Many MLMs require that a person recommit their desire to be a distributor every year by signing and paying a small fee. This process eliminates drop outs from the companies' roles.*

Sales Volume: *Calculated both in personal sales volume (what you personally sell) known as PSV, or group sales volume (what everyone in your downline sells) often shown as GSV.*

Saturation: *The point at which all potential prospects have been converted. Extremely unlikely.*

Sponsor(ing): *The act of showing your company's products and plan to potential distributors and motivating them to sign up. This is extremely important to building an MLM business.*

Stairstep/Breakaway: *A type of compensation plan where any individual and their downline the organization can become independent after that person reaches a pre-defined level of achievement. The original sponsor continues to collect bonuses and overrides on the breakaway group's volume.*

Upline: *The line of sponsorship between a particular distributor and all the sponsoring levels above.*

Unilevel: *A compensation plan that allows a distributor to sponsor as many people as desired, with no breakaways. This is commonly associated more with direct selling.*

INTRODUCTION TO COMPANY PROFILES

BY DIRK JOHNSON

The following group of thirty-six network marketing companies represents the most successful MLM companies in the United States, some of which are among the most stable of any type of company in the world.

With three exceptions, two pages (a "spread") have been devoted to each of the companies profiled in this section. Amway Corporation, Mary Kay Cosmetics, Inc., and Shaklee USA have each received an additional spread devoted to them in recognition of their longevity and their role as trailblazers for the network marketing industry.

The left hand page of each spread contains information such as the company's address and phone number, when it was founded and by whom, available statistics regarding the financial condition and size of the company, the company policy regarding "buy backs" (or product return policy) and inventory, and a brief description of the company's product line.

Two marks of a legitimate network marketing business opportunity are a generous product return policy, and the lack of a requirement for maintaining inventory. All of the companies profiled have a generous product return policy, though some are more generous than others. None of the companies requires an inventory, and some have mechanisms to actively discourage the building of an inventory.

Following is a description of the elements of the right hand page of each spread:

Distributor Discount Off Retail: Some companies set a definite retail price while providing the products to their distributors at a fixed wholesale cost, some suggest a retail price and officially participate only in wholesale pricing, while yet others deal strictly in retail pricing, extending discounts to distributors from the retail price. In order to standardize reporting for the purposes of comparison, we have treated suggested retail prices and fixed retail prices as equivalent.

Qualification Period: Refers to the period of time in which a group and/or personal sales volume is considered to qualify the distributor for a higher bonus structure.

Compression: Refers to whether or not the volume below an inactive downline distributor skips that inactive distributor, and is designated as part of the volume of the inactive distributors' sponsor for the purpose of calculating bonuses. This aspect is usually most important in the higher levels of a stairstep/breakaway plan—after the distributor has already achieved success.

Minimum Qualifying Purchase: Refers to the amount of volume, if any, a distributor must personally generate to qualify for bonuses and overrides on his or her downline. Usually this volume can be met by purchases for personal use, but the intent of the requirement is generally that the products be sold, and that the person being paid be active. In many plans, there is a minimum qualifying purchase at the early stages of the plan but not at the higher stages, the successful distributor being in those cases rewarded for their work by relaxed requirements. For the purposes of this book, the minimum qualifying purchase refers only to the early stages of building a network.

Support: Marketing support from the company can be an extremely valuable asset to a distributor's efforts, especially at the beginning. We include a brief indication of the types of support provided by each company. In some cases, companies offer much more support than space has allowed for us to report, but a quick comparison can be made, and further information obtained either by calling the company directly, or by sending in the Reader Service Card on page 30.

Initial Fee. The initial fee is the charge for registration, initial sales materials and handbook, and usually a sampling of the company's product. These items are generally sold at or near cost, and do not constitute a significant revenue stream for any of the companies included in the section.

Levels Locked In?: The question is whether, once achieved, a level in a marketing plan is retained regardless of performance. In some companies, once you have achieved a certain level, you can never lose it, though restrictions may still apply to bonus payments if you are inactive; in other companies, it is possible to fall back one or more levels through failure to satisfy certain qualification requirements.

Named Levels: A description of the company's marketing/compensation plan employing, as far as possible, the terminology the particular company uses. We have used the words "level" and "generation" synonymously, though some companies insist upon the distinction as described in the glossary.

Additional Levels/Other: Due to space limitations, it is usually not possible to give even a brief description of every level in a plan. This is especially true for companies who have been in existence for many years, because these companies have added new levels as distributors exceeded the potential of the former plan. Every effort has been made to be clear and accurate—but the ultimate authority regarding a company's plan remains the company itself.

Chart of One Month Incomes: Calculations, based upon the marketing plan, for a fixed number of types of organization. The numbers in the left-hand column refer to your organization. For example, 3/3/3 would mean that you sponsored three people, who in turn each sponsored three people, who each in turn sponsored three people. Likewise for 4/4/4, 5/5/5, and 6/4/2. The numbers to the right of this column indicate the amount of money you would personally generate, based upon the override and bonus structure of the plan, *exclusive of any profit on personal sales* if each and every person in your organization were to purchase a volume of $200, $250, and $300 respectively.

The fact that these figures are exclusive of any retail profit margin should be carefully noted, because some companies are oriented toward individual, high-volume retail sales.

The chart, and the graph next to it, are the result of an effort to standardize the marketing plans of a wide variety of companies. To some degree, this is impossible. Yet, as with the Dow Jones Industrial Average, which is a market indicator rather than a defining market factor, a standardized form of analysis for the early stages of a marketing plan can yield some useful comparative information.

For instance, low numbers in the chart and on the graph do not necessarily indicate a worse marketing plan, nor do high numbers necessarily indicate a better plan. Low numbers at the begin-

ning may simply point the way to very high numbers at the higher levels, or to a focus upon personal selling, and high numbers at the beginning may point to reduced incomes at the higher levels. They may, but do not necessarily.

Networker's Index: The graph on each right hand page is a representation of the configuration 6/4/2, with each and every distributor, including yourself, using or selling no more, and no less, than $250 of products in a month.

The configuration of 6/4/2 was chosen because it is more reasonable to fill than, say, a 5/5/5. The amount $250 was used as a median amount. Some plans work better with $200, and some with $300: but, again, this is a standard against which other scenarios can be tested.

"Level 1" refers to you before you have sponsored anyone, "Level 2" refers to you plus your six personally sponsored distributors, "Level 3" refers to you, your personal six, and each of their personally sponsored four; "Level 4" refers to you, your personal six, their personal four, and each of their personally sponsored two. Thus, at "Level 4", there are a total of 79 distributors in your organization, each of whom is "doing" $250 in volume.

"The Networker's Index" and the "Chart of One Month Incomes" both assume that each level has been achieved in one month. Some companies have restrictions which would not allow such a rapid change of level. In these cases, the graph has been computed as though it were allowed, in order to display the income potential at the covered levels, rather than in the specified time.

Some companies have requirements for width before a certain bonus level can be achieved. The chart and graph assume that the given volume satisfies the requirement. Other companies have a minimum personal purchase requirement to receive bonuses in excess of the amount used in the graph and chart. In these cases, the requirement is assumed to have been met, but the figures have not been adjusted to reflect the higher volume that would have resulted.

The charts and graphs are for comparison only, and should in no way be construed or used as a definitive statement regarding the earning power of any of the opportunities presented. ∎

AMERICAN IMAGE MARKETING, INC. (AIM)

3904 E. FLAMINGO, NAMPA, ID 83687
800-456-2682 FOR GENERAL INFORMATION
800-456-2462 FOR CREDIT CARD ORDERS
800-766-5133 FOR FAX ORDERS

History
Founded 1982 by Dennis J. Itami and Ronald A. Wright, with Barleygreen as their first product. They have since expanded to include a wide range of herbal products.

Financials *Not rated; privately held*

General Statistics
Total 1993 Sales: *$42 million; 1992 $39 million*
Total Distributors: *75,000*
Foreign Countries: *Canada, Mexico, Taiwan, Hong Kong, New Zealand, Australia*

Method of Product Distribution *Delivered to distributor, delivered to customer*

Association Membership *N/A*

Inventory Policy *No requirement*

Product Return Policy *90% within 90 days for distributors, 100% to customers*

The Product Line: American Image Marketing offers a variety of unusual products, from Barleygreen nutritional supplement to Mayfine skin care products.

Nutritional Products: Barleygreen, made from the juice of young barley plants, contains a wide array of nutrients, including more than a dozen vitamins as well as enzymes, amino acids, and chlorophyll; Just Carrots, a half pound of carrots becomes a 10 gram serving of 100% pure carrot juice crystals; Herbal Fiberblend is a formulation of herbs and fiber—one tablespoon contains 10.9 grams of dietary fiber; Superzymes contain thousands of sprouts packed into a single tablet; Aloe Gold is a concentrated aloe beverage; Activated Ginko Extract is an extract from the Ginko Balboba tree in Japan, which has been used in that country as a nutritional supplement for centuries; Mountain Meadows Bee Propolis; Catalyst Altered Water makes water "wetter" by reducing the surface tension of the water; Pure Delight Energy Bars; Mountain Meadows Bee Pollen; Composure, an herb formula containing a balance of 8 herbs; Corbicula contains the nutrients found in freshwater clams, in a cream-colored powder.

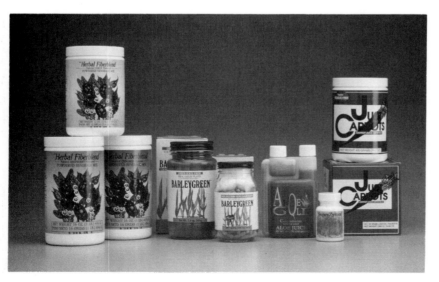

MARKETING/COMPENSATION PLAN

PLAN CATEGORY *Stairstep/Breakaway*
DISTRIBUTOR DISCOUNT OFF RETAIL *40 - 60%*
QUALIFICATION PERIOD *Level Dependent*
COMPRESSION *No*

MINIMUM QUALIFYING VOLUME *$150/$300*
SUPPORT *Videos, Workshops, Literature, Newsletters*
LEVELS LOCKED IN? *Yes*
INITIAL FEE *$25*

NAMED LEVELS

Retailer: *Retailers do not receive override bonuses; retail profit from personal sales*

Manager: *6% of personal and 1st level Retailers; no overrides paid on Managers* **Qualification:** *450 Business Volume Points in 3 Consecutive Months*

Supervisor: *12% personal and 1st level Retailers; 6% 1st level Managers; no overrides paid on Supervisors* **Qualification:** *3,000 Business Volume Points during any 3 consecutive months; personal volume of 150 or more*

Director: *18-21% of personal and 1st level Retailers; 12-15% 1st level Managers; 6-9% 1st level Supervisors; 6% 1st level Directors; 3% 2nd level Directors; 2% 3rd level Directors* **Qualification:** *6,000 Business Volume Points during any 3 consecutive months; personal volume of 300 or more*

Star Sapphire Director: *Director Benefits plus 1-2% 4th level Directors* **Qualification:** *Director with three 1st level Directors in any one month*

Royal Emerald Director: *Star Sapphire Director benefits plus 1% 5th level Directors* **Qualification:** *Director with six 1st level Directors in any one month*

Additional Levels (Contact Company For Details): *Blue Diamond Director; Chairman's Club Director*

Other: *Leadership Performance Bonus*

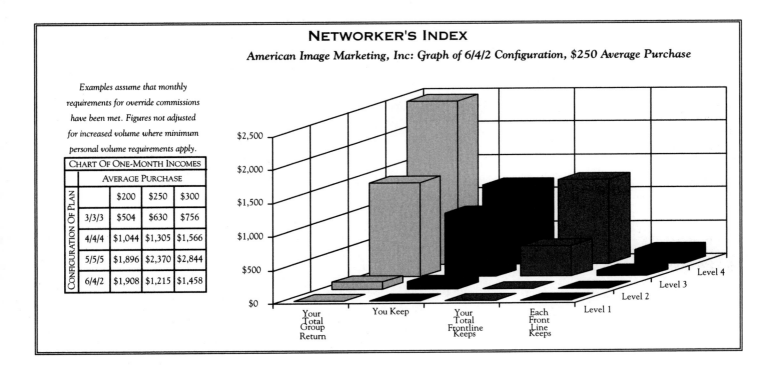

NETWORKER'S INDEX

American Image Marketing, Inc: Graph of 6/4/2 Configuration, $250 Average Purchase

Examples assume that monthly requirements for override commissions have been met. Figures not adjusted for increased volume where minimum personal volume requirements apply.

CHART OF ONE-MONTH INCOMES

CONFIGURATION OF PLAN	AVERAGE PURCHASE		
	$200	$250	$300
3/3/3	$504	$630	$756
4/4/4	$1,044	$1,305	$1,566
5/5/5	$1,896	$2,370	$2,844
6/4/2	$1,908	$1,215	$1,458

ADVANTAGE MARKETING SYSTEMS, INC. (AMS)

2601 NORTHWEST EXPRESSWAY, SUITE 1210, OKLAHOMA CITY, OK 73112
405-842-0131 VOICE
800-866-4267 VOICE

History
A public company founded in 1988 by John Hail. AMS merged with Pacific Coast International in April of 1989.

Financials *Not rated, publicly held, traded OTC, incorporated OK*

General Statistics
Total 1993 Sales: $8.5 Million; 1992 $5.9 million
Total Distributors: 37,000
Foreign Countries: N/A

Method of Product Distribution *Picked up by distributor, delivered to distributor, delivered to customer*

Association Membership *N/A*

Inventory Policy *No requirement*

Product Return Policy *30-day guarantee*

The Product Line: The AMS Consumer card is a membership buying service which obtains discounts for the holder in the following categories:

Travel Services provide discounts on: over 1,450 hotels and motels in the U.S.; car rentals; cruises; and airfares through a full-service travel agency.

Consumer's Choice membership extends guaranteed lowest available price on over 1,700 and 500,000 name brand products such as Panasonic, Cuisinart, Hewlett-Packard, Mohawk, Sony, Lenox China, Apple Computer, Texas Instruments, Microsoft, Sealy, Armstrong, Tiffany, Kenwood, Craftmaster, Vanity Fair, Cleveland Lamp Co., Black & Decker, American Tourister, General Electric, Signet, Marshall, Gibson, Martin, Pitney-Bowes, Cross, IBM, Minolta, Kirsch, Bose, Pioneer, Oneida, Sharp, Uniden, Zenith, Pentax, Rainbow, RCA, Rolex.

A Gift Catalog makes over 400 items available at wholesale. $250 annual credit in advantage checks can be used for up to 50% of purchase price.

In addition, the AMS consumer card offers access to grocery coupons, Allnet long distance telephone service, automobile discounts, vision discounts, prescription drugs, a legal telephone consultation service and over 200,000 college fund sources.

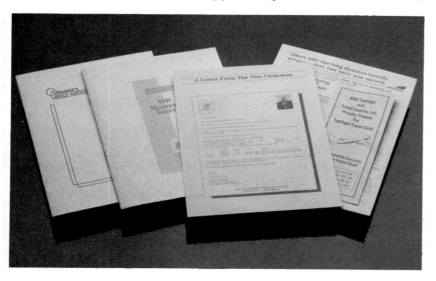

MARKETING/COMPENSATION PLAN

PLAN CATEGORY *Stairstep/Breakaway*
DISTRIBUTOR DISCOUNT OFF RETAIL *37%*
QUALIFICATION PERIOD *One Month*
COMPRESSION? *Yes*

MINIMUM QUALIFYING VOLUME *$95*
SUPPORT *Videos, Workshops, Literature, Newsletters*
LEVELS LOCKED IN? *Yes*
INITIAL FEE *$129.95*

NAMED LEVELS

Associate: *No override bonuses are paid to Associates.*

Partner: *$5 on personal and all 1st level Associate sales* **Qualification:** *Purchase 6 memberships at wholesale from upline.*

Senior Partner: *$14 on 1st level partners; $19 on 1st level Associate and Personal Sales.* **Qualification** *personal wholesale volume of $1,700 in first 30 days OR personal wholesale volume of $2,280 in any month OR 5 1st level Partners over any time period OR organizational volume of $3420 with a maximum of $1140 in any one leg*

Executive Partner: *Senior Partner Benefits plus Leadership Bonus: $4 on 1st level breakaway Senior Partners, $3 on 2nd Level Senior Partners, $2 on 3rd - 5th level Senior Partners; $6 Senior Partner Renewals* **Qualification:** *1 First Level Senior Partner*

Ambassador: *$4 on organization sales to next Ambassador; Leadership Bonus; $18 on 1st Level Partner Sales; $23 on Personal and 1st Level Associate Sales; $6 Ambassador Renewals* **Qualification:** *5 First Level Senior Partners*

Crown Ambassador: *$4 on all sales to next Crown Ambassador; $8 on all sales to next Ambassador; Leadership Bonus; $22 on 1st level partners; $27 on 1st level Associates and Personal* **Qualification:** *1 First Level Ambassador*

Additional Levels (Contact Company For Details): *N/A*

Other Bonuses: *Corporate bonus, Telephone bonus*

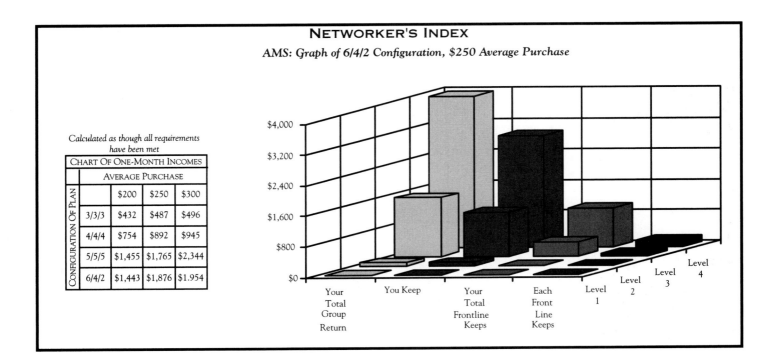

NETWORKER'S INDEX

AMS: *Graph of 6/4/2 Configuration, $250 Average Purchase*

Calculated as though all requirements have been met

CHART OF ONE-MONTH INCOMES

CONFIGURATION OF PLAN	AVERAGE PURCHASE		
	$200	$250	$300
3/3/3	$432	$487	$496
4/4/4	$754	$892	$945
5/5/5	$1,455	$1,765	$2,344
6/4/2	$1,443	$1,876	$1.954

AMWAY CORPORATION

7575 FULTON STREET, ADA, MI 49355-0001
616-676-6000 VOICE
616-676-8140 FAX

History
Founded 1959 by Rich DeVos and Jay Van Andel in the basements of their homes, one product, and a handful of distributors. See pages 60-61 for a detailed history.

Financials *A10 rating; privately held; incorporated in MI*

General Statistics
Total 1993 Sales: *$4.5 Billion; 1992: $3.9 Billion*
Total Distributors: *More than 2 Million*
Foreign Countries: *Global (see pages 144-145)*

Method of Product Distribution *Picked up by distributor; delivered to customer; delivered to distributor*

Association Membership *DSA*

Inventory Policy *No requirement*

Product Return Policy *Distributors 100%; Customers 100%*

The Product Line:
Amway Corporation manufactures and/or private labels several hundred goods and services which fall into the following categories: food & beverage; commercial agricultural; health care; pets; weight control; cosmetics, fragrances, dental care, and skin care; lighting; car care; education; janitorial; household cleaners; garden care; home security; air treatment; water treatment; cookware; Amway VISA credit card; motoring plan; mortgage network; realty service; moving service; health care discount program; MCI/Amway long distance service. These items are available from distributors only.

Amway cleaning products contain only biodegradable surfactants. They are not tested on animals; Amway uses packaging containing recycled materials when available; products are concentrated, reducing the size of the packaging and resulting in less solid waste.

In addition, Amway publishes a "Personal Shoppers® Service" catalog. The issue expiring July 31, 1993 is numbered to 224 pages, and contains items from a wide array of manufacturers. A sample list includes: Kenwood, London Fog, Hamilton Beach, Bushnell, Seiko, Quaker,Lipton, Magnavox, Maidenform, Playtex, Calico, Johnson & Murphy, and Ross. Catalog items can be purchased directly from Amway via "800" number with a distributor's information and credit card, or from the distributor.

MARKETING/COMPENSATION PLAN

PLAN CATEGORY *Stairstep/Breakaway*
DISTRIBUTOR DISCOUNT OFF RETAIL *15% - 49%*
QUALIFICATION PERIOD *One Month*
COMPRESSION? *Yes*

MINIMUM QUALIFYING VOLUME *N/A*
SUPPORT *Videos, Workshops, Literature, Newsletters, Seminars*
LEVELS LOCKED IN? *No*
INITIAL FEE *$102*

QUALIFICATION LEVELS

Distributor: *Profit earned from 15% to 49% discount off retail; bonus of 3% to 25%, in nine increments (the percentage based upon Point Value (PV), which averages approximately 50% of wholesale price) paid on Business Volume (BV)*

Silver Producer: *25% bonus on personal BV; up to 25% bonus on group BV* **Qualification:** *7500 group PV in one month*

Direct Distributor: *Silver Producer benefits plus potential for 4% of each personally sponsored Direct Distributor* **Qualification:** *maintain 7500 group PV for any six months of year and sponsor one 25% group and maintain 2500 personal PV or sponsor two 25% groups*

Ruby Direct Distributor: *Direct Distributor benefits plus 2% of BV of personal group volume* **Qualification:** *15,000 group BV in month*

Pearl Direct: *Profit Sharing Direct benefits plus 1% of the BV of all second level groups down to and including the first Pearl or above* **Qualification:** *three personally sponsored 25% groups in any given month*

Emerald Direct: *Pearl Direct benefits plus a share of .25% of total national BV per month, paid annually* **Qualification:** *Three qualified 25% groups for six months in the fiscal year.*

Additional Levels (Contact Company For Details): *Diamond Direct; Executive Diamond Direct; Double Diamond Direct; Triple Diamond Direct; Crown Direct; Crown Ambassador Direct*

Other Bonuses: *Par bonus; Profit Sharing; Executive Diamond Bonus; Founders' Bonus; trips*

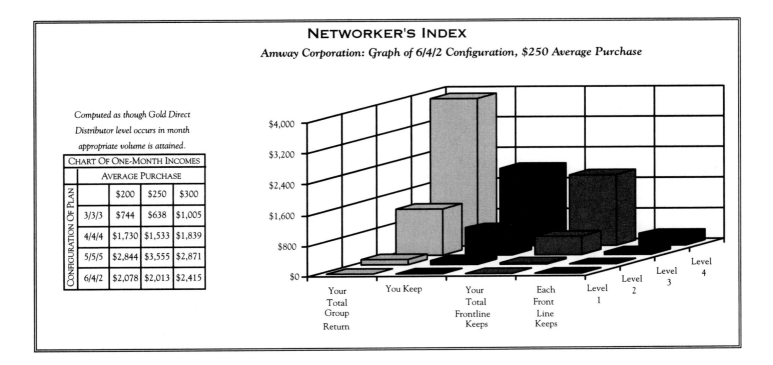

NETWORKER'S INDEX

Amway Corporation: Graph of 6/4/2 Configuration, $250 Average Purchase

Computed as though Gold Direct Distributor level occurs in month appropriate volume is attained.

CHART OF ONE-MONTH INCOMES			
	AVERAGE PURCHASE		
	$200	$250	$300
3/3/3	$744	$638	$1,005
4/4/4	$1,730	$1,533	$1,839
5/5/5	$2,844	$3,555	$2,871
6/4/2	$2,078	$2,013	$2,415

AMWAY CORPORATION

Founded in 1959 by Jay Van Andel and Rich DeVos, Amway Corporation has grown over the past three decades into a multi-billion dollar global company. It all began with a pair of enterprising young men operating from the basements of their homes to supply one product to a small group of distributors. Amway now offers hundreds of products manufactured by the company in Ada, Michigan, plus thousands of brand-name products through its catalog. The small group of distributors has grown to more than two million worldwide.

When Van Andel and DeVos founded Amway, they had already been successful business owners and distributors for Nutrilite Products, a California-based company offering a line of food supplements through direct sales. Amway's first product was L.O.C. (Liquid Organic Cleanser). SA8 Laundry Detergent was introduced the following year, and Amway moved from the basements of Van Andel and DeVos to a former garage on Fulton Road in Ada.

Amway, however, was not a company to be built around one product or even a group of products. Rather, Van Andel and DeVos built the company around a unique distribution system—independent Amway distributors who market Amway products in their own communities. They knew ambitious people could achieve their dreams if provided with the means to start a business with a small investment, a solid sales plan, and quality products. The products were also consumable, which meant there would be a continuing demand.

DeVos and Van Andel also recognized the importance of communication with distributors from the beginning. The very first piece of equipment they purchased was a printing press.

In 1962, Amway added the Ruby Direct Distributor level to its compensation plan.

By 1963, Amway had added Shoe Spray, Car Care products, and Amway Queen Cookware to its line of products. In that year, Amway of Canada Ltd. opened for business, and their private fleet of trucks had expanded to sixteen, and revenues had reached twenty-one million dollars.

In 1964, the Crown Distributor level was added to the compensation plan and Dish Drops Liquid Detergent and the first women's fragrances were added to the product line. Home office employees exceeded five hundred, and revenues had reached twenty-five million dollars.

By 1969, Amway had acquired its first aircraft, a twin-engine Piper Aztec. The Sweet Shot breath freshener and the first Satinique products, Creme Rinse and Cosmetics, had been introduced, bringing the total product line to more than 150 items. At that time, Amway also introduced the Personal Shoppers Catalog.

By 1972, Amway had acquired two yachts, the Enterprise and the Enterprise II, added a ten-passenger Lockheed Jetstar to its air fleet, purchased Nutrilite Products, Inc., experienced its first Crown Distributorship, and opened Amway of Australia Pty. Ltd. Revenues exceeded $180 million.

In 1977, Dick and Bunny Marks reached the top of the Amway compensation plan by becoming Crown Ambassadors, and Michel and Cecile Chapdelaine became Crowns after only five years in the business.

By 1980, Amway boasted 750,000 distributors worldwide, had opened in the U.K., Hong Kong, West Germany, Malaysia, France, The Netherlands, the Republic of Ireland, Japan, Switzerland, and had distributors in Belgium; acquired the Enterprise III for its cruise fleet; opened a manufacturing facility in Canada; purchased the Peter Island resort; acquired Mutual Broadcasting System, Inc.; expanded its Ada facilities to more than 2.5 million square feet; experienced its first Crown Ambassador Direct Distributorships in Canada and Germany, its first Diamond Direct Distributorships in the U.K. and in The Netherlands, and its first Emerald Direct Distributor in the Ireland. Total employees exceeded 3,000 and corporate revenue is $825 million, and estimated retail sales exceeded one billion dollars.

On April 23, 1981, former U.S. President Gerald Ford and other dignitaries joined Amway's co-founders in dedicating the ten million dollar Research and Development Building in Ada. More than 250 scientists, technicians, and other support staff were now working at Amway World Headquarters.

1982 was a year of economic hardship for many countries. Some businesses reluctantly pulled back and retrenched; others had to close their doors forever. For Amway, though, 1982 was a record-breaking year. The worldwide distributor organization numbered one million. Amway Taiwan Ltd. opened. Corporate employees worldwide numbered seven thousand. Operating from the Amway hangar at Kent County International Airport, the company's 17 pilots and 11 support staff kept Amway's two BAC 1-11's, three Cessna Citations, and two helicopters flying a total of 1.1 million miles annually. Amway President Rich DeVos appeared at motivational rallies in fifteen cities across the United States. To meet this intense schedule Amway purchased a Boeing 727 aircraft. In a move to become more active in the home electrical/electronic device field, Amway acquired the Statitrol Division of Emerson Electric Company. Corporate revenue topped $1.2 billion, and estimated retail sales exceeded $1.5 billion.

By 1984, the company's twenty-fifth anniversary, the Amway product line had grown to include more than three hundred products. Over 350 million pounds of finished products were shipped from Ada. Among these products were Artistry Cosmetics, produced for the first time at Ada in a new eleven million dollar plant.

The one hundred thousand foot facility featured explosion-proof rooms for a high degree of safety. A lipstick casting machine was one of only four in the United States. A heat reclamation system was designed to be so energy efficient that system heat was required only during sub-zero temperatures. From receiving raw materials to final packaging, 175 employees could produce 95 percent of the entire Amway personal care line.

Around this time, Amway began to offer not only its own products, but the brand-name products and services of other companies through its Personal Shoppers Catalog. Some of the companies for which Amway distributors market products and services include Coca Cola and MCI. Amway now offers more than four hundred products of its own, plus an additional five thousand brand-name products through this catalog.

Amway blazed the trail for multi-level marketing companies by achieving victory in court cases challenging the legality of network marketing. In fact, the Amway marketing plan is now a primary benchmark for legal judgements regarding the soundness of a network marketing company

. As the number of independent distributors increased and the product line multiplied, Amway facilities expanded to meet the greater demands. Manufacturing plants, distribution warehouses, research and development facilities, and administrative office buildings have risen along a 1.2 mile stretch of Fulton Street East. Amway's Ada headquarters consists of more than 3.3 million square feet under one roof on more than 400 acres of land, (up from 2,400 square feet in 1960) which more than 20,000 people tour each year. The company also has facilities across the United States and affiliates in more than fifty countries and territories. The number of Amway employees worldwide reached 10,000 in 1992.

In underdeveloped countries and those formerly under communist rule, people are enthusiastically embracing the Amway opportunity, not only because of a desire in those markets for quality products, but because Amway offers individuals an inexpensive way to own their own business.

The Amway truck fleet now logs more than three million miles a year—equivalent to one hundred trips around the world; the company now has twenty-one full-time pilots to fly employees and distributors in seven corporate aircraft; each of its more than thirteen thousand Direct Distributors worldwide has a name-plate somewhere in the Amway halls.

Amway's plans for the future include continued expansion of facilities to better serve world markets. New markets are being opened at a rate of three or four countries each year. For the fiscal year ended August 31, 1990, Amway set a record sales mark of $2.2 billion at estimated retail prices. The following year, sales increased by 40 percent, to the $3.1 billion mark, and topped the $3.9 billion mark for 1992.

In 1992, Amway ensured its future direction as a family business by forming the Policy Board, composed of the cofounders and the eight DeVos and Van Andel children. Rich DeVos announced his retirement as President. His eldest son, Dick, was appointed his successor.

In a recent joint letter, Amway founders Jay Van Andel and Rich DeVos stated:

From the beginning, we've prided ourselves on the equal opportunity of the Amway business. It's an opportunity open to people from all walks of life—people with varying religious convictions, political affiliations, nationalities, ethnic backgrounds, and racial origins. Amway distributors...work together to achieve financial independence by following the Amway Sales and Marketing Plan and observing the Code of Ethics and Rules of Conduct. On all other issues not specifically affecting the operation of their Amway businesses, Amway distributors have the right to hold differing viewpoints, without their status as Amway distributors or their business relationships with other distributors... Amway has been such a huge success because it is not restrictive. Because it is accessible to everyone. Because it can be tailored to meet the needs of the individual. ■

BRITE INTERNATIONAL

2595 EAST 3300 SOUTH, BOX 9191, SALT LAKE CITY, UT 84109
801-487-5891 VOICE
801-487-8371 FAX

History
Founded 1982

Financials *Not rated, privately held, incorporated UT*

General Statistics
Total 1993 Sales: *est. $1.5 Million*
Total Distributors: *1,800*
Foreign Countries: *Canada*

Method of Product Distribution *Delivered to distributor*

Association Membership *DSA*

Inventory Policy *No Requirement*

Product Return Policy *90% buyback in 90 days*

The Product Line: Children's musical educational materials and games intended to develop and promote self-esteem, rhythm, physical coordination, love, caring, nutrition, character, attitudes, drug and alcohol abuse prevention, personal safety, and patriotism.

MARKETING/COMPENSATION PLAN

PLAN CATEGORY *Stairstep/Breakaway*
DISTRIBUTOR DISCOUNT OFF RETAIL *26%*
QUALIFICATION PERIOD *One Month*
COMPRESSION? *Yes*

MINIMUM QUALIFYING VOLUME *$75*
SUPPORT *Brochures, Tapes, Videos*
LEVELS LOCKED IN? *No*
INITIAL FEE *$59.00*

QUALIFICATION LEVELS

Representative: *No overrides are paid to Representatives*

Associate: *4% of personal volume* **Qualification:** *$400 Team Business Volume over any period of time*

Advanced Associate: *8% of volume* **Qualification:** *$800 Team Business Volume over any period of time*

Manager: *12% of volume* **Qualification:** *$1,200 Team Business Volume in one month*

Advanced Manager: *16% of volume* **Qualification:** *$1,600 Team Business Volume in one month*

Director: *20% of volume* **Qualification:** *$2,000 Team Business Volume in one month or $1,600 in two consecutive months; $1,000 must be unencumbered volume*

Executive Director: *Director benefits; 5% of 1st generation Directors* **Qualification:** *Director; one 1st generation Director; $800 Maintenance Requirement.*

Bronze Director: *Executive Director benefits; 4% of 2nd Generation Directors* **Qualification:** *Director; two 1st generation Directors; $700 Maintenance Requirement*

Additional Levels (Contact Company For Details): *Silver Director Gold Director; Diamond Director; Presidential Director*

Other Bonuses: *N/A*

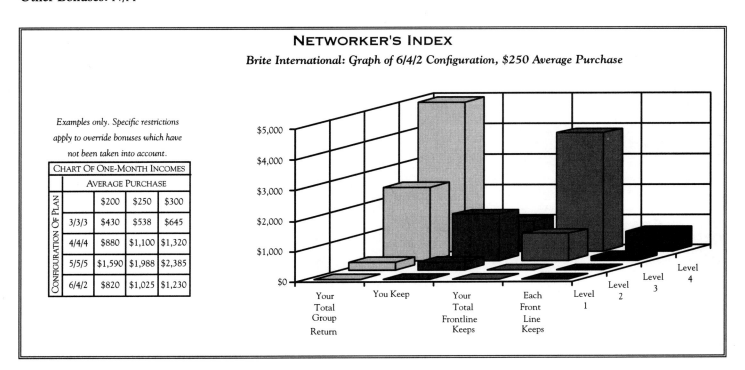

NETWORKER'S INDEX
Brite International: Graph of 6/4/2 Configuration, $250 Average Purchase

Examples only. Specific restrictions apply to override bonuses which have not been taken into account.

CHART OF ONE-MONTH INCOMES			
	AVERAGE PURCHASE		
CONFIGURATION OF PLAN	$200	$250	$300
3/3/3	$430	$538	$645
4/4/4	$880	$1,100	$1,320
5/5/5	$1,590	$1,988	$2,385
6/4/2	$820	$1,025	$1,230

CAMBRIDGE DIRECT SALES

2801 SALINAS HIGHWAY, BUILDING F, MONTEREY, CA 93940-6420
408-373-2300 VOICE
408-373-7167 FAX
800-443-2584 (800-356-0082—AREA CODES 312, 309, 815) VOICE

History
Founded 1979

Financials *Not rated, privately held, incorporated CA*

General Statistics
Total 1993 Sales: *est. $3.5 Million*
Total Distributors: *3,000*
Foreign Countries: *N/A*

Method of Product Distribution *Not available*

Association Membership *DSA*

Inventory Policy *No requirement*

Product Return Policy *Not Available*

The Product Line: Cambridge Direct Sales markets a total system for weight management and lifetime nutrition called the Cambridge Integrated System. This system consists of a nutritionally complete meal replacement formula, a self-directed behavior modification program, and a combination walking and body-shaper program designed to fit every goal and lifestyle. Companion products are available to support the elements of the integrated system. Cambridge has also introduced a new line of skin care products that provide "nutrients for the skin," as well as a new diet formula called Cambridge Diet 2000, designed to incorporate the latest breakthrough discoveries in the field of nutrition.

The cornerstone of the various programs is the Cambridge Food for Life Nutritional Formula. The formula is a scientifically engineered food providing 100% of the U.S. RDA for protein, vitamins, and minerals, along with electrolytes and trace elements recommended for good health by the National Academy of Sciences in 420-480 calories per day. It is available in over 10 flavors as a cereal, soups, pudding dessert, drinks, and bars.

Cambridge Direct Sales markets its products and programs, supported by a Program Guide, through a network of consultants who assist with program selection and provide non-medical support.

MARKETING/COMPENSATION PLAN

PLAN CATEGORY *Stairstep/Breakaway*
DISTRIBUTOR DISCOUNT OFF RETAIL *25%*
QUALIFICATION PERIOD *Level Dependent*
COMPRESSION? *Yes*

MINIMUM QUALIFYING VOLUME *$150/$300*
SUPPORT *Videos, Workshops, Literature, Newsletters*
LEVELS LOCKED IN? *No*
INITIAL FEE *$25*

QUALIFICATION LEVELS

Consultant: *Purchase products at wholesale; 6% rebate on purchases $150-$299; 12% rebate on purchases of $300 or more*

Manager: *12% of Group Volume, in addition to personal volume rebate* **Qualification:** *3000 Group Volume (of which the maximum personal purchase is 1500); 5 active first-level Consultants (active = $150 minimum monthly order or sponsor one new consultant with minimum $300 order)*

Director: *24% of Group Volume, in addition to personal volume rebate; 12% of 1st level Managers* **Qualification:** *5000 Group Volume (of which the maximum personal purchase is 2000); 10 1st level active Consultants*

Bronze Director: *Director Benefits plus 5% on 1st generation Directors* **Qualification:** *1 First Level Directors*

Silver Director: *Bronze Director Benefits plus 5% 2nd Generation Directors* **Qualification:** *2 First Level Directors*

Gold Director: *Silver Director Benefits plus 5% 3nd Generation Directors* **Qualification:** *4 First Level Directors*

Platinum Director: *Gold Director Benefits plus 5% 4th Generation Directors* **Qualification:** *8 First Level Directors*

Additional Levels (Contact Company For Details): *Diamond Director, Retirement Level*

Other Bonuses: *President's/Chairman's Bonus Pools; retreats*

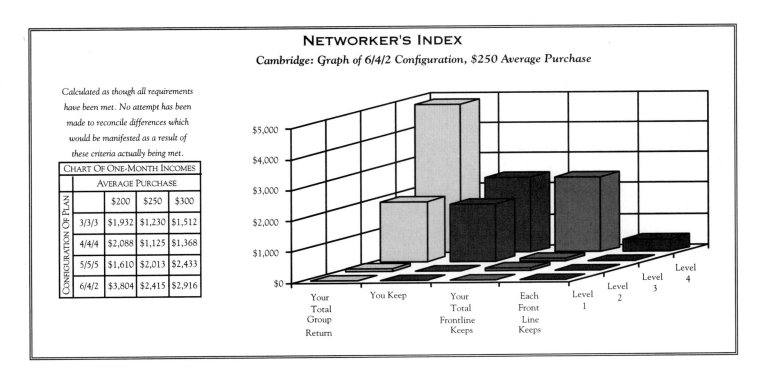

NETWORKER'S INDEX

Cambridge: Graph of 6/4/2 Configuration, $250 Average Purchase

Calculated as though all requirements have been met. No attempt has been made to reconcile differences which would be manifested as a result of these criteria actually being met.

CHART OF ONE-MONTH INCOMES

CONFIGURATION OF PLAN		AVERAGE PURCHASE		
		$200	$250	$300
	3/3/3	$1,932	$1,230	$1,512
	4/4/4	$2,088	$1,125	$1,368
	5/5/5	$1,610	$2,013	$2,433
	6/4/2	$3,804	$2,415	$2,916

CARCO INTERNATIONAL, INC.

PO BOX 528, BELLEVILLE, IL, 62222
618-236-2726 VOICE
800-366-2728 VOICE
618-236-2826 FAX

History
Founded in 1981 by Jim Rompel, Dave Rompel, and Mary Beth Schaltenbrand. Restructured in 1992 with new compensation plan and new products.

Financials *Not rated, privately held, incorporated IL*

General Statistics
Total 1993 Sales: *Not Available*
Total Distributors: *10,000*
Foreign Countries: *N/A*

Method of Product Distribution *Delivered to distributor; delivered to customer*

Association Membership *MLMIA*

Inventory Policy *No requirement*

Product Return Policy *100% 30 days; 90% 30-60 days*

The Product Line: Carco manufactures and/or private labels more than 60 products, in the following categories: Nutrition, personal care, homeopathic medicines, skin care, water filtration, aloe vera, and environmentally friendly cleansers and detergents.

Nutritional and personal care products include: Hi Potency II Multi Vitamin With Minerals, Energy, Cal-Mag Plus, Super C-plex, Vitamin E-400 (Mixed Toc), Beta Care, Stress All-B 50, Garlic and Parsley, Fiber Supreme, Spirulina, Weight Control Formula Caps, Aqua Supreme II water filtration system, Aqua Mistique water catalyst gel and mist, Aloe Supreme Juice, Aloe Supreme Lotion, Aloe Supreme Jelly, Aloe Supreme Body Shampoo, Aloe Supreme Liniment, Aloe Supreme Shampoo, Aloe Supreme Conditioner, and Aloe Supreme Tooth Polish, A•Dora Facial Creme, Homeopathic Energy, Joint/Muscle, Arnica, Rheumatism, Hay Fever/Alergy, Sinus, Indigestion, Headache, Pain, Daily Care, Calendula lotion, cough syrup.

Home care products include: Environmentally-friendly laundry detergent, stain remover, organic cleanser, Blue Bolt concentrated cleaner and automatic dishwashing cleaner.

MARKETING/COMPENSATION PLAN

PLAN CATEGORY *Expandable Matrix*
DISTRIBUTOR DISCOUNT OFF RETAIL *25%*
QUALIFICATION PERIOD *One Month*
COMPRESSION? *N/A*

MINIMUM QUALIFYING VOLUME *$36.00*
SUPPORT *Videos, Workshops, Literature, Newsletters*
LEVELS LOCKED IN? *Yes*
INITIAL FEE *$5.00 Lifetime; Free to Preferred Customers*

QUALIFICATION LEVELS

Preferred Customer: *Purchase products at 25% discount* **Qualification:** *enrolled by Member (free)*

Member: *Earn 25% retail profit; 25% commission on products purchased by personally enrolled Preferred Customers; 7% of all products purchased by 5 levels of downline Members; 2% of all product purchased by Preferred Customers of five levels of downline Members; an additional 5% on all products purchased by personally enrolled Members (12% total) and their Preferred Customers (7% total)* **Qualification:** *purchase membership kit; $36.00 monthly volume in products or product coupons (redeemable at any time up to one year for any product). The $36.00 volume qualifies on all levels for bonuses, commissions, overrides and profits.*

Additional Levels (Contact Company For Details): *N/A; the simplest plan known.*

Other Bonuses: *N/A*

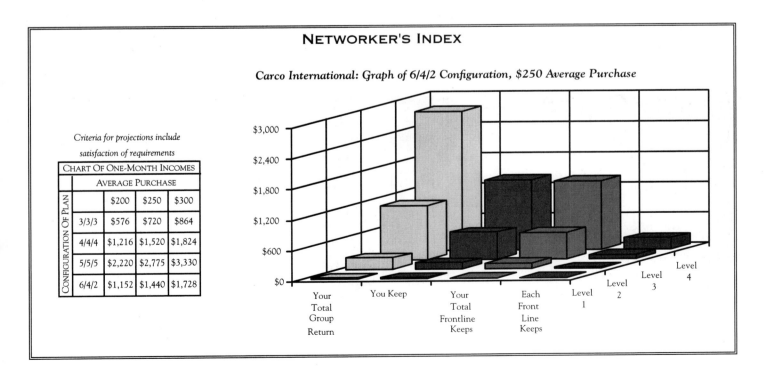

NETWORKER'S INDEX

Carco International: Graph of 6/4/2 Configuration, $250 Average Purchase

Criteria for projections include satisfaction of requirements

CHART OF ONE-MONTH INCOMES			
	AVERAGE PURCHASE		
	$200	$250	$300
3/3/3	$576	$720	$864
4/4/4	$1,216	$1,520	$1,824
5/5/5	$2,220	$2,775	$3,330
6/4/2	$1,152	$1,440	$1,728

CELL TECH

1300 MAIN STREET, KLAMATH FALLS, OR 97601
800-800-1300 VOICE
503-884-1869 FAX

History
Founded in 1982 by Daryl Kollman, one of the first researchers in the U.S. to cultivate microalgae for human consumption, and Marta Kollman, a business woman.

Financials *Not rated, privately held, incorporated OR*

General Statistics
Total 1993 Sales: *$20 Million*
Total Distributors: *34,000*
Foreign Countries: *Canada*

Method of Product Distribution *Delivered to Distributor, Picked up by Distributor*

Association Membership *N/A*

Inventory Policy *No requirement*

Product Return Policy *Not Available*

The Product Line: Cell Tech's core product is freeze-dried Super Blue Green™ Algae—*Aphanizomenon flos-aquae*—harvested from the pristine Upper Klamath Lake in the Cascade mountains of south-central Oregon. The 200 million pounds of Super Blue Green™ Algae produced by the lake each year, combined with its natural isolation, has inhibited industrial and recreational use of the lake.

Cell Tech's literature informs us that algae have been used as staple foods in human dietary traditions throughout the world, and that freshwater algae also formed a part of many traditions as in parts of Africa and Central America. "The Kanembu natives of the Lake Chad region in Africa have traditionally harvested and eaten blue-green algae, using a processing method similar to that used by the Aztec civilization to remove Spirulina from Lake Texcoco."

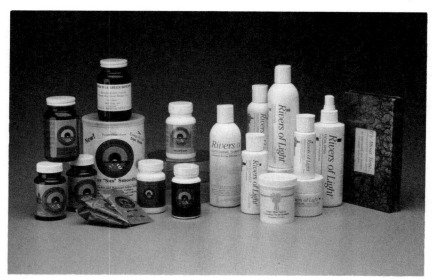

Nutritional products include: Super Blue Green™ Omega Sun, Alpha Sun, Acidophilus, Enzymes; Super Sprouts and Algae; Super Sun Smoothie; BG Bites

Cell Tech also manufactures Rivers Of Light, a skin-care system including a skin cleanser, facial spray, skin creme and "Moisture Mystique" and a line of clothing called "Fun Wear" made of all-natural fibers

MARKETING/COMPENSATION PLAN

PLAN CATEGORY *Stairstep/Breakaway*
DISTRIBUTOR DISCOUNT OFF RETAIL 30-40%
QUALIFICATION PERIOD *Level Dependent*
COMPRESSION *No*

MINIMUM QUALIFYING VOLUME *$50/$100*
SUPPORT *Videos, Workshops, Literature, Newsletters*
LEVELS LOCKED IN *No*
INITIAL FEE *Not available*

QUALIFICATION LEVELS

Consumer: *Purchases made at standard distributor discount; income derived from retail-sale profit margins*

Assistant Leader: *5% personal and 1st level Consumer volume* **Qualification:** *Cumulative (no time limit) group volume of $251.00; $50 purchase*

Associate Leader: *10% personal and 1st level Consumer volume; 5% 1st level Assistant Leader Volume* **Qualification**: *Cumulative (no time limit) group volume of $501.00; $50 personal*

Group Leader: *15% personal and 1st level Consumer volume; 10% Assistant Leaders; 5% Associate Leaders* **Qualification:** *$751.00 in one month; $50 personal purchase; 5 Distributors, at least 3 1st level; $50 personal purchase*

Leader: *20% personal and 1st level Consumer volume; 15% Assistant Leaders; 10% Associate Leader Volume; 5% Group Leaders* **Qualification:** *$1,501 volume; 10 distributors (5 first level); $50 personal purchase*

Executive: *25% personal and 1st level Consumer; 20% Assistant Leaders; 15% Associate Leaders; 10% Group Leaders; 5% Leaders* **Qualification:** *$3,001 Volume; 20 Distributors (5 first level); $50 personal purchase*

Amethyst: *Executive bonus plus: bonus on executives: 1st level 9%; 2nd level 7%; 3rd level 5%; 4th level 2%; 5th level 2%; 6th level 1%* **Qualification:** *Executive qualifications; one 1st level executive; $100.00 personal purchase*

Additional Levels (Contact Company For Details): *Ruby; Sapphire; Emerald; Topaz; Diamond; Double Diamond*

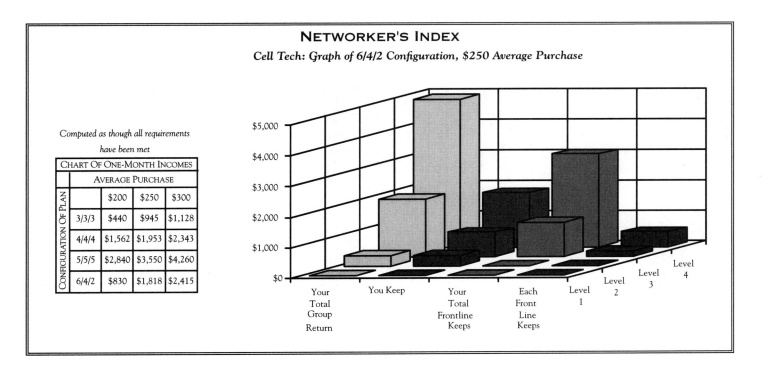

NETWORKER'S INDEX

Cell Tech: Graph of 6/4/2 Configuration, $250 Average Purchase

Computed as though all requirements have been met

CHART OF ONE-MONTH INCOMES			
	AVERAGE PURCHASE		
	$200	$250	$300
3/3/3	$440	$945	$1,128
4/4/4	$1,562	$1,953	$2,343
5/5/5	$2,840	$3,550	$4,260
6/4/2	$830	$1,818	$2,415

DIAMITE CORPORATION

1625 McCANDLESS DRIVE, MILPITAS, CA 95035
408-945-1000 TELEPHONE

DIAMITE
CORPORATION

History
In 1983 Rudy Revak became president. He changed the marketing plan and introduced nutritional, personal care, and home care products.

Financials *Not rated; privately held; incorporated NV*

General Statistics
Total 1993 Sales: *$50 Million*
Total Distributors: *43,000*
Foreign Countries: *Canada, Japan, Bahamas*

Method of Product Distribution *Picked up by distributor; delivered to distributor; delivered to customer*

Association Membership *DSA*

Inventory Policy *No requirement*

Product Return Policy *Distributors 90% of resalable merchandise; Customers 100%*

The Product Line: Diamite Corporation manufacturers and/or private labels over 50 products. These products are: Vitality Aloe Vera Plus, Vitality Nutritional Drink, Vitality Fiber Tablets, Vitality Fiber Bar Plus, Vitality Night Trimming System (part of the Simply Perfect diet plan), Vitality Multi-Fiber Blend, Vitality Whole Orange C Complex, Vitality Calcium Plus, Vitality Omega III Concentrate, Vitality Snack Bar Plus; DEJA VU® Personal Care line — Aloe Vera Facial Scrub, Conditioning Facial Cleanser, Herbal Toner, Hydrating Eye Formula, Daytime Collagen Complex, Night Time Collagen Complex, Vital Protection Complex™, Skin Care Lotion, Bath & Shower Gel,

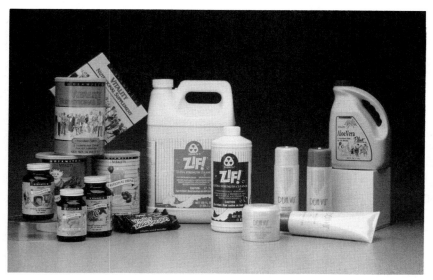

Aloe Vera Gel Plus Herbs, Replenishing Shampoo, Revitalizing Conditioner—Water Enhancement System, ZIF! Extra Strength Cleaner, Liquid Concentrate Cleaner, Laundry Detergent Concentrate.

The majority of Diamite's products are nutritional and personal care products. Most of the personal care products contain Aloe. ZIF! Extra Strength Cleaner and Liquid Concentrate are biodegradable, phosphate-free, and concentrated. Laundry Detergent Concentrate is biodegradable with controlled phosphate.

The Diamite Water Enhancement System is NSF listed for reduction of chlorine, THMs, and pesticides. The filter cartridge is replaceable, and the unit taps directly into the cold-water line.

MARKETING/COMPENSATION PLAN

PLAN CATEGORY *Stairstep/Breakaway*
DISTRIBUTOR DISCOUNT OFF RETAIL 30-50%
QUALIFICATION PERIOD *Two Months*
COMPRESSION *Yes; Volume Pooling*

MINIMUM QUALIFYING VOLUME *N/A*
SUPPORT *Videos, Workshops, Literature, Newsletters*
LEVELS LOCKED IN *No*
INITIAL FEE *Not Available*

QUALIFICATION LEVELS

V.I.P. Customer: *Discount on purchased products; no retailing*

Associate Member: *discount on purchased products up to 50%; income derived from retail-sale profit margins*

Ruby Member: *up to 8% of Group Volume (GV)* **Qualification**: *250 Point Value (PV)*

Group Manager: *up to 12% Bonus on GV* **Qualification**: *1,000 PV in one month; Purchase Business Literature Kit; Submit Group Manager application*

Group Coordinator: *up to 25% GV* **Qualification:** *3,000 adjusted Group PV + 100 Personal PV*

Team Coordinator: *Group Coordinator benefits plus 3% of entire downline* **Qualification:** *Group Coordinator; 3 qualified group coordinator legs*

Team Director: *Group Coordinator benefits plus 5% of entire downline* **Qualification:** *Group Coordinator; 6 qualified group coordinator legs*

Additional Levels (Contact Company For Details): *First Level Continuous Training Bonus, Second Level Continuous Training Bonus, Team Director, Diamond Director; Double Diamond Director, Triple Diamond Director, Executive Diamond Director*

Other Bonuses: *President's/Chairman's Bonus Pools, Director Incentive Bonuses, Profit Sharing Team Bonus, Travel Bonus, Group Coordinator Incentive Bonus.*

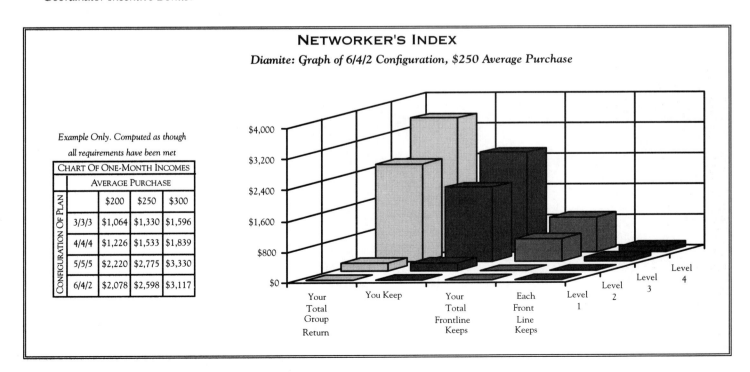

NETWORKER'S INDEX
Diamite: Graph of 6/4/2 Configuration, $250 Average Purchase

Example Only. Computed as though all requirements have been met

CHART OF ONE-MONTH INCOMES			
	AVERAGE PURCHASE		
CONFIGURATION OF PLAN	$200	$250	$300
3/3/3	$1,064	$1,330	$1,596
4/4/4	$1,226	$1,533	$1,839
5/5/5	$2,220	$2,775	$3,330
6/4/2	$2,078	$2,598	$3,117

DISCOVERY TOYS, INC.

2530 ARNOLD DRIVE, SUITE 400, MARTINEZ, CA 94553
510-370-3400 VOICE

History
Founded by President Lane Nemeth

Financials *Not rated; privately held*

General Statistics
Total 1993 Sales: *$50.1 - 100 million*
Total Distributors: *25,000*
Foreign Countries: *Australia, Canada, Japan, Mexico*

Method of Product Distribution *Delivered to distributor, delivered to customer*

Association Membership *DSA*

Inventory Policy *No requirement*

Product Return Policy *90% within 90 days for distributors, 100% to customers*

The Product Line: Discovery Toys manufacturers and distributes a wide range of games and toys designed to enhance learning through play. Age categories begin with the early years; the oldest age category begins with 8 year olds.

For age categories beginning with the early years and 3 year olds, toys are available which are designed to enhance hearing and listening skills. Age-specific products for all age groups include toys and games designed to enhance: seeing and perceiving; touching and grasping; eye-hand coordination; large muscle movement; speaking, listening, reading, and writing ; taking care of the body and getting around in the world; imagination, dramatic play, drama, art, and music; self-nurturing, self-esteem, and relationships; cause-effect problem-solving and relationships.

Discover Toys also offers the "Gateway to the Imagination®" book club, available in individual club selections or as a complete 30-book set which in both cases offer age-appropriate story selections. Club selections are available every six weeks.

Age selections for the "Gateway to the Imagination®" are 2½ years, 3 years, 3-3½ years; 4-4½ years, and 5 years.

MARKETING/COMPENSATION PLAN

PLAN CATEGORY *Stairstep/Breakaway*
DISTRIBUTOR DISCOUNT OFF RETAIL *50 - 60%*
QUALIFICATION PERIOD *Level Dependent*
COMPRESSION *No*

MINIMUM QUALIFYING VOLUME *Level Dependent*
SUPPORT *Videos, Workshops, Literature, Newsletters*
LEVELS LOCKED IN? *No*
INITIAL FEE *Not available*

QUALIFICATION LEVELS

Educational Consultant: *Earn 22% commission on Personal Sales (PS)* **Qualification:** *to remain active, $100 per quarter*

Star Educational Consultant: *Earn additional 3% on PS; 1% override on Personal Group Sales (PG)* **Qualification:** *January: 300 PS, 500 PS+PG; February, 300 PS, 900 PS+PG; March , April: 400 PS, 1,200 PS+PG; May, June, July: 400 PS, 1,400; August: 500 PS, 1,600 PS+PG; September 700 PS, 2,200 PS+PG; October: 1,400 PS, 4,800 PS+PG; November: 2,000 PS, 6,400 PS+PG; December: 800 PS, 3,000 PS+ PG; Personal sales can be used to meet the PS+PG requirement on a monthly basis.*

Manager: *Earn 27-32% commission on PG; 3-10% override on PG; 3-4% override on 1st level* **Qualification:** *Recruit and qualify at least 7 Educational Consultants of which 5 must be direct recruits; 1st Quarter (January — March: 1,400 PS 3,000 PS+PG; 2nd Quarter (April-June): 1,800 PS 4,600 PS+PG; 3rd Quarter (July-September): 2,300 PS, 6,000 PS+PG; 4th Quarter (October-December): 6,500 PS, 16,400 PS+PG; Maintenance Qualifications: 1st Quarter (January — March: 1,000 PS, 2,600 PS+PG; 2nd Quarter (April-June): 1,200 PS 4,000 PS+PG; 3rd Quarter (July-September): 1,600 PS, 5,200 PS+PG; 4th Quarter (October-December): 4,200 PS, 14,200 PS+PG*

Advanced Manager: *Manager benefits plus 1% override on 2nd level* **Qualification:** *Have one first level Manager (FL); 1st Quarter (January — March: 1,800 PS, 5,400 PS+PG, 10,400 PS+PG+FL; 2nd Quarter (April-June): 2,400 PS 8,200 PS+PG, PS+PG +FL 15,600; 3rd Quarter (July-September): 3,200 PS, 10,800 PS+PG, 21,400 PS+PG+FL; 4th Quarter (October-December): 8,600 PS, 31,600 PS+PG, 62,600 PS+PG+PL; Maintenance Qualifications: PS+PG & PS+PG+FL the same as level qualification; PS requirements: 1st Quarter (January — March: 1,400; 2nd Quarter (April-June): 1,800; 3rd Quarter (July-September): 2,300; 4th Quarter (October-December): 6,500;*

Additional Levels (Contact Company For Details): *Senior Manager; Sterling Senior Manager; Sales Director Gold Sales Director; Emerald Sales Director; Diamond Sales Director; Blue Diamond Director; Chairman's Club Director*

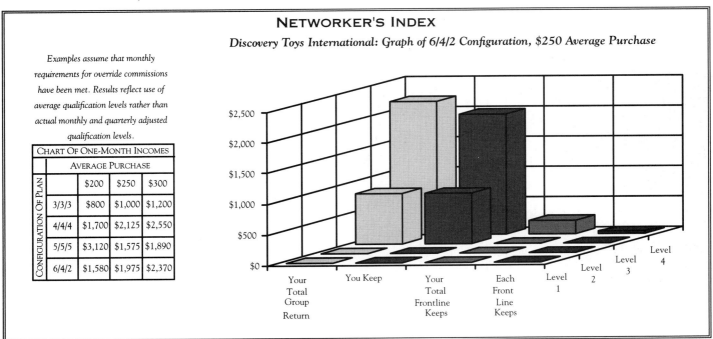

NETWORKER'S INDEX

Discovery Toys International: Graph of 6/4/2 Configuration, $250 Average Purchase

Examples assume that monthly requirements for override commissions have been met. Results reflect use of average qualification levels rather than actual monthly and quarterly adjusted qualification levels.

CHART OF ONE-MONTH INCOMES

CONFIGURATION OF PLAN	AVERAGE PURCHASE		
	$200	$250	$300
3/3/3	$800	$1,000	$1,200
4/4/4	$1,700	$2,125	$2,550
5/5/5	$3,120	$1,575	$1,890
6/4/2	$1,580	$1,975	$2,370

ENRICH INTERNATIONAL

748 NORTH 1340 WEST, OREM, UT 84057
801-226-2600 VOICE
801-226-8232 FAX
800-748-4334 ORDER LINE
800-999-6222 CANADIAN ORDER LINE

History
Founded in 1977 as Nature's Labs, it was purchased and converted from Direct Sales to MLM in 1985 by Kenneth Brailsford and David Lisonbee. Kenneth Brailsford is currently owner and president, and David Lisonbee Senior Vice President.

Financials *Not available*

General Statistics
Total 1993 Sales: *est.* $75 Million; 1992 $24,839,000
Total Distributors: 75,000
Foreign Countries: Canada, Malaysia, Mexico

Method of Product Distribution *Picked up by distributor, delivered distributor, delivered to customer*

Association Membership *DSA, MLMIA*

Inventory Policy *No requirement*

Product Return Policy *100% guarantee for customers; distributor policy not available*

The Product Line:
Enrich's product line began with simple herbs in capsule form. It has since been expanded to include a variety of health-oriented products. The product line can be grouped into four categories: all-body systems, weight control systems, concentrated products, combinations, single herbs, homeopathics, extracts, vitamins and minerals, and ointments.

REV and Enhance are two all-body systems offered exclusively by Enrich. REV has a lemon taste and is used to build energy, tone muscles, and for vitamins. Enhance is a mint-flavored mineral drink that combines essential minerals with natural herbs. It is used to increase stamina, vitality, and a sense of well-being.

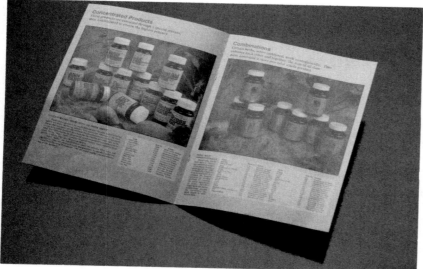

The Enrich weight loss product line includes glandular, digestive, and intestinal systems. The concentrated product line and the combination herb line consist of formulas for respiratory, nervous, circulation, digestive, liver/gall, urinary, glandular, and skeletal systems. There are 37 popular and useful herbs in Enrich's single herb line, and 23 extracts for virtually every system of the body in their extract line. 7 homeopathic formulas, 14 vitamin/mineral formulas, and 6 ointments and creams fill out Enrich's natural product line.

Enrich introduced Aeon Skin Treatment System, with Epidermal Growth Factor (EGF), in 1993.

MARKETING/COMPENSATION PLAN

PLAN CATEGORY *Stairstep/Breakaway*
DISTRIBUTOR DISCOUNT OFF RETAIL *Up to 30%*
QUALIFICATION PERIOD *Level Dependent*
COMPRESSION? *Yes*

MINIMUM QUALIFYING VOLUME *$100*
SUPPORT *Videos, Workshops, Literature, Newsletters*
LEVELS LOCKED IN? *Yes*
INITIAL FEE *$35.00*

QUALIFICATION LEVELS

Distributor: *Up to 46% retail profit margin (mark-up on wholesale)*

Silver Distributor: *5% rebate on personal sales volume and 5% commission on personally sponsored Distributor Personal Group Sales Volume (PGSV) and Silver Distributor Personal Sales Volume (PSV)* **Qualification:** *$300 cumulative PGSV*

Gold Distributor: *10% on PSV and Distributor PGSV; 5% on 1st level Gold Distributor PSV* **Qualification:** *$1,000 cum. PGSV*

Platinum Distributor: *15% on PSV and 1st level Distributor PGSV; 10% on PGSV of 1st level Silver Distributors; 5% on PSGV of 1st level Gold Distributors and on PSV of 1st level Platinum Distributors* **Qualification:** *$3,000 cumulative PGSV*

Diamond Distributor: *20% on PSV and 1st level Distributor PGSV; 15% on PGSV of 1st level Silver Distributors; 10% on PSGV of 1st level Gold Distributors; 5% on PGSV of 1st level Platinum Distributors and on PSV of 1st level Diamond Distributors* **Qualification:** *$5,000 cumulative PGSV*

Manager *25% on PSV and 1st level Distributor PGSV; 20% on PGSV of 1st level Silver Distributors; 15% on PSGV of 1st level Gold Distributors; 10% on PGSV of 1st level Platinum Distributors; 5% on PGSV of 1st level Diamond Distributors* **Qualification:** *$1,000 PGSV in one month*

Additional Levels (Contact Company For Details) *Senior Manager, Supervisor, Director, Senior Director, Executive Director, Presidential Director (breakaways paid up to nine levels deep)*

Other Bonuses *New Manager Bonus; Car Allowance Program*

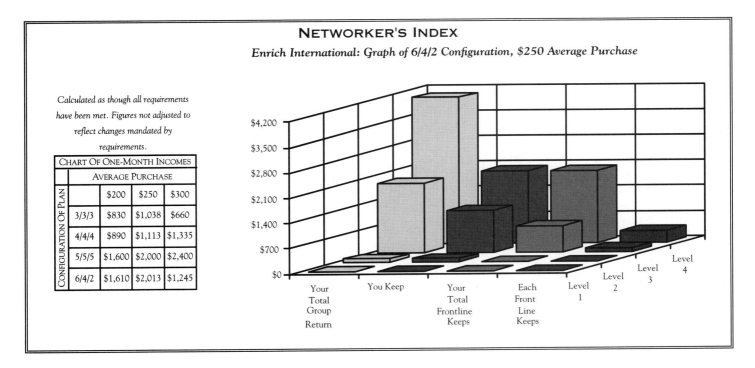

NETWORKER'S INDEX

Enrich International: Graph of 6/4/2 Configuration, $250 Average Purchase

Calculated as though all requirements have been met. Figures not adjusted to reflect changes mandated by requirements.

CHART OF ONE-MONTH INCOMES

CONFIGURATION OF PLAN	AVERAGE PURCHASE		
	$200	$250	$300
3/3/3	$830	$1,038	$660
4/4/4	$890	$1,113	$1,335
5/5/5	$1,600	$2,000	$2,400
6/4/2	$1,610	$2,013	$1,245

HERBALIFE INTERNATIONAL

PO BOX 80210, LOS ANGELES, CA 90080-0210
310-410-9600 VOICE
310-216-7454 FAX

History
Founded 1980 by Mark Reynolds Hughes, Chairman of the Board and President

Financials *Not rated; public company traded OTC; Incorporated in NV*

General Statistics
Total 1993 Sales: *est. $102 Million*
Total Distributors: *250,000*
Foreign Countries: *Global (See page 144-145)*

Method of Product Distribution *Not available*

Association Membership *DSA*

Inventory Policy *No requirement*

Product Return Policy *90% within one year to distributors*

The Product Line: An Herbalife flagship product, Thermojetics™, is a blend of 21 health-enhancing botanicals including ancient Chinese herbs and herbs from the Amazon rain forest. The aim of Thermojetics™ is the creation of a more desirable energy balance in the body, so that excess body fat may be reduced. The complete system is composed of one "Beige" and one "Green."

The Cellular Nutrition Program, which is composed of Nutritional Protein Drink Mix Formula 1 (which comes in French Vanilla, Dutch Chocolate, and Wild Berry), Multivitamin-Mineral & Herbal Tablets Formula 2 (which has 31 vitamin, mineral, and other nutritional factors), and Cellactivator Formula 3 (which is a combination of 12 botanical factors).

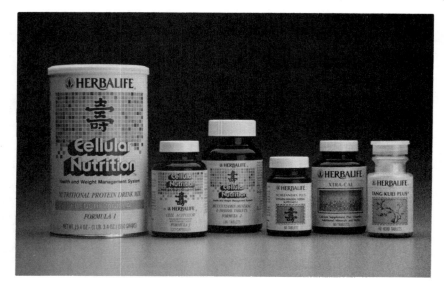

Additional health and weight management system products include: N.R.G.—Natures Raw Guarana, C ell-U-Loss (a vitamin, mineral, and herbal formula), Activated Fiber Tablets, Herbal Aloe beverage, Herbalifeline (high in Omega 3 fatty acids), Schizandra Plus (combats cell damage from environmental toxins), Male Factor 1000, Tang Kuie Plus (for women), and others.

In addition, Herbalife markets a range of both men's and women's skin-care products, as well as sun-tanning lotion and shampoo.

MARKETING/COMPENSATION PLAN

PLAN CATEGORY *Stairstep*
DISTRIBUTOR DISCOUNT OFF RETAIL *17% - 33%*
QUALIFICATION PERIOD *Level Dependent*
COMPRESSION? *Yes*

MINIMUM QUALIFYING VOLUME *$100*
SUPPORT *Videos, Workshops, Literature, Newsletters*
LEVELS LOCKED IN? *No*
INITIAL FEE *No*

QUALIFICATION LEVELS

Distributor: *Income earned by 25%-50% markup on wholesale*

Supervisor: *50% personal discount; 5% override to three levels; 8-25% wholesale profit on items sold to distributors* **Qualification:** *$4,000 group volume in one month or $2,000 for two consecutive months*

National Expansion Team: *Supervisor benefits plus 2% Organizational Production Bonus* **Qualification**: *Not available*

Millionaire Team: *National Expansion Team Benefits plus up to 4% Organizational Production Bonus Qualification:* *Not available*

President's Team: *Millionaire Team benefits plus up to 6% Organizational Production Bonus* **Qualification:** *Not available*

Additional Levels (Contact Company For Details): *Not available*

Other Bonuses: *Not available*

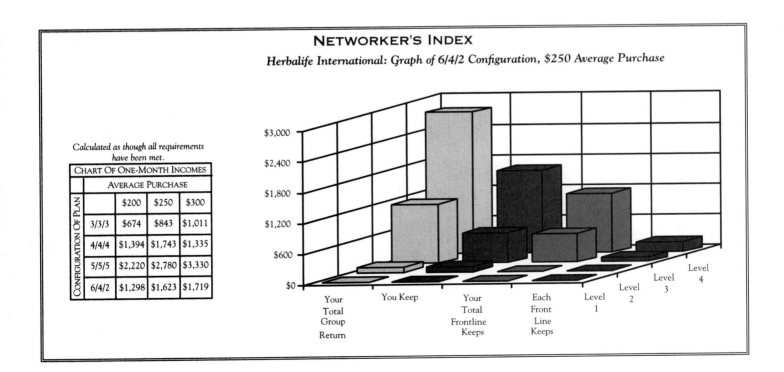

NETWORKER'S INDEX

Herbalife International: Graph of 6/4/2 Configuration, $250 Average Purchase

Calculated as though all requirements have been met.

CHART OF ONE-MONTH INCOMES			
	AVERAGE PURCHASE		
CONFIGURATION OF PLAN	$200	$250	$300
3/3/3	$674	$843	$1,011
4/4/4	$1,394	$1,743	$1,335
5/5/5	$2,220	$2,780	$3,330
6/4/2	$1,298	$1,623	$1,719

JAPAN LIFE AMERICA CORPORATION

4160 WILSHIRE BOULEVARD, LOS ANGELES, CA 90010
213-954-1781 VOICE
213-954-1785 FAX

JAPAN LIFE

History
Founded 1975 in Isezaki City, Japan; Opened in New York and Los Angeles 1984, began U.S sales operations in 1985

Financials *Not rated; privately held; Incorporated CA*

General Statistics
Total 1993 Sales: *est $7 Million (U.S.) $50 Million (worldwide)*
Total Distributors: *4,500 (U.S.)*
Foreign Countries: *Global (See page 144-145)*

Method of Product Distribution *Delivered to distributor and customer*

Association Membership *DSA*

Inventory Policy *None allowed (products stocked in company-owned showrooms)*

Product Return Policy *N/A*

The Product Line: Japan Life manufactures and markets a line of futons, futon comforters, bed frames, pillows, pads, and personal comfort items, many of which employ multiple low-gauss magnets to enhance their effects.

The Japan Life flagship product is the JL Sleep System, which includes the Dream Futon Comforter, the Sleep Pad, and the Pillow. The Dream Futon Comforter, contains over 70% goose down. To ensure that the down feathers cannot escape from the comforter, an extremely fine, soft fabric is used; this fabric is created by the Japan Life FeatherGuard process, in which natural cotton yarn is spun in air jet textile machines, resulting in a high density fabric. The quilting is machine sewn, with an average of 6 to 7 stitches per centimeter. To ensure an especially strong border, morning cord (a specially braided cord) is employed as a further measure against feather loss.

The Japan Life sleep pad is composed of six layers of varying materials and textures designed to give firm support to the human body and a gentle massage during.

Japan Life's pillow is made of three layers of materials designed to give firm but flexible support for the head during sleep.

MARKETING/COMPENSATION PLAN

PLAN CATEGORY *Stairstep/Breakaway*
DISTRIBUTOR DISCOUNT OFF RETAIL *10% & 25%*
QUALIFICATION PERIOD *Two Months*
COMPRESSION? *No*

MINIMUM QUALIFYING VOLUME *$100*
SUPPORT *Brochures, Showrooms*
LEVELS LOCKED IN? *No*
INITIAL FEE *$25*

QUALIFICATION LEVELS

Business Associate: *10% discount on purchases; profits derived from retail-sale profit margins*

Distributor: *25% personal discount; 15% of 1st level Business Associates volume* **Qualification:** *$5,000 accumulative two-month total volume*

Senior Distributor: *distributor bonus plus 5% of personal and 1st level Distributor Group volumes* **Qualification**: *Accumulative total group volume of $7,500 in two consecutive months; $100 personal volume*

Executive Distributor: *Distributor Bonus plus 10% on personal and Direct Distributor volumes, and 5% of 1st level Senior Distributor Volume* **Qualification:** *$15,000 volume over two consecutive months; $100 personal volume*

Bronze Star Distributor: *Distributor benefits plus 15% personal and Direct Distributor volumes; 10% Senior Distributor Volume; 5% Executive Distributor Volume; 5% 1st level Bronze Star Distributors* **Qualification:** *$30,000 over two months; $3,000 retail sales volume; $100 personal volume*

Silver Star Distributor: *Distributor Benefits plus 20% personal and Direct Distributor volumes; 15% Senior Distributor Volume; 10% Executive Distributor Volume; 5% Bronze Star Distributor Volume; 5% 1st level Silver Star Distributors; 5% 2nd level Silver Star Distributors.* **Qualification:** *$60,000 volume over two consecutive months; $3,000 retail sales volume; $100 personal volume*

Additional Levels (Contact Company For Details): *Gold Star Distributor, Diamond Star Distributor, Super Star Distributor*

Other Bonuses: *N/A*

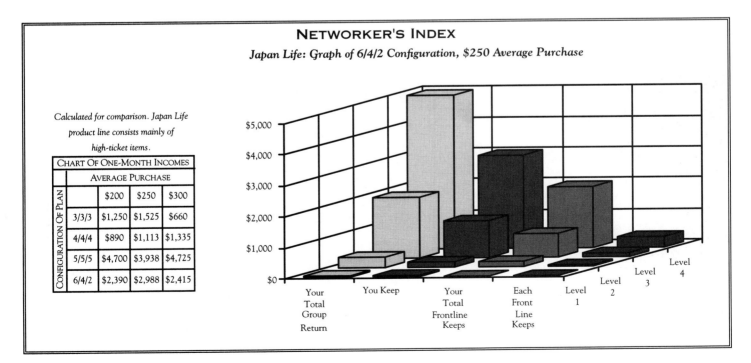

NETWORKER'S INDEX
Japan Life: Graph of 6/4/2 Configuration, $250 Average Purchase

Calculated for comparison. Japan Life product line consists mainly of high-ticket items.

CHART OF ONE-MONTH INCOMES			
	AVERAGE PURCHASE		
	$200	$250	$300
3/3/3	$1,250	$1,525	$660
4/4/4	$890	$1,113	$1,335
5/5/5	$4,700	$3,938	$4,725
6/4/2	$2,390	$2,988	$2,415

CONFIGURATION OF PLAN

KARLA JORDAN INTERNATIONAL

3505 NORTH 124TH STREET, BROOKFIELD, WI 53005
414-783-5575 VOICE

History
Founded by Karla Jordan in 1984 in her home when she found herself alone with four children and no business. She had become interested in handcrafted jewelry in the early 1970s while teaching deaf children on a Navajo reservation.

Financials *Not rated, privately held, incorporated WI*

General Statistics
Total 1993 Sales: *$5.2 Million*
Total Distributors: *5,100*
Foreign Countries: *Norway and Sweden*

Method of Product Distribution *Picked up by distributor, delivered to distributor*

Association Membership *N/A*

Inventory Policy *No requirement*

Product Return Policy *Not available*

The Product Line: Karla Jordan Kollections Ltd. markets women's clothing and accessories, ranging from limited edition, handcrafted jewelry to versatile apparel, moonbags, and watches.

Karla Jordan's clothing line is manufactured of cotton/poly knitwear, along with matched accessories. Ensembles include a white Dolman tunic, black narrow pant, and sequined applique collar; oversized tee, blazer, sash, and narrow pant; Dolman tunic, stretch belt, and swing skirt; an all-black combo of four 16" tubes used variously as belts and tops, with swing skirt (Items for these and many other ensembles are sold individually). There are panty hose, crossover belts, cardigans, "wrinkled" metal belt buckles as well as many other items

Jewelry and accessories include a two-part Santa Fe Collection, one part a Black/Silver/Crystal ensemble of necklace, bracelet, bracelet watch, and a choice of dangling or button earrings, each sold individually; the other part composed of similar items made of carnelian, turquoise, unakite, overlay and patina. There are also onyx, opal, mother-of-pearl, paua, pen shell, jade, purple quartz, obsidian, teal, gold, sterling, copper, and/or topaz gem pins, earrings, bolos, bracelettes, bezels, watches, and rings; bead, faux pearl, freshwater pearl, and nugget strands, necklace extenders, belt buckles, purses, and moonbags.

MARKETING/COMPENSATION PLAN

PLAN CATEGORY *N/A*
DISTRIBUTOR DISCOUNT OFF RETAIL *25% - 35%*
QUALIFICATION PERIOD *Level Dependent*
COMPRESSION? *Yes*

MINIMUM QUALIFYING VOLUME *$150/$300*
SUPPORT *Certification, training, catalogs, brochures*
LEVELS LOCKED IN? *No*
INITIAL FEE *$48 or $250*

QUALIFICATION LEVELS

Consultant: *Earn 25% to 35% retail profit; the higher of the two following schedules (paid on jewelry accessories only): (1) 3% on Personal Active Consultants (PACs) for 1-3 PACS; 4% on PACs for 4 PACs; 5% on PACs for 5 PACs; 6% on PACs for 6 or more PACs or (2) 3% Personal Consultant (PC) & 1 level for up to $3,999 volume; 4% PC & 1 level for $4,000-$7,999 volume; 5% PC & 1 level for $8,000-$11,999 volume; 6% PC & 1 level for $12,000 and more volume*

Senior Consultant: *Consultant benefits plus the higher of the two following schedules for Apparel Accessories: (1) 1% on Personal Active Consultants (PACs) for 1-3 PACS; 2% on PACs for 4 PACs; 2% on PACs for 5 PACs; 2% on PACs for 6 or more PACs or (2) 1% Personal Consultant (PC) & 1 level for up to $3,999 volume; 2% PC & 1 level for $4,000-$7,999 volume; 2% PC & 1 level for $8,000-$11,999 volume; 2% PC & 1 level for $12,000 and more volume* **Qualification:** *Four Qualified PCs; $3,000 combined Jewelry Accessories (JA) and Apparel Accessories (AA) volume; $1,000 JA & AA combined retail personal volume in one month.*

Unit Director: *Senior Consultant benefits plus 2% of AA and the following paid on PC & 2 Levels: 3% for 1-5 PACs or up to $5,000 volume; 4% for 6 PACs or $6,000 to $10,999 volume; 5% for 7 PACs or $11,000 to $14,999 volume; 6% for 8 (or more) PACS or $15,000 (or more) volume* **Qualification:** *either 8 consultants on PC level, 5 on 1st level, 2 on 2nd level or a representative on each of these levels totalling 20; nine qualified consultants, four of which are PC; $6,000 downline volume (JA & AA); $1,000 personal retail volume (JA & AA) in month and two previous months; complete Unit Director Development Program*

Additional Levels (Contact Company For Details): *Agency Director; Executive Director; Generation Agency Director*

Other Bonuses: *Conference Bonus; President's Bonus; Car Bonus; Profit Sharing Bonus; Pay Off Home Mortgage Bonus*

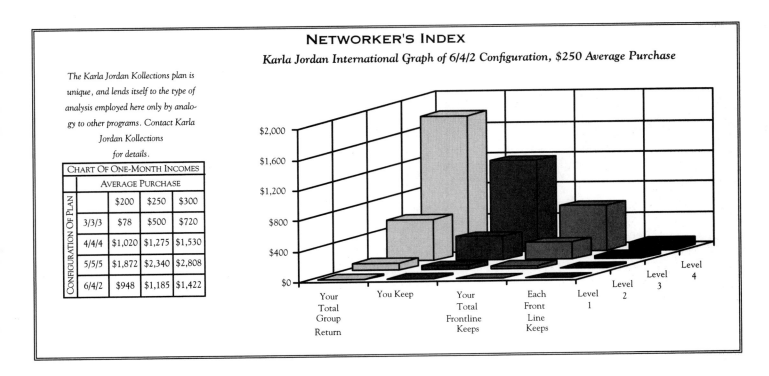

NETWORKER'S INDEX

Karla Jordan International Graph of 6/4/2 Configuration, $250 Average Purchase

The Karla Jordan Kollections plan is unique, and lends itself to the type of analysis employed here only by analogy to other programs. Contact Karla Jordan Kollections for details.

CHART OF ONE-MONTH INCOMES			
	AVERAGE PURCHASE		
CONFIGURATION OF PLAN	$200	$250	$300
3/3/3	$78	$500	$720
4/4/4	$1,020	$1,275	$1,530
5/5/5	$1,872	$2,340	$2,808
6/4/2	$948	$1,185	$1,422

LIGHT FORCE

1115 THOMPSON AVENUE #5, SANTA CRUZ, CA 95062
408-462-5000 VOICE
408-476-9630 FAX

History
Founded 1979 by Christopher Hills. Light Force cultivates and harvests a proprietary strain of Spirulina, and manufacturs Spirulina-based nutrients worldwide.

Financials *Not rated; privately held; incorporated CA*

General Statistics
Total 1993 Sales: *Not available*
Total Distributors: *10,000*
Foreign Countries: *N/A*

Method of Product Distribution *Delivered to customer, delivered to distributor*

Association Membership *MLMIA*

Inventory Policy *No requirement*

Product Return Policy *100% 60-days for customers; 90% 90-days for distributors*

The Product Line: Light Force formulas are based upon Spirulina, believed to have the broadest nutritional profile of any known food; Spirulina is a high-protein, vitamin-rich vegetable plankton, and widely cultivated for its value as a staple-food and highly digestible protein source.

In mid–1992, Light Force introduced a line of formulas with Flanagan Microclusters®. Microclusters are used as microscopic transport vehicles to reduce the size of nutrients and carry them rapidly into cells. Microcluster products include Phycotena Microclusters®, PhycoCreme®, Artichoke Micro™, ExCELLerate™, and C rystal Energy®.

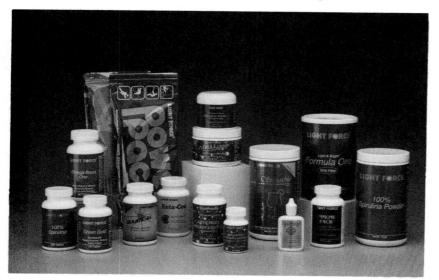

Other important Light Force's products and formulas include Immune Pack with Phycotene®, MagiCal™, Extra-Cee, Power Pack, Slim Pack™, Mega-Life™, and Beta Bears for Children, which are vitamin and nutrient supplement packages of individually wrapped dosages in tablet form. Power Pack, for example, contains Spirulina, papaya enzyme, Tienchi ginseng, bee pollen niacin, calcium gluconate, and vitamin B-6.

All of Light Force's products are preservative and additive free.

MARKETING/COMPENSATION PLAN

PLAN CATEGORY *Stairstep/Breakaway*
DISTRIBUTOR DISCOUNT OFF RETAIL *25-50%*
QUALIFICATION PERIOD *One or Two Month*
COMPRESSION *No*

MINIMUM QUALIFYING VOLUME *None*
SUPPORT *Videos, Workshops, Literature, Newsletters*
INITIAL FEE *Not available*
LEVELS LOCKED IN? *Yes*

QUALIFICATION LEVELS

Member/Distributor: *25% discount on product; income derived from retail-profit margins*

Star Distributor: *33% discount on product; 8% of personal and 1st level Distributors & Members* **Qualification:** *$500 volume in one or two months*

Manager: *41%% discount on product; 8% of personal & 1st level Star Distributors* **Qualification:** *$2,000 volume in one or two months*

Director: *50% discount on product; 8% of personal managers* **Qualification:** *$4,000 in 1 or 2 months*

Senior Director: *Director benefits plus 5% on 3 levels of Directors* **Qualification:** *Director with a Director in any of first three levels; $2,000 Volume*

Executive Director: *Senior Director benefits plus 1% of 4th level Director* **Qualification:** *Director with two 1st level Directors; $2,000 Volume*

Senior Executive Director: *Senior Director Benefits plus 2% of 4th level Director and 1% of 5th level Director* **Qualification:** *Director with four 1st level Directors; $2,000 Volume*

Additional Levels (Contact Company For Details): *Diamond Director, Master Diamond Director*

Other: *Bonus Bucks; President's Club; Networking Bonus; Leadership Bonus*

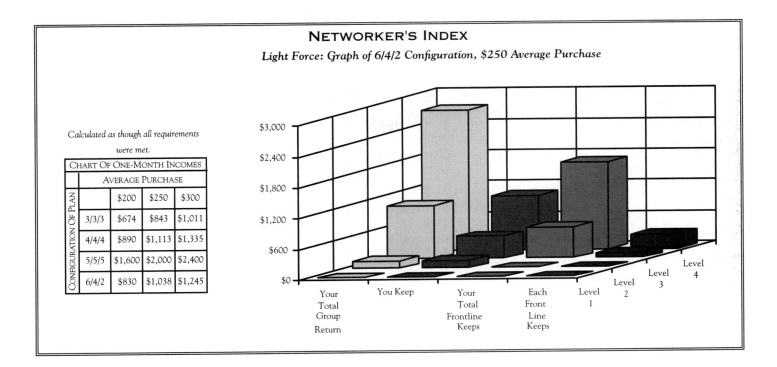

NETWORKER'S INDEX

Light Force: Graph of 6/4/2 Configuration, $250 Average Purchase

Calculated as though all requirements were met.

CHART OF ONE-MONTH INCOMES

CONFIGURATION OF PLAN	AVERAGE PURCHASE		
	$200	$250	$300
3/3/3	$674	$843	$1,011
4/4/4	$890	$1,113	$1,335
5/5/5	$1,600	$2,000	$2,400
6/4/2	$830	$1,038	$1,245

LITE & RITE

PO BOX 70725, SEATTLE, WA 98707-1525
206-547-2006 VOICE
206-547-4011 FAX

History
Founded in July, 1988 by Dr. Irvin Miller (a Naturopathic Physician) and Bonnie Miller, a health therapist, to market Dr. Miller's herbal weight-loss formula.

Financials *Not rated; privately held*

General Statistics
Total 1993 Sales: $10 Million
Total Distributors: 12,000
Foreign Countries: N/A

Method of Product Distribution *Delivered to distributor, delivered to customer*

Association Membership *N/A*

Inventory Policy *No requirement; stockpiling actively discouraged by rule requiring sale of at least 70% of all products previously purchased.*

Product Return Policy *90% in 30 days*

The Product Line: Dr. Miller's Exclusive Formula #1, a 100% natural product made with a combination of four herbs: epitonin, purple willow, kelp, and berberis vulgaris. It comes in bottles of 225 caplets or capsules.

Harmonizer, a blend of twenty-two herbs in a base of trace minerals, comes in bottles of 120 caplets.

Thinergy, Lite & Rite's weight management enhancer, is a complement to Formula #1. One serving of Thinergy is 210 calories when taken with apple juice, contains protein, has no fat, and includes over 20 vitamins and minerals. The powder comes in a 21 ounce canister.

VitaMin is a powdered nutritional supplement providing 100% U.S. RDA of 14 vitamins and minerals, plus 2% fiber. Virtually flavorless, the powder can be mixed with any juice. Formulated for those who don't like swallowing pills. VitaMin comes in a 1-pound canister.

MARKETING/COMPENSATION PLAN

PLAN CATEGORY *Stairstep/Breakaway*
DISTRIBUTOR DISCOUNT OFF RETAIL *20-40%*
QUALIFICATION PERIOD *Level Dependent*
COMPRESSION *Yes*

MINIMUM QUALIFYING VOLUME *$100/$400*
SUPPORT *Videos, Workshops, Literature, Newsletters*
LEVELS LOCKED IN *Yes*
INITIAL FEE *$30*

QUALIFICATION LEVELS

Associate*: 20% discount on product purchases; income derived from retail-sale margins*

Manager: *25% discount on product purchases; 5% bonus on 1st level Associates Group Volume (GV)* **Qualification:** *Accumulated $400 Volume in three months; $100 personal volume*

Coordinator: *30% discount on product purchases; 10% of 1st level Associates, 5% on 1st level Managers* **Qualification:** *Accumulated $1,200 volume; $100 personal volume*

Supervisor: *35% discount on product purchases; 15% of 1st level Associates GV; 10% on 1st level Managers GV; 5% on 1st level Coordinators GV* **Qualification:** *$3,600 volume, at least $1,000 in qualifying month; $100 personal volume*

Director: *40% discount on product purchases; 20% of 1st level Associates GV; 15% on 1st level Managers GV; 10% on 1st level Coordinators GV; 5% on 1st level Supervisors GV* **Qualification:** *$7,200 GV volume, at least $2,000 in qualifying month; $100 personal volume*

Bronze Star Director: *Director Benefits plus 5% 2 levels of Directors GV* **Qualification:** *Director with one 1st level Director; $400 personal volume, or $1,000 Group Volume of which $100 is personal*

Additional Levels (Contact Company For Details): *Silver Star Director, Gold Star Director; Ruby Star Director; Diamond Star Director; Ambassador; Premier; Presidential*

Other Bonuses: *VIP Bonus*

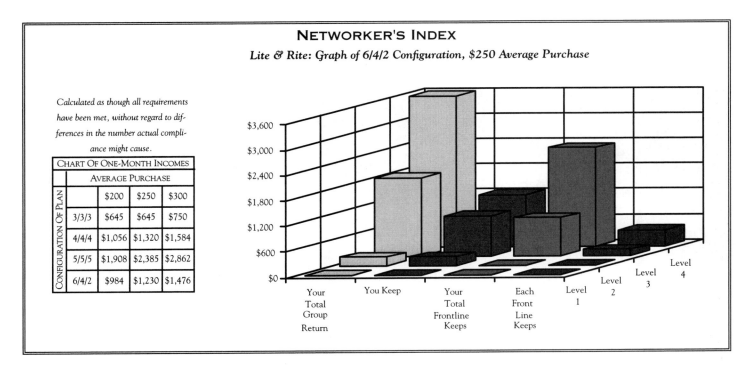

NETWORKER'S INDEX
Lite & Rite: Graph of 6/4/2 Configuration, $250 Average Purchase

Calculated as though all requirements have been met, without regard to differences in the number actual compliance might cause.

CHART OF ONE-MONTH INCOMES		AVERAGE PURCHASE		
CONFIGURATION OF PLAN		$200	$250	$300
	3/3/3	$645	$645	$750
	4/4/4	$1,056	$1,320	$1,584
	5/5/5	$1,908	$2,385	$2,862
	6/4/2	$984	$1,230	$1,476

MARY KAY COSMETICS, INC.

8787 STEMMONS FREEWAY, DALLAS, TX75247
214-630-8787 VOICE

History

Friday, September 13, 1963 Mary Kay opened her doors in a small Dallas storefront with nine employees and her son, Richard Rogers, now Chairman of the Board and CEO. Mary Kay Cosmetics does not consider itself to be a network-marketing company.

Financials Not rated; privately held; incorporated DE

General Statistics

Total 1993 Sales: est. $520 Million
Total Distributors: 250,000 (Beauty Consultants)
Foreign Countries: Canada, Australia, Germany, Mexico, Argentina, Taiwan

Method of Product Distribution Delivered to consultant, delivered to customer

Association Membership DSA

Inventory Policy no requirement; suggest reinvestment in inventory up to $3,000 wholesale ($6,000 suggested retail), and an additional $600 for supplies, taxes, etc.

Product Return Policy 90% from consultants

The Product Line: Mary Kay Cosmetics offers a complete skin-care program for both women and men, and for dry skin, normal skin, combination and oily skin, combination and normal skin, and for blemish prone skin, producing formulas to cleanse, retexture, freshen, moisture balance and protect these skin types. Also available are a variety of skin supplements.

As well as skin-care, Mary Kay Cosmetics manufactures a full pallette of cosmetics with a wide variety of color and texture types of foundation, eye colors, cheek colors, lipsticks and lip glosses, rouges, concealers, highlighters, eyebrow pencils, eye defining pencils, and lip liner pencils.

The five-step Mary Kay nail care program consists of treatment oil, fortifier, binder, color shield, and protector available in a wide range of colors. The nail care system allows for a balance between hardness and flexibility, and takes into account factors such as moisture, texture, and strength of the nail.

In addition, Mary Kay distributes and trains in the use of fragrances, manicures, hair care, and sun protection.

No animal testing is used in the development or production of any Mary Kay product.

MARKETING/COMPENSATION PLAN

PLAN CATEGORY *N/A*
DISTRIBUTOR DISCOUNT OFF RETAIL *15% - 40%*
QUALIFICATION PERIOD *Level Dependent*
COMPRESSION? *Yes*

MINIMUM QUALIFYING VOLUME *$300*
SUPPORT *Videos, Workshops, Literature, Newsletters, Seminars*
LEVELS LOCKED IN? *No*
INITIAL FEE *$45.00*

QUALIFICATION LEVELS

Beauty Consultant: *Earn income from 40% to 50% discount from retail; skin care classes and facials* **Qualification:** *$300 - $499.99 order for 40% discount; $500 – $799.99 for 45% discount; $800 or more for 50% discount*

Star Recruiter: *4% commission on wholesale of personal recruits;wear red jacket, Star Recruiter Pin* **Qualification:** *3 or 4 active recruits*

Team Leader: *8–12% commission on personal recruits; Team Leader Pin* **Qualification:** *5 or more active recruits*

Team Manager: *up to 12% commission on personal recruits; VIP car or cash; Team Manager Pin and Team Manager scarf; $50–$300 performance bonus based on recruiting and time as Team Manager; Silver or Gold Key Manager Status* **Qualification:** *combined personal/team production of $3,600 for 4 consecutive months; meet requirements of Auto Insurance Program to qualify for use of VIP car*

Director-in-Qualification: *Team Manager benefits* **Qualification:** *Team Manager; 12 active recruits in month prior to submitting commitment card and leadership profile*

Sales Director: *up to 12% on personal recruits; 9 or 13% on unit; $300–$3,500 bonus; Director Recruit bonus; life insurance & disability; Director's plaque, certificate, briefcase; wear Director's suit; earn use of VIP car, pink mid-sized car or Cadillac* **Qualification:** *$16,000 and 30 active consultants in one, two, three, or four months.*

Additional Levels (Contact Company For Details): *N/A*

Other Bonuses: *Conference Bonus; President's Bonus; Car Bonus; Profit Sharing Bonus; Pay Off Home Mortgage Bonus*

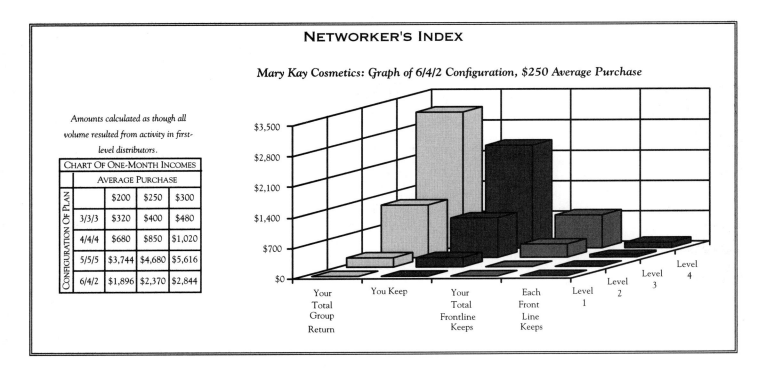

NETWORKER'S INDEX

Mary Kay Cosmetics: Graph of 6/4/2 Configuration, $250 Average Purchase

Amounts calculated as though all volume resulted from activity in first-level distributors.

CHART OF ONE-MONTH INCOMES

CONFIGURATION OF PLAN	AVERAGE PURCHASE		
	$200	$250	$300
3/3/3	$320	$400	$480
4/4/4	$680	$850	$1,020
5/5/5	$3,744	$4,680	$5,616
6/4/2	$1,896	$2,370	$2,844

Mary Kay Cosmetics, Inc.

Mary Kay Cosmetics does not consider itself to be a multi-level marketing company. They are included in this book because many industry experts feel that the company is a trail-blazer for the multi-level marketing industry.

Mary Kay Ash was already a very successful direct sales person in 1963. She was considered one of the top saleswomen in the United States, and had a national reputation as a motivator and trainer. But she had long held onto one dream—to found a company in which the people responsible for its success would share in its success. The dream was of a company that would give women the potential to earn unlimited income.

At that time, Mary Kay also had a product she believed in as well as a very unusual marketing concept—the skin-care class. These classes were limited to five or six individuals and held in the more casual home environment. A trained, independent Beauty Consultant would lead these classes by guiding the guests through a complementary facial using the company's products.

On Friday, September 13, 1963, in a Dallas Texas storefront, Mary Kay Cosmetics began business with Mary Kay, her co-founder and son, Richard Rogers (now chairman of the company), along with nine saleswomen.

Today, the company has a sales force of approximately two hundred thousand independent Beauty Consultants and Sales Directors. The Mary Kay headquarters building is an easily recognized Dallas landmark. In addition, Mary Kay Cosmetics, Inc. owns and operates five regional distribution centers around the country, with approximately one thousand employees. And Mary Kay has produced at least fifty-four millionaires, fourteen of whom are multi-millionaires.

Over the years, Mary Kay Cosmetics has entered international markets, including Canada, Australia, Germany, Mexico, Argentina, and Taiwan.

Since its inception, the company has been based upon the same philosophy: the golden rule of "Do unto others as you would have them do unto you" and an order of priorities of God first, family second, and career third.

Mary Kay Cosmetics' vision is "To be preeminent in the manufacturing, distribution, and marketing of personal care products through our independent sales force. To provide our sales force an unparalleled opportunity for financial independence, career achievement, and personal fulfillment. To achieve total customer satisfaction worldwide by focusing on quality, value, convenience, innovation, and personal service."

Mary Kay Beauty Consultants are not employees. They are self-employed, and each Beauty Consultant's independent contractor status is clearly spelled out by company policy. Beauty Consultants have the freedom to choose their own hours and to use the sales methods which work best for them.

In addition, Beauty Consultants retain the right to determine their own retail pricing for products and whether or not they will follow the company's suggested retail pricing.

Mary Kay Cosmetics offers in-depth training to Beauty Consultants and even legal advise through the company's Legal Department.

Mary Kay Cosmetics, Inc. refers to its marketing and compensation plan as "Dual Marketing," a term emphasizing the separation of corporate management from the network of independent contractors.

The point is that Mary Kay Cosmetics, Inc. does not directly recruit new independent Consultants, but that Consultants and Sales Directors help build the company by sharing the opportunity with others.

This network begins with the Recruiter, Director, and Consultants within what is called a "unit." Along with the company, these people provide training to new Consultants.

This training begins with observation of at least three skin-care classes and is supplemented with videos, audio recordings, workbooks, and guides.

Once the facials have been observed, and some other preliminary work done, Consultants are encouraged to get off to a quick start by booking eight skin care classes and holding at least five of them within two weeks of starting.

Mary Kay Cosmetics offers detailed information regarding how to book and conduct classes, as well as how to follow up on these.

In addition to this sales training, the company stresses to its Consultants that they should become very well-informed about skin, skin care, product ingredients, and the terminology that goes along with this knowledge.

Consultants learn the vocabulary of skin care,

including the meaning and usage of words like dermis, efficacious, fibrocytes, free radicals collagen, comedogenic, photoaging, pH, sebum, exfoliant, and melanocytes.

Consultants are also given an arsenal of facts with which they can guide their business activities. Facts such as the following:

There has been a tremendous increase in the number of women holding professional, managerial, and technical positions.

On average, these women buy and use more cosmetics and have greater disposable income.

The use of birth control pills can lead to more oily or acne prone skin in some women.

Women want products that produce immediate results and provide demonstrable benefits.

Most women think of their skin as sensitive.

Consultants are cautioned to be aware that they can care for the skin, but they should not treat a medical problem which might result in dry or oily skin.

Within this framework, Mary Kay Cosmetics has created the Skin Wellness Program, a public service skin cancer awareness and prevention program designed to teach consumers how to maintain healthy skin.

Mary Kay Cosmetics, Inc. is a Bronze contributor to the World Congress of Dermatology and is permitted to use the World Congress seal.

Following is a partial list of Mary Kay Cosmetics' five-step skin care products, along with ingredients identified by the company as "key:"

Gentle Cleansing Cream Formula 1 For Dry Skin; key ingredients—glycerine, candelilla wax, beeswax, PEG 4 Octanoate

Creamy Cleanser Formula 2 For Normal and Combination Skin; key ingredients—mineral oil, propylene glycol

Deep Cleanser Formula 3 For Oily Skin; key ingredients—camomile extract, quaternium-26

Purifying Bar For Normal, Combination, And Oily Skin; key ingredients—sodium cocoyl isethionate, stearic acid, eucalyptus oil

Moisture Rich Mask Formula 1 For Dry And Normal Skin; key ingredients—hybrid safflower oil, sesame oil, avacado oil, acrylates copolymer, panthenol, stearyl heptanoate

Revitalizing Mask Formula 2 For Combination and Oily Skin; key ingredients—kaolin, bentonite, walnut shell powder, oat flour, quaternium-26, carnauba, candelilla wax, cucumber extract.

Clarifying Mask Formula 3 For Blemish-Prone Skin; key ingredients—kaolin, C12-15 alcohols benzoate, propylene glycol, camomile and lavender extracts

Gentle Action Freshener Formula 1 For Dry Skin; key ingredients—silk amino acids, panthenol, witch hazel extract, menthol

Refining Freshener Formula 2 for Normal, Combination and Oily Skin; key ingredients—quaternium-26, SD Alcohol 40, benzyl alcohol

Blemish Control Toner Formula 3 Acne Medication; key ingredients—salicylic acid, SD Alcohol 40, Dimethicone

Enriched Moisturizer Formula 1 for Dry Skin; key ingredients—soluble animal collagen, panthenol, cetearyl octanoate

Balancing Moisturizer Formula 2 for Normal and Combination Skin; key ingredients—mineral oil, avocado oil, dimethicone

Oil Control Lotion Formula 3 for Oily Skin; key ingredients—acrylates copolymer, cyclomethicone, glycereth-26

Day Radiance Cream Foundation for Dry Skin; key ingredients—propylene glycol dicaprylate/dicaprate, cetyl ricinoleate

Day Radiance Liquid Foundation for Normal and Combination Skin; key ingredients—mineral oil, dimethicone

Oil-Free foundation for Oily Skin; key ingredients—kaolin, talc, nylon 12

After three years of research, Mary Kay Cosmetics came to a determination of the variety of possible skin tones and the distribution of skin tones across the population.

Skin tones were measured according to several criteria then charted on a distribution graph to indicate the largest cluster of skin tones.

The foundation shades were developed to fall within these clusters, tested in the marketplace, and further refined to more exact groups of shades.

At the head of two pages containing 71 photographs of Mary Kay Cosmetics National Sales Directors (the majority of whom are noted as "Mary Kay Millionaire" or "Mary Kay Multi-Millionaire"), reads the caption:

All Mary Kay National Sales Directors are proof that no goal is beyond reach. On their journey to the top, they have demonstrated that it is possible to have a full and nurturing family life while pursuing a rewarding career. From the fulfillment of helping others achieve new levels of growth in their Mary Kay careers to the prestigious gift of the keys to a new pink Cadillac, the rewards are many… ■

Matol Botanical International, Ltd.

1111, 46e Avenue, Lachine, Quebec, Canada H8T3C5
514-639-0730 Voice
514-637-0576 Fax

History
J.F. Robert Boldue and Anthony Jurak founded the company in 1984. Sam Kalenuik became co-partner and co-chairman in 1986.

Financials *Not rated, privately held, incorporated Canada*

General Statistics
Total 1993 Sales: *$249 Million*
Total Distributors: *172,000*
Foreign Countries: *Canada, Mexico, Great Britain, New Zealand*

Method of Product Distribution *Delivered to customer and to distributor.*

Association Membership *DSA, MLMIA*

Inventory Policy *No requirement*

Product Return Policy *100% to customers; 90% to distributors within one year*

The Product Line: Matol Botanical's original, flagship product is Km™, a potassium mineral supplement which is also used as the basis for skin care lotion. Matol also offers the Matola™ line of nutritional products including a variety of meal replacement bars and shakes, a dietary fibre supplement, and a cereal. Km™ is a formulation of 14 botanical elements formulated by Dr. Karl Jurak more than 70 years ago. A synopsis of the plants from which Km™ is formulated follows.

Camomile flower: a sacred flower to the ancient Egyptians and Romans. Saw Palmetto Berry: consumed

by Native Americans and early American Settlers. Also known as fan palm and sabal. Cascara Sagrada: Native Americans believed Cascara bard was sacred and named it "The Great Herb." Angelica Root: known as a holy plant among ancient Laplanders, who chewed it regularly. Thyme: widely used as a culinary spice, tea and oil. Passion Flower: Early Spanish explorers took samples back to Spain. Gentian root: popular for centuries as a mid-day tea. Licorice root: also known as Spanish or Italian juice root, lickweed, and sweet wood, horehound root, Senega root; Celery seed: native to the British Isles. Sarsparilla root; Alfalfa: used for centuries in many cultures. Dandelion root: residents of Minorca subsisted on nothing but dandelion when the rest of their harvest was destroyed.

MARKETING/COMPENSATION PLAN

PLAN CATEGORY *Stairstep*
DISTRIBUTOR DISCOUNT OFF RETAIL *25-40%*
QUALIFICATION PERIOD *Two Months*
COMPRESSION *Yes*

MINIMUM QUALIFYING VOLUME *$105*
SUPPORT *Audios/Videos/Brochures/Sponsoring Programs*
INITIAL FEE *Not Available*
LEVELS LOCKED IN *Yes*

QUALIFICATION LEVELS

New Distributor:
.25-2 Cases Distributor: *25% discount off retail case price*

Over 2 Cases Distributor: *30% discount off retail case price*

Over 4 Cases Distributor: *35% discount off retail price*

Supervisor: *40% discount off retail price; 15% on .25-2 case distributors; 10% on 2.25-4 case distributors; 5% on 4.25-6 case distributors* **Qualification:** *Accrue 6 cases of volume in 3 consecutive months*

Royalty Qualified Supervisor: *Supervisor benefits plus 5% override on retail sales volume of Supervisors to 3 generations deep* **Qualification:** *2 cases total volume*

Silver Key Supervisor: *Silver Key Supervisor benefits plus 5% override on 4th generation supervisors* **Qualification:** *5-9 qualified Supervisor legs plus two cases total volume*

Gold Key Supervisor: *Royalty Qualified Supervisor benefits plus 5% override on 5th generation Supervisors* **Qualification:** *10 qualified Supervisor legs plus two cases total volume*

Additional Levels (Contact Company For Details): *Field Advisory Supervisor, Executive Field Advisory Supervisor*

Other Bonuses: *Retail Volume Bonus; Leadership Bonus (potential to collect 5% on whole volume of entire downline)*

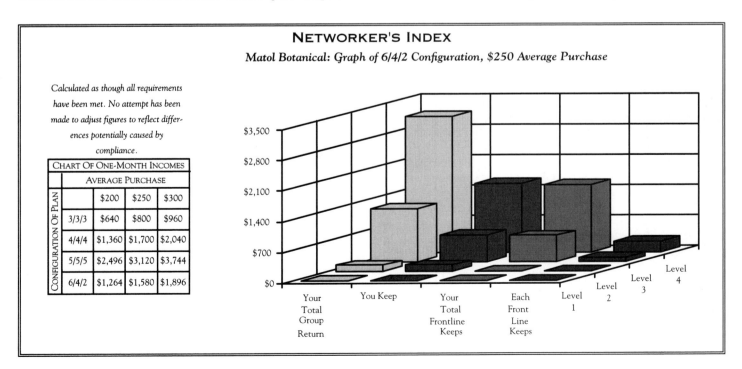

NETWORKER'S INDEX

Matol Botanical: Graph of 6/4/2 Configuration, $250 Average Purchase

Calculated as though all requirements have been met. No attempt has been made to adjust figures to reflect differences potentially caused by compliance.

CHART OF ONE-MONTH INCOMES			
	AVERAGE PURCHASE		
	$200	$250	$300
3/3/3	$640	$800	$960
4/4/4	$1,360	$1,700	$2,040
5/5/5	$2,496	$3,120	$3,744
6/4/2	$1,264	$1,580	$1,896

Melaleuca, Inc.

3910 South Yellowstone, Idaho Falls, ID 83402
800-282-3000 Voice

History
Founded 1985 by Frank Vandersloot, Roger Ball, and Allen Ball. As of 1993, Melaleuca's official position is that they are not an MLM

Financials *Not rated; privately held; incorporated in ID*

General Statistics
Total 1993 Sales: *$200 Million*
Total Distributors: *150,000 (130,000 U.S.)*
Foreign Countries: *Canada, Puerto Rico, Virgin Islands*

Method of Product Distribution *Delivered to customer, delivered to distributor*

Association Membership *DSA, MLMIA*

Inventory Policy *Product shipped directly to customers; inventory actively discouraged*

Product Return Policy *100% to customers; 90% to distributors*

The Product Line:
Melaleuca has a product line of more than 55 nutritional, medicinal, personal care, and home hygiene products. The basis of many of Melaleuca's products is the oil of Australia's Melaleuca alternifolia tree. Melaleuca oil contains over 48 natural compounds that together, according to product literature, outperform aloe vera in treating skin conditions.

Melaleuca holds exclusive rights to a process called "fructose compounding,' which binds minerals to a fructose molecule to make minerals more easily used by the body; its leading product is called the Vitality Pak, a vitamin and mineral supplement which utilizes fructose compounding. Melaleuca's products also contain combinations of more than 30 common and exotic plants, among them camomile, ginseng, golden seal, lemongrass, rosemary, and passion flower, as well as natural oils extracted from the coconut, jojoba, macadamia nut, apricot, sesame seed, and wintergreen plants; and camphor, menthol, aloe, and arnica plant extracts.

The major categories of Melaleuca's product line are Nutrition (vitamins and minerals), Medicine Chest (melaleuca based skin gels, ointments, creams, and oils; shampoo, dental care, acne medicine and douche), Personal Care (melaleuca based liquid and bar soaps, body lotion and hand cream, suntan lotions, anti-perspirants, bath oil, shampoo and conditioner, hair sprays, lip-balms and fragrances), Facial Care (moisturizers, cleansers, masks, and toners), and Home Care (laundry, bath, floor and dish cleansers).

MARKETING/COMPENSATION PLAN

PLAN CATEGORY *Unilevel Matrix*
DISTRIBUTOR DISCOUNT OFF RETAIL *37%*
QUALIFICATION PERIOD *Level Dependent*
COMPRESSION? *Yes*

MINIMUM QUALIFYING VOLUME *29/75 Bonus Points*
SUPPORT *Videos, Workshops, Leterature, Newsleters*
LEVELS LOCKED IN? *No*
INITIAL FEE *$19.00*

QUALIFICATION LEVELS

Marketing Executive: *37% discount on purchases; Product Introduction Bonus (PIB) of 25% of bonus points over 100 of personal and 1st level new Customers; 7% of 1st 100 BP of 2nd month Customers and Marketing Executives to 2nd level* **Qualification:** *one customer (Direct or Insured: contact company for details) or one Marketing Executive; 29 personal Bonus Points (BP)*

Bronze Executive: *PIB; 7% to 3rd level; listed in monthly publication; certificate* **Qualification:** *2 1st level Customers; 100 organization BP; 29 personal BP*

Silver Executive: *PIB; 7% to 4th level; listed in monthly publication; certificate* **Qualification:** *4 1st level Customers; 500 organization BP; 29 personal BP*

Gold Executive: *PIB; 7% to 7th level; Gold Executive Personal Enrollee Bonus: 20% of personal enrollees purchases if Gold has 16 or more active personal enrolled customers; Leadership Bonus; $500; lapel pin; certificate* **Qualification:** *8 active Customers; 1,000 BP organization volume; 75 personal BP; maintain status at least 3 consecutive months.*

One-Star Gold Executive: *Gold Executive benefits plus one-time $250 One Star Bonus; $1,000 Leadership Bonus* **Qualification:** *Gold Executive plus 1 1st level Gold Executive; 2500 BP organization volume*

Additional Levels (Contact Company For Details): *Two-Star Gold Executive; Three-Star Gold Executive; Four-Star Gold Executive; Ruby Executive; Diamond Executive; Corporate Diamond Executive*

Other Bonuses: *Ruby and Diamond Executive New Car Bonus; Ruby First Level Expansion*

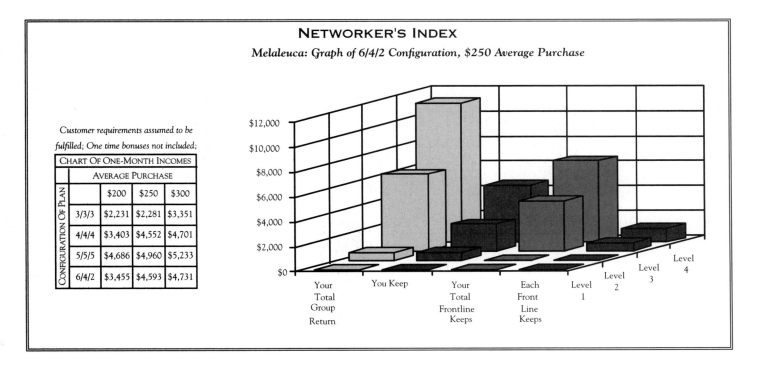

NETWORKER'S INDEX
Melaleuca: Graph of 6/4/2 Configuration, $250 Average Purchase

Customer requirements assumed to be fulfilled; One time bonuses not included;

CHART OF ONE-MONTH INCOMES			
	AVERAGE PURCHASE		
CONFIGURATION OF PLAN	$200	$250	$300
3/3/3	$2,231	$2,281	$3,351
4/4/4	$3,403	$4,552	$4,701
5/5/5	$4,686	$4,960	$5,233
6/4/2	$3,455	$4,593	$4,731

MULTI-PURE CORPORATION

21339 NORDHOFF STREET, CHATSWORTH, CA 91311
818-341-7577 VOICE

History
Founded in 1970 by H. Allen Rice, CEO; Alvin E. Rice, President. Became MLM in 1982

Financials *Not rated; privately held*

General Statistics
Total 1993 Sales: *Not available*
Total Distributors: *100,000*
Foreign Countries: *global (see pages 144-145)*

Method of Product Distribution *Delivered to customer, delivered to distributor*

Association Membership *N/A*

Inventory Policy *No requirement*

Product Return Policy *100%, 30-day guarantee; 10 year warranty*

The Product Line: Multi-Pure Corporation is a drinking water treatment product manufacturer many of whose products are tested and certified under NSF (National Sanitation Foundation, an independent testing and certification agency that sets quality standards for a wide variety of home and industrial products) Standards No.42 and No. 53 for aesthetic effects and health effects of drinking-water treatment systems.

Multi-Pure water treatment systems utilize a solid carbon block main filter and an outershell of 304 stainless steel. The systems provide .75 gallon of water per minute @ 60 psi. The replacement filter has a capacity for about 500 gallons of water.

Multi-Pure water treatment systems are NSF listed for removal of the following contaminants: Asbestos 99%+; Chlorine class I (taste, odor, and chlorine reduction are the three classifications for this listing, class I is the highest); cysts 99%+ (including *giardia Lamblia*); 2,4-D 99%+; lead 99%+; lindane 99%+; particulate matter (down to submicron range)99%+; THMs (trihalomethanes) 99%+; TCE (trichloroethylene) 99%+; turbidity 99%+; and VOCs (volatile organic chemicals) 99%+.

Multi-pure water treatment systems are also certi-fied, regestered, or listed in the states of California, Colorado, Iowa, Massachusetts.

MARKETING/COMPENSATION PLAN

PLAN CATEGORY *Unilevel 4*
DISTRIBUTOR DISCOUNT OFF RETAIL *$49.95*
QUALIFICATION PERIOD *N/A*
COMPRESSION *No*

MINIMUM QUALIFYING VOLUME *N/A*
SUPPORT *Videos, Workshops, Literature, Newsletters*
LEVELS LOCKED IN *No*
INITIAL FEE *$15.00*

QUALIFICATION LEVELS

Junior Builder: *$49.95 discount on first and subsequent purchases; 20% commission on 2nd and subsequent purchases; 5% commission on 1st level sales; 2% Commission on 2nd level sales*

Executive Builder: *25% commission on personal purchases; 5% commission on 1st level sales; 2% commission on 2nd level sales; 0.5% commission on 3rd - 9th level sales; 1% commission on replacement filter sales to 9th level; 3% Activity Bonus on 1st level sales; 1% activity Bonus on 2nd level sales; 5% Roll-up bonus* **Qualification:** *$700 Personal Net Volume over any time period; $500 in Group Net Volume in month to qualify for Activity and Roll-up bonuses*

Senior Builder: *30% commission on personal purchases; 5% commission on 1st level sales; 2% commission on 2nd level sales; 0.5% Commission on 3rd - 9th level sales; 2% on replacement filter sales to 9th level; 4% Activity Bonus on 2nd level sales; 2% Activity Bonus on 3rd level sales; 0.5% Activity Bonus on 3rd - 9th level sales; 10% Roll-up Bonus* **Qualification:** *$5,000 Personal Net Volume over any period of time; $1,000 Group Net Volume in month to qualify for Activity and Roll-up bonuses*

Master Builder: *35% commission on personal purchases; 5% commission on 1st level sales; 2% commission on 2nd level sales; 0.5% commission on 3rd - 9th level sales; 5% Activity bonus on 1st level sales; 3% Activity Bonus on 2nd level sales; 1% Activity Bonus on 3rd - 9th level sales; 15% Roll-up Bonus* **Qualification:** *$15,000 Personal Net Volume over any time period; $2,000 Group Net Volume in month to qualify for Activity and Roll-up bonuses.*

Additional Levels (Contact Company For Details): *N/A*

Other Bonuses: *N/A*

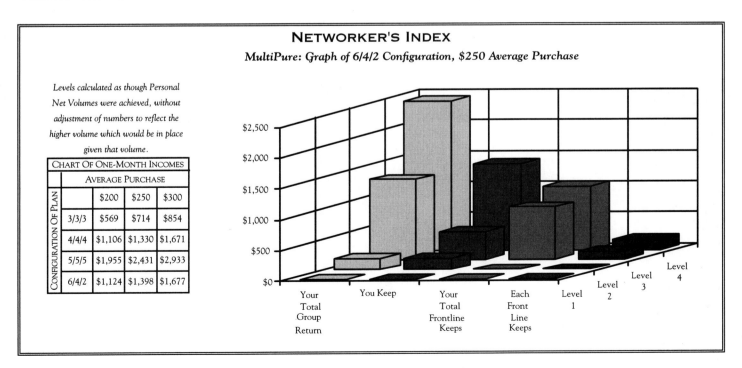

NETWORKER'S INDEX

MultiPure: Graph of 6/4/2 Configuration, $250 Average Purchase

Levels calculated as though Personal Net Volumes were achieved, without adjustment of numbers to reflect the higher volume which would be in place given that volume.

CHART OF ONE-MONTH INCOMES

CONFIGURATION OF PLAN	AVERAGE PURCHASE		
	$200	$250	$300
3/3/3	$569	$714	$854
4/4/4	$1,106	$1,330	$1,671
5/5/5	$1,955	$2,431	$2,933
6/4/2	$1,124	$1,398	$1,677

THE NANCI CORPORATION

7633 EAST 63RD PLACE, TULSA, OK 74133
918-254-7700 VOICE
800-825-8848 PRODUCT ORDER LINE
800-765-8848 PRODUCT ORDER FAX

History
Founded in 1986 by Nanci Masso, Chairman of the Board, and Eli Masso, President. Nanci Masso was a finalist for 1991 Entrepreneur of the Year sponsored by Ernst & Young, Merrill Lynch, and Inc. Magazine

Financials *Not rated; privately held, incorporated OK*

General Statistics
Total 1993 Sales: Proj. $50 million; 1992 $37 million
Total Distributors: 50,000
Foreign Countries: Canada, Mexico, Japan

Method of Product Distribution *Picked up by distributor, delivered to distributor, delivered to customer*

Association Membership *MLMIA*

Inventory Policy *No requirement*

Product Return Policy *30-day 100% to customers; 90-day 90% to distributors*

The Product Line: Nanci provides nutrition and weight control for all ages. All Nanci's exceptional products are based on SF-10—Nanci's proprietary 100% soluble fiber—and offers nutrition formulated for each individual age group—children, adolescents, adults, and senior citizens. The product line offers programs for nutritional stability, weight loss, and weight gain. Robert Kowalski, author of the best-selling book, *The Eight Week Cholesterol Cure* has endorsed Nanci products in his most recent book, *Eight Steps to a Healthy Heart.*

Supportive products include Genuine Homestyle Cookies—available in Oatmeal Raisin and Chocolate Chip—individually wrapped and packaged 30 to a box; Candi-fiber bars, with only 150 calories per 1.52 oz. bar; and Plus, a daily vitamin and mineral supplement.

Nanci also carries French Impressions, a personal-care product line composed of original creations by Michael Stern, whose previous accomplishments include creating and marketing fragrances for such prominent celebrities as Oscar de la Renta, Perry Ellis, Valentino, Catherine Deneuve, and Cher. The line includes bath and shower gel, body lotion, body powder, and eau de parfum.

Nanci has recently announced the addition of the Silent Sentry water filtration system.

MARKETING/COMPENSATION PLAN

PLAN CATEGORY *Stairstep/Breakaway*
DISTRIBUTOR DISCOUNT OFF RETAIL *15% - 40%*
QUALIFICATION PERIOD *Level Dependent*
COMPRESSION? *Yes*

MINIMUM QUALIFYING VOLUME *$36/60*
SUPPORT *Videos, Workshops, Literature, Newletters*
LEVELS LOCKED IN? *Yes*
INITIAL FEE *$19.95*

QUALIFICATION LEVELS

Distributor: *20% discount on product purchased from sponsor or company*

Direct Order Distributor: *20% discount on purchases (retained through all levels; add rebates to discounts for total discount)*

Counselor: *5% rebate on personal purchases; 5% of 1st level Direct Order Distributors 5% of 1st level Distributors* **Qualification:** *$500 Accumulated Personal Group Sales Volume (PGSV)*

Advisor: *10% rebate on personal purchases; 5% of 1st level Counselors; 10% of 1st level Direct Order Distributors;* **Qualification:** *$1,500 Accumulated PGSV, of which $1,000 is in qualifying month*

Supervisor: *15% rebate on personal purchases; 5% of 1st level Advisors; 10% of 1st level Counselors; 15% of 1st level Direct Order Distributors* **Qualification:** *$3,000 Accumulated PGSV, of which $1,500 is in qualifying month*

Additional Levels (Contact Company For Details): *Ambassador; Bronze Ambassador; Silver Ambassador; Gold Ambassador; Diamond Ambassador; Double Diamond Ambassador; Triple Diamond Ambassador*

Other Bonuses: *Conference Bonus; President's Bonus; Car Bonus; Profit Sharing Bonus; Pay Off Home Mortgage Bonus; Millionaire's Bonus; Special Features; Inactive Distributor Bypass; Ambassador Roll-up; Compression of Downline Leadership; Bonus Review*

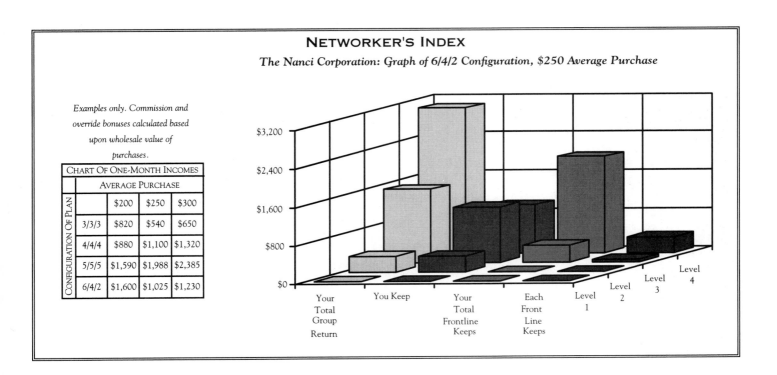

NETWORKER'S INDEX

The Nanci Corporation: Graph of 6/4/2 Configuration, $250 Average Purchase

Examples only. Commission and override bonuses calculated based upon wholesale value of purchases.

CHART OF ONE-MONTH INCOMES			
	AVERAGE PURCHASE		
	$200	$250	$300
3/3/3	$820	$540	$650
4/4/4	$880	$1,100	$1,320
5/5/5	$1,590	$1,988	$2,385
6/4/2	$1,600	$1,025	$1,230

NEWAYS

150 EAST 400 NORTH, PO BOX 651, SALEM, UTAH 84653
801-423-2800 VOICE
801-423-2350 FAX

History
Founded 1987 by Thomas & Dee Mower. Manufactures own products. 20,000 Square Foot offices; 60,000 Square Foot Manufacturing Facility.

Financials *Not rated, privately held, incorporated UT*

General Statistics
Total 1993 Sales: *$45 Million; 1992 $32 Million*
Total Distributors: *35,000*
Foreign Countries: *Global (see pages 144-145)*

Method of Product Distribution *Delivered to distributor, delivered to customer*

Association Membership *MLMIA*

Inventory Policy *No requirement*

Product Return Policy *100% in 30 days; 90% in 60 days.*

The Product Line: Neways manufactures products which can be placed into 6 categories: cosmetics based on biological extracts; ancient Chinese and latest science for health products; dental hygiene line; professional salon line; acrylic nail line for home or salon; weight loss products.

Neways cosmetics are based on biological extracts and do not contain propylene glycol, mineral oil, or sodium laureth sulfates (common ingredients in moisturizers) because, according to company information, propylene glycol is an industrial anti-freeze that coats and suffocates skin cells. Nor do they contain bentonite or kaolin (ingredients found in several makeup foundations) because it's "the same suffocating substance used to fight fires," according to Neways founder/research scientist Thomas Mower. Animal testing is not used in the development of Neways cosmetics.

When a trove of Ming dynasty medical records was discovered, researchers gained a rare glimpse of Ming science. After an exhaustive analysis of these manuscripts it was concluded that Ming herbalists, in their quest for life-promoting formulas, used several research procedures commonly used in today's modern-research facilities.

Neways has secured marketing rights for more than 1,200 Imperial formulas found in the Ming medical documents.

MARKETING/COMPENSATION PLAN

PLAN CATEGORY *Stairstep/Breakaway*
DISTRIBUTOR DISCOUNT OFF RETAIL *40% to 60%*
QUALIFICATION PERIOD *Level Dependent*
COMPRESSION? *Yes*

MINIMUM QUALIFYING VOLUME *$100*
SUPPORT *Videos, Workshops, Literature, Newsletters, Audios*
LEVELS LOCKED IN? *Yes*
INITIAL FEE *$29.95*

QUALIFICATION LEVELS

Distributor: *5% bonus on personal order of $100 or more*

Supervisor: *10% bonus on Personal Volume & Distributors* **Qualification:** *$1000 cumulative volume, $250 in qualifying month.*

Manager: *15% on Personal Volume; 5% on 1st level Supervisors; 15% on 1st level Distributors and their downlines* **Qualification** *$3,000 cumulative volume, $1000 is in qualifying month*

Executive: *20% Personal Volume; 5% 1st level Managers; 10% on 1st level Supervisors; 20% on 1st level Distributors and their downlines* **Qualification:** *$6,000 cumulative, $1,000 during qualifying month; no more than 80% from single leg*

Executive Leadership: *Executive bonus plus 8% on 1st level Executives; 7% on 2nd level Executives; 5% on 3rd level Executives* **Qualification:** *Executive level plus one 1st level Executive;*

Senior Executive: *Executive Leadership bonus plus 5% on 4th level Executives* **Qualification** *Executive plus three 1st level Executives*

Master Executive: *Senior Executive bonus plus 5% on 5th level Executives* **Qualification:** *Executive plus six 1st level Executives*

Additional Levels (Contact Company For Details): *Presidential Executive; Diamond Presidential; Executive Director; Chairman's Club; Executive Level Payouts as far as 7% on 7th level.*

Other Bonuses: *Production & Training Incentive; Producer Bonus; Personal Retail Bonus;Quarterly Bonus Pool; Executive Leadership Car Bonus and others*

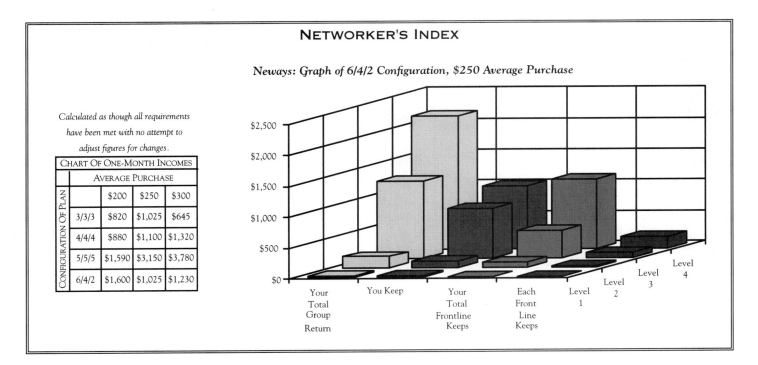

NETWORKER'S INDEX

Neways: Graph of 6/4/2 Configuration, $250 Average Purchase

Calculated as though all requirements have been met with no attempt to adjust figures for changes.

CHART OF ONE-MONTH INCOMES			
	AVERAGE PURCHASE		
	$200	$250	$300
3/3/3	$820	$1,025	$645
4/4/4	$880	$1,100	$1,320
5/5/5	$1,590	$3,150	$3,780
6/4/2	$1,600	$1,025	$1,230

NIKKEN, U.S.A., INC.

WESTWOOD PLACE, #250, 10866 WILSHIRE BOULEVARD, LOS ANGELES, CA 90024
310-446-4300 VOICE
800-669-8859 VOICE
800-669-8856 ORDER FAX

History
Founded by Isamu Masuda in Japan, 1975; established in U.S. April 1989

Financials *Not rated; privately held; incorporated in CA*

General Statistics
Total 1993 Sales: *$40 Million (U.S. only); $1 Billion Worldwide*
Total Distributors: *35,000 (U.S.) 1 Million Foreign*
Foreign Countries: *Global (see pages 144-145)*

Method of Product Distribution *Picked up by distributor, delivered to distributor, delivered to customer*

Association Membership *DSA*

Inventory Policy *No requirement*

Product Return Policy *90% from distributor for one year*

The Product Line: Nikken introduces a new product line each year, drawing upon a worldwide corporate powerhouse for research and development. Following is Nikken's current product line:

The Kenkomattresspad: a layer of rubberthane helps minimize vibrations naturally caused by changes of position made during sleep. The material absorbs and distributes approximately one cup of fluid normally released by the average person during a normal sleep cycle. The material is also highly durable—in compression testing it can undergo as much as 60 compressions per minute for more than 80,000 consecutive repetitions. The texture of the first layer is available with a 100% Merino wool covering.

The Kenkopillow is fashioned from a 4-fold structure of rubberthane, ceramic tile, urethane and a special rubberthane structured to fit the human neck. Helps to keep head cool by helping to dissipate any excess heat given off by the head.

Kenkocreator: designed to roll on the back for a quick "massage." The Kenkoseat is a seat cushion of Australian Merino wool developed for people whose occupations require extended periods of sitting. The Magboy are magnetic balls to be rolled in the hands for refreshment. Magsteps are shoe-inserts designed to give a stimulating and massaging effect to the feet during walking.

MARKETING/COMPENSATION PLAN

PLAN CATEGORY *Stairstep/Breakaway*
DISTRIBUTOR DISCOUNT OFF RETAIL *20%*
QUALIFICATION PERIOD *1 or 2 months*
COMPRESSION? *Yes*

MINIMUM QUALIFYING VOLUME *$100*
SUPPORT *Videos, Workshops, Literature, Newsletters*
LEVELS LOCKED IN? *Yes*
INITIAL FEE *$49*

QUALIFICATION LEVELS

Associate Distributor: *Earns 10% markup on retail sales*

Direct Distributor: *Earns 25% markup on retail sales ; 15% of 1st level Associate Distributor volume* **Qualification:** *$500 1-month Group Sales Volume; $100 Personal Sales Volume (PSV)*

Senior Distributor: *Direct Distributor benefits plus 5% rebate on PSV; 5% on 1st level Direct Distributors* **Qualification:** *$2,500 combined 2-month Group Sales Volume; $100 PSV*

Executive Distributor: *10% rebate on PSV; 5% on 1st level Senior Distributors; 10% on 1st level Direct Distributors* **Qualification:** *$7,500 combined 2-month Group Sales Volume; $100 PSV*

Bronze Distributor: *15% rebate on PSV; 5% on 1st level Executive Distributors; 10% on 1st level Senior Distributors; 15% on 1st level Direct Distributors* **Qualification:** *$15,000 combined 2-month Group Sales Volume; $100 PSV*

Silver Distributor: *25% rebate on PSV; 10% on 1st level Bronze Distributors; 15% on 1st level Executive Distributors; 20% on 1st level Senior Distributors; 25% on 1st level Direct Distributors; 5% Leadership Bonus on 2 levels of Silver Distributors* **Qualification:** *$40,000 combined 2-month Group Sales Volume, of which $8,000 is in qualifying month; 1-2 1st level Silver Distributors & $100 PSV & $3,000 "Modified" Group Sales Volume for Leadership Bonus*

Additional Levels (Contact Company For Details): *Gold Distributor; Platinum Distributor; Diamond Distributor; Royal Diamond Distributor*

Other Bonuses: *Vacation Months, Automobile, Home Mortgage Programs*

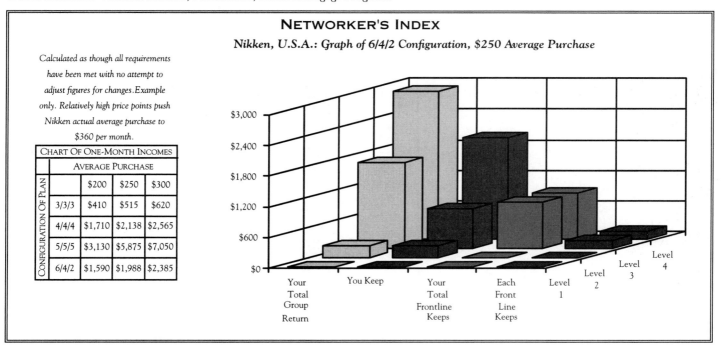

NETWORKER'S INDEX
Nikken, U.S.A.: Graph of 6/4/2 Configuration, $250 Average Purchase

Calculated as though all requirements have been met with no attempt to adjust figures for changes. Example only. Relatively high price points push Nikken actual average purchase to $360 per month.

CHART OF ONE-MONTH INCOMES			
	AVERAGE PURCHASE		
CONFIGURATION OF PLAN	$200	$250	$300
3/3/3	$410	$515	$620
4/4/4	$1,710	$2,138	$2,565
5/5/5	$3,130	$5,875	$7,050
6/4/2	$1,590	$1,988	$2,385

Noevir U.S.A., Inc.

1095 S.E. MAIN STREET, IRVINE, CA 92714
714-660-1111 VOICE
714-660-9562 FAX

NOEVIR

History
Parent company founded 1964 by Hiroshi Okura in Japan as J.H. Okura and Company; name changed to Noevir Co. Ltd. 1978; Noevir, Inc. established in U.S.A. 1982

Financials *Not rated; privately held; incorporated CA*

General Statistics
Total 1993-1994 Sales: *$30 Million $1.2 billion worldwide (parent commpany)*
Total Consultants: *40,000 U.S.; 350,000 worldwide (parent company)*
Foreign Countries: *Japan, Korea, Canada, Taiwan, Germany (parent company)*

Method of Product Distribution *Picked up by consultant, delivered to consultant, delivered to customer*

Association Membership *DSA*

Inventory Policy *No requirement*

Product Return Policy *90% for one year.*

The Product Line: Noevir manufactures a line of natural and herbal skin care products, cosmetics, and personal care, and nutritional products.

Noevir's basic skin care lines include Noevir 003, for all skin types, which begins with three essential steps (cleanse, tone, and moisturize) The other line within the basic care category is Series 4, for drier skin types. Four steps soothe dry or chapped skin with 19 herbal extracts, wheat germ oil, and other natural ingredients.

The Noevir advanced skin care lines include Noevir 95, a six-step program for all skin types, and Noevir 105 for drier skin. As an option to the 105 line, Noevir 505 toner and moisturizers provide Noevit's ultimate in moisture. Noevir special treatment products include three types of facial masks; medicated skin care; three specially formulated moisturizers; neck cream; night cream; a pigmentation correction system; and two eye treatment products.

Noevir also offers body and bath products, shampoos, conditioners, and fragrance. In addition, Noevir manufactures Royal Reflections, a complete line of cosmetics.

The Most recent addition to the Noevir family of products is the Inner Care Nutrition Series.

MARKETING/COMPENSATION PLAN

PLAN CATEGORY *Stairstep/Breakaway*
DISTRIBUTOR DISCOUNT OFF RETAIL *30%*
QUALIFICATION PERIOD *Level Dependent*
COMPRESSION? *Yes*

MINIMUM QUALIFYING VOLUME *$100*
SUPPORT *Videos, Workshops, Literature, Newsletters*
LEVELS LOCKED IN? *No*
INITIAL FEE *Not Available*

QUALIFICATION LEVELS

Sponsoring Consultant: *Earn 30% retail sales margin; 5% of 1st line Consultants' Personal Volume*

Unit Leader: *5% of personal volume and on Consultants to 2 levels* **Qualification:** *5 1st level Consultants; 500 Group Volume Points*

Director-In-Qualification: *5% of personal volume and 1st 3 levels* **Qualification:** *There is a complex set of requirements to meet Director qualifications through this program. Contact Noevir for an explanation. In a six month period, 5 front-line consultants, and progress through levels of $1,500, $2,000, $2,500, $3,000 in orderly succession.*

Quick-Start Director: *In first month, paid as Director-in-Qualification, in second month as Director* **Qualification:** *10 active 1st level Consultants (200 Personal Volume Points per year); 30 Consultants in organization; $9,000 Group Volume*

Unit Director: *12% on Group Volume $2,000-$2,999; 13% on $3,000-$4,999; 14% on $5,000-$9,999; 15% on $10,000-$14,999; 16% on $15,000-$19,999; 17% on $20,000 and above.* **Qualification:** *Quick Start Director-in-Qualification completed.*

Senior Director: *7% override on 1st level breakaway groups* **Qualification:** *1 1st level Director; $2,000 Group Volume per month*

Senior Director Elite: *7% override on 1st level breakaway groups; 3% on 2nd level breakaway groups* **Qualification:** *2 1st level Director; $2,000 Group Volume per month*

Additional Levels (Contact Company For Details): *Executive Director; Executive Director Elite; Diamond Director; Diamond Director Elite; Double Diamond Director*

Other Bonuses *N/A*

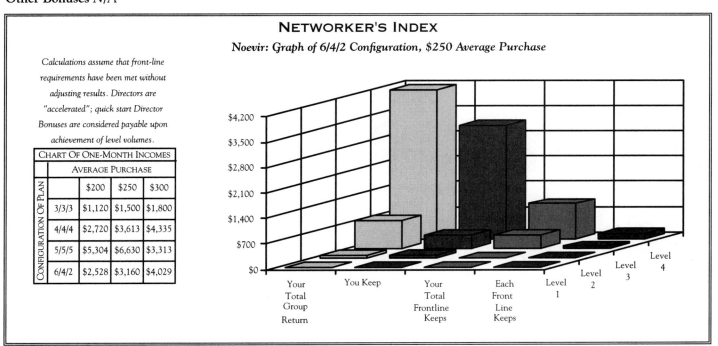

NETWORKER'S INDEX
Noevir: Graph of 6/4/2 Configuration, $250 Average Purchase

Calculations assume that front-line requirements have been met without adjusting results. Directors are "accelerated"; quick start Director Bonuses are considered payable upon achievement of level volumes.

CHART OF ONE-MONTH INCOMES			
	AVERAGE PURCHASE		
	$200	$250	$300
3/3/3	$1,120	$1,500	$1,800
4/4/4	$2,720	$3,613	$4,335
5/5/5	$5,304	$6,630	$3,313
6/4/2	$2,528	$3,160	$4,029

(CONFIGURATION OF PLAN)

NonScents

767 Kenrick, Suite 110, Houston, TX 77077
713-847-0281 Voice
800-866-6367 Voice
713-847-0285 Fax

History
Founded 1987

Financials *Not rated; privately held*

General Statistics
Total 1993 Sales: *est. 3 Million*
Total Distributors: *14,000*
Foreign Countries: *Canada, New Zealand, Australia, Hong Kong*

Method of Product Distribution *Picked up by distributor, delivered to distributor, delivered to customer*

Association Membership *N/A*

Inventory Policy *No requirement*

Product Return Policy *No*

The Product Line: Airborne odors, smoke, and bacteria will "piggy-back" on dust particles, which have a positive molecular ion charge; NonScents has a negative molecular ion charge which attracts these particles and their riders, ridding the environment of their odoriferous effects.

According to Dr. Paul J. Roper, Technical Director of NonScents, zeolites are a complex group of naturally occurring minerals. More than 40 different types are found in nature, but only a few are found in quantities large enough to be commercially useful. Zeolites have channels which provide enormous internal surface areas within the zeolite crystals. The most common naturally occurring zeolite is the mineral clinoptilolite. This is the type of zeolite that occurs in NonScents products.

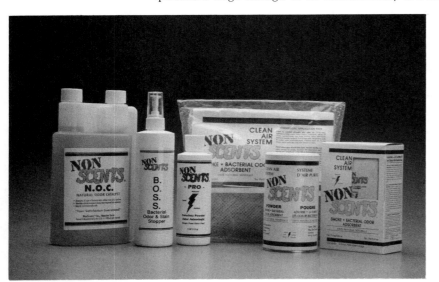

The ionic pore diameter of NonScents clinoptilolite is approximately 4.0 Å (angstrom), more than sufficient to allow normal elemental and simple polarized molecules to be adsorbed into these ionic pores (adsorption, as distinct from absorption is, according to Webster, the adhesion in an extremely thin layer of molecules...as of gasses...to the surfaces of solid bodies or liquids with which they are in contact).

NonScents products come in a variety of forms, and can be used in many different contexts where odor removal is desired or required.

MARKETING/COMPENSATION PLAN

PLAN CATEGORY *Stairstep/Breakaway*
DISTRIBUTOR DISCOUNT OFF RETAIL *25% - 50%*
QUALIFICATION PERIOD *One Month*
COMPRESSION? *Yes*

MINIMUM QUALIFYING VOLUME *N/A*
SUPPORT *literature*
LEVELS LOCKED IN? *Yes*
INITIAL FEE *Not Available*

QUALIFICATION LEVELS

Representative: *Earn 25% discount on retail sales*

Qualified Distributor: *35% discount on retail sales; 10% on personally sponsored Representatives* **Qualification:** *four cases in group volume in one month*

Supervisor: *50% discount on retail sales; 15% on personally sponsored Qualified Distributors; 25% on personally sponsored Qualified Distributors* **Qualification:** *either ten cases group volume in one month, with four cases of that being in non-qualifying volume or four cases in group volume in one month to become a Qualified Distributor, and six cases Group Volume, with four cases of that being in non-qualifying volume, in another month to become a Supervisor; must be achieved within 12 months*

Supervisor Royalty Overrides: *Supervisor benefits plus overrides paid on five levels of downline q ualified Supervisors, the amounts dependent upon your group volume, as follows:your group volume 4 cases—6% first level, 5% second level, 4% third level, 2.5% fourth level, 2.5% 5th level; your group volume 3 cases—3.5% first level, 3% second level, 2.5% third level, 2.5% fourth level, 2.5% fifth level; your group volume 2 cases—3% first level, 2.5% second through fifth level; your group volume 1 case—2.5% first through fifth levels* **Qualification:** *Supervisor; to receive International Royalties, a Supervisor must have at least 4 cases of group volume*

Additional Levels (Contact Company For Details): *N/A*

Other Bonuses: *N/A*

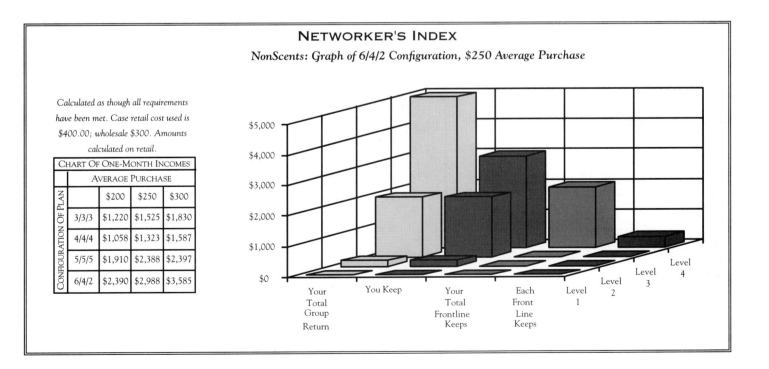

NETWORKER'S INDEX

NonScents: Graph of 6/4/2 Configuration, $250 Average Purchase

Calculated as though all requirements have been met. Case retail cost used is $400.00; wholesale $300. Amounts calculated on retail.

CHART OF ONE-MONTH INCOMES			
CONFIGURATION OF PLAN	AVERAGE PURCHASE		
	$200	$250	$300
3/3/3	$1,220	$1,525	$1,830
4/4/4	$1,058	$1,323	$1,587
5/5/5	$1,910	$2,388	$2,397
6/4/2	$2,390	$2,988	$3,585

NSA, Inc.

4260 Raines Road, Memphis, TN 38118
901-366-9288 Voice

History
Founded in Memphis, 1970, by Jay Martin as a regional marketer of home fire protection equipment. Home water filtration units added to product mix in late 1970s, air filtration in the 1980s, and educational products in the 1990s

Financials *Not rated; privately held; incorporated TN*

General Statistics
Total 1993 Sales: *est. 364 Million*
Total Distributors: *50,000*
Foreign Countries: *Canada, Germany, Taiwan*

Method of Product Distribution *Delivered to distributor*

Association Membership *DSA*

Inventory Policy *No requirement*

Product Return Policy *90% within one year*

The Product Line: The NSA product line falls for the most part into three categories: water filtration, air filtration, and educational products.

The Bacteriostatic Water Treatment Unit is NSA's flagship product. The work of water filtration is done by a granular activated carbon media bed for chlorine absorption and a silver impregnated carbon media bed to inhibit bacteria growth within the unit. The various units and functions range from the 50C countertop version with a 5,000 gallon capacity to the 300H whole house version, with a 75,000 gallon

capacity, and the 744, designed for treatment of problem water. In addition, NSA offers bottle-less water coolers and a Sparkling Water System.

NSA's two air filtration systems, one portable (Personal Air System), the other stationary (Stationary Air System), implement tri-media filter. The Personal unit also employs an electrostatic filter and has a range of 1,200-1,500 cubic feet. The stationary unit also employs a HEPA (high-efficiency particulated air) filter, and has a range of 2,400-3,000 cubic feet.

The WINGS program was NSA's first of several planned entries into the mushrooming education product market; it has been joined by the Family Encyclopedia and other educational products designed for home use.

MARKETING/COMPENSATION PLAN

PLAN CATEGORY *Stairstep/Breakaway*
DISTRIBUTOR DISCOUNT OFF RETAIL *10-35%*
QUALIFICATION PERIOD *One Month*
COMPRESSION? *Yes*

MINIMUM QUALIFYING VOLUME *N/A*
SUPPORT *Videos, Workshops, Literature, Newsletters*
LEVELS LOCKED IN? *Yes*
INITIAL FEE *$35.00*

QUALIFICATION LEVELS

Dealer: *Earns retail sales profit margin*

Direct Distributor: *Dealer benefits plus 8% distributorship Purchase Volume Credits (PVC); 5% of PVC of Direct Distributors and Sales Coordinator's through four generations, with compression* **Qualification:** *$2,000 distributorship PVC OR 2 lines with a bonus qualifier in each plus $1,000 Distributorship PVC (including prior month "excess" PVC), or 3 lines with a bonus qualifier in each*

Senior Direct Distributor: *Direct Distributor benefits; 8% distributorship PVC; 8% downline PVC not under another Senior Direct Distributor* **Qualification:** *$6,000 PVC in one month, or $3,000 distributorship PVC during same month a new Senior Direct Distributor qualifies in your downline, not under another Senior Direct Distributor*

Sales Coordinator: *Senior Direct Distributor benefits; 8% PVC of downline not under another Sales Coordinator ("open" PVC); Promote Out bonus of 5% of "open" downline PVC of 1st qualified Sales Coordinator below you* **Qualification:** *$12,000 in distributorship and/or downline PVC not under another downline Sales Coordinator, or $6,000 in distributorship and/or downline PVC during the same month that a new Sales Coordinator qualifies in your downline, not under another Senior Direct Distributor; For Promote Out Bonus: have $6,000 "open" downline PVC (including prior month "excess" PVC), or $3,000 PVC in your "open" downline and 2 lines with Sales Coordinator in each, or 3 lines with a qualified Sales Coordinator in each*

Additional Levels (Contact Company For Details): *Qualifying National Marketing Director; National Marketing Director*

Other Bonuses: *N/A*

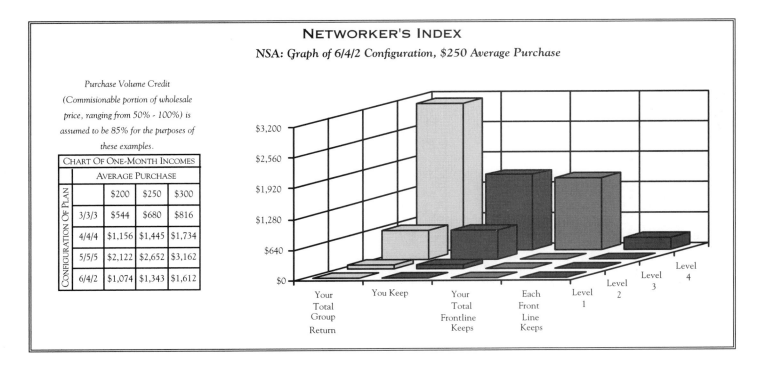

NETWORKER'S INDEX
NSA: Graph of 6/4/2 Configuration, $250 Average Purchase

Purchase Volume Credit (Commisionable portion of wholesale price, ranging from 50% - 100%) is assumed to be 85% for the purposes of these examples.

CHART OF ONE-MONTH INCOMES			
AVERAGE PURCHASE			
	$200	$250	$300
3/3/3	$544	$680	$816
4/4/4	$1,156	$1,445	$1,734
5/5/5	$2,122	$2,652	$3,162
6/4/2	$1,074	$1,343	$1,612

Nu Skin International, Inc.

75 West Center, Provo, UT 84601
800-487-1500 Voice
801-345-1099 Fax (Attention of Lead Distribution Coordinator)

History
Founded 1984 by Blake Roney, after a discussion with his sister at a kitchen table that most personal care products contain mainly waxes and fillers; started with $5,000 capital.

Financials *Not rated; privately held; incorporated UT*

General Statistics
Total 1993 Sales: *Not available*
Total Distributors: *250,000*
Foreign Countries: *Hong Kong, Taiwan, Canada, Australia, New Zealand, Japan*

Method of Product Distribution *Picked up by distributor, delivered to distributor, delivered to customer*

Association Membership *DSA, MLMIA*

Inventory Policy *Distributor must sell or use 80% of monthly product purchases, and document sales to at least five customers*

Product Return Policy *90% for shelf-life of product, unlimited in time*

The Product Line:
Nu Skin International manufactures and markets more than 70 products sold through two product divisions: Nu Skin Personal Care, a line of hair, skin, and personal care products that include the Face Care System, Hair Care System, Body Care System, Nu Colour, and Jungamals for children; the InteriorDesign Nutritionals division includes supplements, health foods, and drinks.

Nu Skin's Face Care System consists of items ranging from Face Lift (With Activator), Facial Scrub, Extra Gentle Exfoliant Scrub, and Celltrex® to Nutriol® Eyelash and Mascara, Intensive Eye Complex to Clay Pack, NaPCA Moisturizer, Rejuvenating Cream and PH Balance.

The Hair Care System consists of several choices of shampoos and hair conditioners. The Body Care System covers the ground from Mineral Bath to Body Smoother through Hand Lotion and Body Bar to Deodorant to Sunright™ tanning and sun-protection systems. Nu Colour consists of eight shades of oil-free moisturizing finish. Jungamals is a line of personal care products for children.

Interior Design Nutritionals consists of products designed to reduce fat intake, maintain optimal health, aid in proper weight management, and

MARKETING/COMPENSATION PLAN

PLAN CATEGORY *Stairstep*
DISTRIBUTOR DISCOUNT OFF RETAIL *30%*
QUALIFICATION PERIOD *Level Dependent*
COMPRESSION? *Yes*

MINIMUM QUALIFYING VOLUME *$100 (executive only)*
SUPPORT *Videos, Workshops, Literature, Newsletters*
LEVELS LOCKED IN? *Yes*
INITIAL FEE *$35.00*

QUALIFICATION LEVELS

Distributor: *Profit earned by 43% markup on wholesale; Personal Sales Incentive Bonus paid on Personal Sales Volume (PSV) points—1% for 750-999 PSV points; 2% for 1,000-1,499 PSV points; 3% for 1,500-1,999 PSV points; 4% for 2,000 PSV points*

Executive: *paid bonuses on Group Sales Volume points (GSV) as follows—9%/2,000; 10%/4,000; 11%/5,000; 12%/10,000; 13%/25,000; 14%/50,000* **Qualification:** *after achieving 2,000 GSV, complete a three-month qualification period in each of those months maintaining at least 500 points PSV, retailing at least 80% of PSV to a minimum of five retail customers, have five active distributor lines; in addition, in month one have 2,000 GSV, month two 2,500 GSV, month three 3,000 GSV; to retain Executive status, maintain 2,000 GSV, 100 PSV points 80% of which is bought or sold to a minimum of five documented retail customers*

Gold Executive: *Executive benefits; 5% of GSV of 1st level Executives* **Qualification:** *Executive; one 1st level Executive*

Lapis Executive: *Gold Executive benefits; 5% GSV of 2nd level Executives* **Qualification:** *Executive; two 1st level Executives*

Ruby Executive: *Lapis Executive benefits; 5% GSV of 3rd level Executives* **Qualification:** *Executive;four 1st level Executives*

Emerald Executive: *Ruby Executive benefits; 5% GSV of 4th level Executives* **Qualification:** *Executive; six 1st level Executives*

Additional Levels (Contact Company For Details): *Diamond Executive, Blue Diamond Executive paying 5% to 6 levels of Executives*

Other: *Expanding Link Bonus; for all levels, at least 80% of personal product volume must be either used or sold to at least 5 documented customers.*

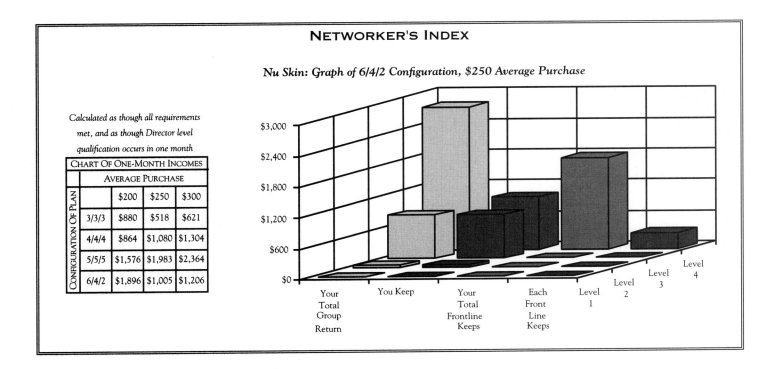

NETWORKER'S INDEX

Nu Skin: Graph of 6/4/2 Configuration, $250 Average Purchase

Calculated as though all requirements met, and as though Director level qualification occurs in one month

CHART OF ONE-MONTH INCOMES

CONFIGURATION OF PLAN	AVERAGE PURCHASE		
	$200	$250	$300
3/3/3	$880	$518	$621
4/4/4	$864	$1,080	$1,304
5/5/5	$1,576	$1,983	$2,364
6/4/2	$1,896	$1,005	$1,206

NUTRITION FOR LIFE INTERNATIONAL

8801 JAMEEL, SUITE 100, HOUSTON, TX 77040
713-460-1976 VOICE
713-460-9049 FAX

History
Founded October, 1984 by David Bertrand and Jana Mitcham

Financials *Publicly Held*

General Statistics
Total 1993 Sales: *$15 Million est.*
Total Distributors: *30,000*
Foreign Countries: *Canada, Phillipines, Korea*

Method of Product *Distribution Delivered to distributor and Customer*

Association Membership *N/A*

Inventory Policy *No requirement*

Product Return Policy *100% 30-days/90 day exchange*

The Product Line: Among Nutrition For Life's fastest moving products are Requin 3 (whole shark cartilage); Premium Antioxidants formulation: Master Key Plus, Oraflow Plus, Grand Master, and Yummies for children; RNA/DNA products for both men and women; Nutri-cookies, in four flavors, go well together with Leanlife, Nutrition For Life's thermogenic, chromium weight management product; Nutique Nutritional Skin Care—a system designed for men and women to reflect the radiant glow of youth. Personal Defendere (personal alarm) and the Clean Sip water filter straw are also very popular.

Nutrition For Life's products encompass a Life Cycle made up of eight categories: air and water filtration systems, food and weight management products, vitamins & minerals, homeopathics and special formulas, Nutique hair & skin care, self-improvement programs, and a complete line of environmentally friendly cleaning concentrates for all areas of the home.

Air and water filtration systems are available, as are EPA listed radon test kits. Water filtration systems include KDF/carbon and reverse osmosis media. Undercounter, shower head units, and in-line filters are available.

Food and weight management includes complex carbohydrate foods, protein shakes, food wafers and whey beverage. The vitamins and minerals, herbal and homeopathic categories contain proprietary mixtures as well as singles like Co Q-10, Golden Seal, Garlic, Milk Thistle, Ginkgo Biloba, etc. Specialty products include Bio Enhanced water, Collis Curve Toothbruch, toothpaste, and long distance telephone service.

MARKETING/COMPENSATION PLAN

PLAN CATEGORY *Modified Breakaway Matrix*
DISTRIBUTOR DISCOUNT OFF RETAIL *25-35%*
QUALIFICATION PERIOD *Cumulative*
COMPRESSION? *Yes*

MINIMUM QUALIFYING VOLUME *$40*
SUPPORT *Videos, Workshops, Literature, Newsletters*
LEVELS LOCKED IN? *No*
INITIAL FEE *$35.00*

QUALIFICATION LEVELS

Distributor: *Distributors earn 30-40% markup on retail sales*

Executive (A): *Distributor benefits plus 20% (20% if on Order Insurance Program (OIP) and 45% possible with Transfer Volume Policy and 40% retailer's bonus) of downline distributor volume; 1% of 1st, 2nd, & 3rd level Executives* **Qualification:** *$1,500 cumulative Group Volume (GV) in any period ($1,200 if on OIP)*

Bronze Executive (B, C, & D): *Distributor Benefits Plus Executive (A) benefits; 10% of 4th or 5th level Executives (or both)* **Qualification:** *$80 personal sales volume (PSV); 4 or 5 personally enrolled distributors or executives*

Bronze Exeuctive (E): *Bronze Executive (D) benefits plus 3% on 6th level Executives* **Qualification:** *$80 PSV; 3 personally enrolled distributors or Executives*

Silver Exeuctive (F, G, H, or I): *Bronze Executive (E) benefits plus 3%-15% on 7th level Executives* **Qualification:** *$80-$160 PSV; 4 -7 personally enrolled distributors or Executives*

Gold Exeuctive (J): *Silver Executive (I) benefits plus 18% on 7th level Executives* **Qualification:** *$160 PSV; 8 personally enrolled distributors or Executives*

Additional Levels (Contact Company For Details): *Platinum Executives receive an additional 2% on all enrollee levels*

Other Bonuses: *40% Retailer's Bonus, Car Bonus; Quarterly Production Bonuses; Executive Recognition Levels; Master Bonus*

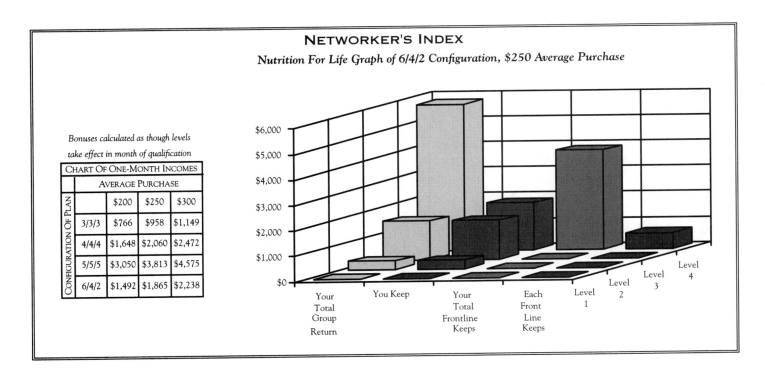

NETWORKER'S INDEX

Nutrition For Life Graph of 6/4/2 Configuration, $250 Average Purchase

Bonuses calculated as though levels take effect in month of qualification

CHART OF ONE-MONTH INCOMES			
AVERAGE PURCHASE			
CONFIGURATION OF PLAN	$200	$250	$300
3/3/3	$766	$958	$1,149
4/4/4	$1,648	$2,060	$2,472
5/5/5	$3,050	$3,813	$4,575
6/4/2	$1,492	$1,865	$2,238

OXYFRESH USA, INC.

PO BOX 3723, SPOKANE, WA 99220
509-924-4999 VOICE
509-924-5285 FAX

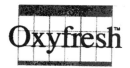

History
Founded in January of 1984 in Spokane, Washington. Since 1986, led by CEO Richard Brooke, Oxyfresh has averaged a 30% annual growth.

Financials *Not rated; privately held; incorporated WA*

General Statistics
Total 1993 Sales: *$13 Million; $11 Million 1992*
Total Distributors: *13,000*
Foreign Countries: *Canada and Mexico scheduled for 1994*

Method of Product Distribution *Delivered to distributor, delivered to customer*

Association Membership *MLMIA*

Inventory Policy *No requirement*

Product Return Policy *100% for 120 days; 100% of current support materials, no time limit.*

The Product Line: Oxyfresh products contain Oxygene™, a proprietary active ingredient.. Oxygene is a selection of organic and inorganic oxidizing agents effective in eliminating odors, including bad breath, foot odor, mildew, and onions. These odors are caused by compounds containing sulfur bonds in their molecular structure. Oxygene is a deodorizing and cleansing formula that breaks sulfur bonds and eliminates their ability to produce odors.

The Oxyfresh product line can be classified under five categories: the Aiyana™ Skin Care line, Dental Care, Personal Care, Household Hygiene, and Pet Care.

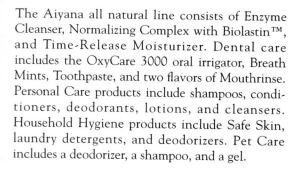

The Aiyana all natural line consists of Enzyme Cleanser, Normalizing Complex with Biolastin™, and Time-Release Moisturizer. Dental care includes the OxyCare 3000 oral irrigator, Breath Mints, Toothpaste, and two flavors of Mouthrinse. Personal Care products include shampoos, conditioners, deodorants, lotions, and cleansers. Household Hygiene products include Safe Skin, laundry detergents, and deodorizers. Pet Care includes a deodorizer, a shampoo, and a gel.

The Oxyfresh line contains no animal products. Animal testing is not used on any Oxyfresh product.

MARKETING/COMPENSATION PLAN

PLAN CATEGORY *Stairstep/Breakaway*
DISTRIBUTOR DISCOUNT OFF RETAIL *29%*
QUALIFICATION PERIOD *Level Dependent*
COMPRESSION? *Yes*

MINIMUM QUALIFYING VOLUME *$120*
SUPPORT *Videos, Workshops, Literature, Newsletters*
LEVELS LOCKED IN? *Some*
INITIAL FEE *$20*

QUALIFICATION LEVELS

Product Representative: *Earn profit from 29% discount from retail*

Coordinator: *5% bonus on Personal Volume (PV)* **Qualification:** *$300 Group Volume (GV) over any period*

Director: *20% bonus on PV; 15% on all coordinators in group, regardless of level; 5% Director Generation Bonus through 1st two levels of qualified Directors* **Qualification:** *either $1,500 GV each month for three consecutive months or $3,000 GV*

Executive Director: *5% Director Generation Bonus through the first three levels of qualified Directors* **Qualification:** *Qualify self and any four personally sponsored Director legs in any month*

Senior Director: *Executive Director Benefits plus 3% Bonus on the fourth level of qualified Directors* **Qualification:** *Qualify self and establish any four personally sponsored Director legs for three consecutive months*

Master Director: *Senior Director Benefits plus share in 2% of the company's sales pro-rated to share of contribution; compensation available on the fourth month* **Qualification:** *Qualify self and establish any eight personally sponsored Director legs for three consecutive months*

Additional Levels (Contact Company For Details): *Master Instructor; State and Regional Directors earn up to 50% front-end and 35% back-end Generation Bonus*

Other Bonuses: *National Achievers' Club members earn free Leadership Seminars and week-long vacations.*

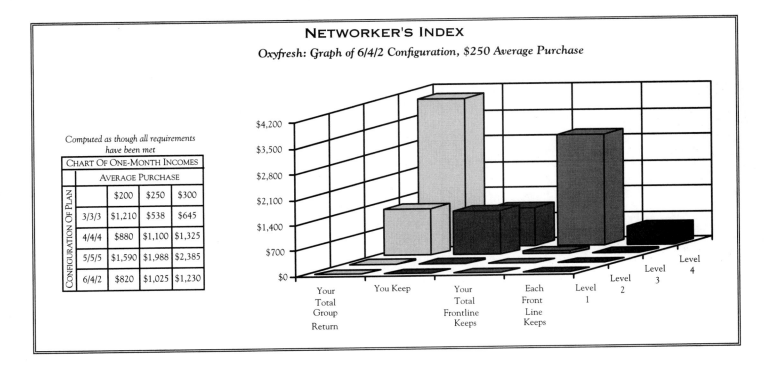

NETWORKER'S INDEX

Oxyfresh: Graph of 6/4/2 Configuration, $250 Average Purchase

Computed as though all requirements have been met

CHART OF ONE-MONTH INCOMES

CONFIGURATION OF PLAN	AVERAGE PURCHASE		
	$200	$250	$300
3/3/3	$1,210	$538	$645
4/4/4	$880	$1,100	$1,325
5/5/5	$1,590	$1,988	$2,385
6/4/2	$820	$1,025	$1,230

RELÌV

PO BOX 406, CHESTERFIELD, MO 63005-4006
314-537-9715 VOICE

History
Founded in 1988 by Robert L. and Sandy Montgomery

Financials *Not rated; publicly owned (1,400 shareholders); incorporated MO*

General Statistics
Total 1993 Sales: *est. 50 Million*
Total Distributors: *48,000*
Foreign Countries: *Australia, New Zealand, Canada*

Method of Product Distribution *Delivered to distributor, delivered to customer*

Association Membership *N/A*

Inventory Policy *No requirement*

Product Return Policy *90%*

The Product Line: Relìv products are based on nutritional formulas patented by Dr.. Ted Kalogris and manufactured by Relìv, directed by Dr. Carl Hastings. These products are:

Relìv Classic™, the original formula containing every vitamin and mineral recommended by the U.S. Government, plus a blend of proteins and herbs, manufactured under license from the owner of U.S. patent #4,737,364.

Relìv Now™, based on the formula of Relìv Classic™, with a vanilla flavor.
Relìv Ultrim-Plus™, a cholesterol-free weight control product containing the nutritional content of Relìv Now™.

Relìv Ultrabar™, a granola snack containing the same vitamins and minerals as Relìv Now™.

Relìv Innergize™, a thirst-quenching beverage formulated to be taken before, during, and after exercise. Its effects result from a combination of fructose and complex carbohydrates, along with patented supplements such as Chromemate® and Optizinc™, trademarks of InterHealth Company, U.S,. Patent Nos. 4,932,855 and 4,954,492.

MARKETING/COMPENSATION PLAN

PLAN CATEGORY *Stairstep/Breakaway*
DISTRIBUTOR DISCOUNT OFF RETAIL *25%-45%*
QUALIFICATION PERIOD *One Month*
COMPRESSION? *Yes*

MINIMUM QUALIFYING VOLUME *N/A*
SUPPORT *Videos, Workshops, Literature, Newsletters, Training*
LEVELS LOCKED IN? *Yes*
INITIAL FEE *$29.95*

QUALIFICATION LEVELS

Retail Distributor *Earn 25% retail sales profit margin*

Affiliate: *30% discount on purchases 5% of wholesale on 1st level Retail Distributors* **Qualification:** *700 Personal Group Retail Volume (PGPV) in one month*

Key Affiliate: *35% discount on purchases; 5% of wholesale on 1st level Affiliates; 10% of wholesale on 1st level Retail Distributors* **Qualification:** *2,000 PGPV in one month*

Senior Affiliate: *40% discount on purchases; 5% of wholesale on 1st level Key Affiliates; 10% of wholesale on 1st level Affiliates; 15% of wholesale on 1st level Retail Distributors* **Qualification:** *3,000 PGPV in one month*

Master Affiliate: *45% discount on purchases; 5% of wholesale on 1st level Senior Affiliates; 10% of wholesale on 1st level Key Affiliates; 15% of wholesale on 1st level Affiliates; 20% of wholesale on 1st level Retail Distributors* **Qualification:** *5,000 PGPV in one month*

Additional Levels (Contact Company For Details): *2-5% override on personally sponsored Master Affiliates and their groups that have broken away, through up to 5 levels.*

Other: *Audio Support; Commissions and overrides based on suggested retail pricing*

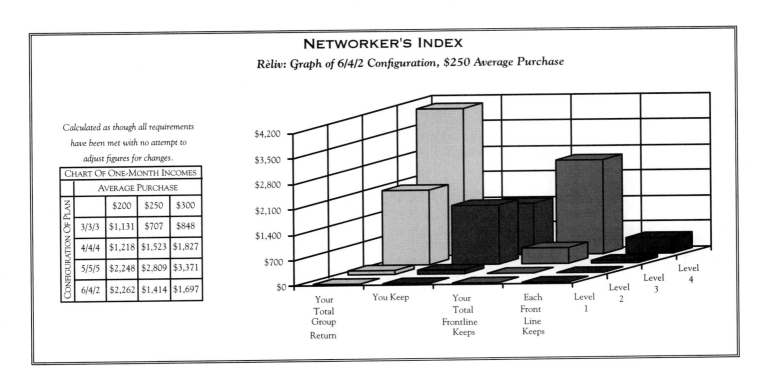

NETWORKER'S INDEX
Rèliv: Graph of 6/4/2 Configuration, $250 Average Purchase

Calculated as though all requirements have been met with no attempt to adjust figures for changes.

CHART OF ONE-MONTH INCOMES

CONFIGURATION OF PLAN	AVERAGE PURCHASE		
	$200	$250	$300
3/3/3	$1,131	$707	$848
4/4/4	$1,218	$1,523	$1,827
5/5/5	$2,248	$2,809	$3,371
6/4/2	$2,262	$1,414	$1,697

SHAKLEE U.S. INC.

SHAKLEE TERRACES, 444 MARKET STREET, SAN FRANCISCO, CA 94111
415-954-3000 VOICE
1-800-SHAKLEE VOICE

History
Founded in 1956 by Dr. Forrest C. Shaklee, Sr. (1894-1985) as a family venture which became a NYSE/Fortune 500 company before being acquired in 1989 by Yamanouchi Pharmaceutical Company, Ltd., the second largest pharmaceutical company in Japan

Financials *Not rated; Privately held; incorporated DE*

General Statistics
Total 1993 Sales: *$459 million; 1992 $423 Million*
Total Distributors: *One Million*
Foreign Countries: *Global (see page 144–145)*

Method of Product Distribution *Delivered to distributor, delivered to customer*

Association Membership *DSA*

Inventory Policy *No requirement*

Product Return Policy *100% for distributors who resign*

The Product Line: Shaklee U.S. has five product lines: nutritional supplements, household cleaning products, personal care products, home water treatment systems, and CareerTrack tapes and seminars.

Shaklee nutritional supplements are unconditionally guaranteed and most are Kosher certified. Products include Instant Protein, Meal Shakes, Energy Bars, Vita-Lea®, Fiber Plan, Formula 1®, EPA Natural Marine Lipid Concentrate, Lecithin, Beta Carotene, Calcium Complex, Vita-C®, Vita-E®, B-Complex, Zinc, Iron plus vitamin C, Diet Tablets, Herb-Lax®, Pro-Lecin® Nibblers, Performance®, and Physique™, among others.

Shaklee BestWater® systems are available in models from countertop to whole-house systems. They are all backed by independent laboratory testing.

Household products are all phosphate-free and include Basic-H® Concentrated Organic Cleanser to Basic-D® Automatic Dishwashing Concentrate to Basic-L® Laundry Concentrate to name a few.

Shaklee offers "The Healthy Approach to Beauty" with a complete line of skin and hair care products, as well as cosmetics, baby care, and daily care product lines.

MARKETING/COMPENSATION PLAN

PLAN CATEGORY *Stairstep/Breakaway*
DISTRIBUTOR DISCOUNT OFF RETAIL *15%–33%*
QUALIFICATION PERIOD *One Month*
COMPRESSION? *Yes*

MINIMUM QUALIFYING VOLUME *Level dependent*
SUPPORT *Videos, Audios, Workshops, Literature, Newsletters*
LEVELS LOCKED IN? *No*
INITIAL FEE *$7.50*

QUALIFICATION LEVELS

Member: *Purchase product at 15% discount from Suggested Retail Price (SRP)*

Distributor: *Earn 27% discount from SRP; bonus of 2% of Purchase Volume (PV) on 100-499 Unit Value (UV); 5% of PV on 500-999 UV* **Qualification:** *100 UV in month*

Assistant Supervisor: *Earn 27% discount from SRP; 10% of PV at 100-1499 UV; 15% of PV at 1500-1999 UV; 21% of PV on 1000-2999 UV* **Qualification:** *1000 group UV in month*

Supervisor: *Earn 33.3% discount from SRP; bonus of 25% of PV at 3000-6999 UV; 27% of PV at 7000 UV or more* **Qualification:** *3000 Group UV in month.*

Senior Supervisor: *Supervisor benefits plus 5% onPV of 1st level Sales Leaders, i.e. Supervisors and up; 3% on PV of 2nd level Sales Leaders; 1% on PV of 3rd level Sales Leaders* **Qualification:** *3–8 First Level Sales Leaders (need not be personally sponsored, and may be acquired through compression)*

Additional Levels (Contact Company For Details): *Coordinator; Senior Coordinator; Key Coordinator, Senior Key Coordinator, Master Coordinator (Master Coordinators may go on to reach incremental Special Incentive Levels)*

Other Bonuses: *Expense-paid Convention/Incentive Travel; Bonus Car Program; GRO (Growth Reward Opportunity Program; 1% for Cash; Master Special Incentive Bonus; Reduced Activity Residual Bonus* **Important Note:** *Discounts and Bonuses at the Member, Distributor, and Assistant Supervisor levels are suggested only. Members of all levels are independent business people and free to determine for the prices they charge and the bonuses they pay. UV (Unit Value) and PV (Point Volume) are non-monetary values assigned to each Product. Total UV for a month determines one's qualification level; total PV for the month is the figure used to calculate bonuses*

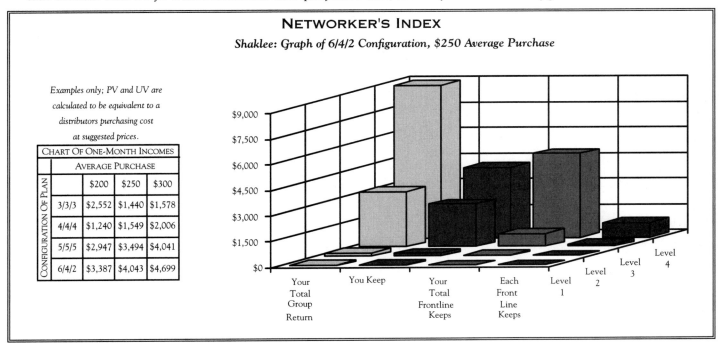

NETWORKER'S INDEX
Shaklee: Graph of 6/4/2 Configuration, $250 Average Purchase

Examples only; PV and UV are calculated to be equivalent to a distributors purchasing cost at suggested prices.

CHART OF ONE-MONTH INCOMES			
	AVERAGE PURCHASE		
	$200	$250	$300
3/3/3	$2,552	$1,440	$1,578
4/4/4	$1,240	$1,549	$2,006
5/5/5	$2,947	$3,494	$4,041
6/4/2	$3,387	$4,043	$4,699

Shaklee U.S. Inc.

Dr. Forrest C. Shaklee, Sr. (1894-1985) was a man ahead of his time. He believed that the health of the environment is entwined with the health of every person who inhabits it. In 1956 he began a family venture with the idea of manufacturing products in harmony with nature. The venture rapidly became a New York Stock Exchange-listed Fortune 500 company.

Now, more than three decades later, Shaklee is a well-established and respected health industry leader. In 1989, it was acquired by a very large and successful Japanese firm, Yamanouchi Pharmaceutical Co., Ltd. Both Shaklee Corporation and Shaklee Japan are owned by Yamanouchi Pharmaceutical Company, Ltd.

Shaklee Corporation subsidiaries include Shaklee U.S., Inc., Shaklee Mexico, and Shaklee Canada, with additional businesses in Singapore, and Malaysia; Bear Creek Corporation, a direct mail subsidiary that includes Harry and David, the nation's largest direct mail marketer of fine fruits and gourmet foods, and Jackson & Perkins, a leading supplier of roses and other plants.

Its 221-acre Norman, Oklahoma plant—a size equivalent to seven football fields—is one of the largest and most advanced nutritional supplement facilities in the world. Rigid quality controls and modern production methods are used to manufacture nutritional supplements such as Shaklee brand vitamins, minerals, and food supplements.

In the Norman facility, over 145 employees, including chemists, biologists, engineers, and technicians, produce these products with state-of-the-art manufacturing services which include direct compression blending, fluid bed granulation, tablet compression, tablet coating, powder mixing technology, powder packaging, extruded bar snacks, bottle, can, and pouch packaging, and quality control laboratories.

Over 252 different kinds of in-stock raw materials are maintained in conditions that protect the integrity of each ingredient, while an indoor temperature of 75 degrees Fahrenheit, with 50 percent relative humidity, is precisely maintained at all times to ensure consistent product freshness.

The Norman plant ships approximately one million pounds of products to Shaklee distribution centers across the nation, and over 120,000 pounds of products to Japan, each month to meet increasing domestic and international demand.

In addition, over 140 employees work at distribution centers in Bedford Park, Illinois; Dayton,

New Jersey; and La Palma, California, serving thousands of Shaklee Sales Leaders and their millions of customers across the country, each maintaining 606 different products in stock, for a total inventory of products and sales support literature valued at approximately $6.2 million per center.

Over 26,000 incoming orders are received at the centers each month. On a daily basis, the centers ship 1,250 product orders adding up to approximately 40,000 cases of product.

Shaklee has spent over $80 million on research and development. New nutritional product concepts are evaluated by independent research scientists from such institutions as Scripps Clinic, the University of California at San Diego, Columbia University, Stanford University, and the University of Texas.

Independent research studies on products are conducted by researchers at leading universities, including Harvard University, The University of California at San Francisco, and the University of Texas. In the past decade alone, Shaklee is responsible for more than 60 research abstracts and articles published in major scientific journals throughout the world.

The Shaklee Scientific Advisory Board, a group of nationally recognized physicians and scientists, provides expertise in nutrition, bio-chemistry, cardiovascular health, and sports medicine.

Current members of the board are: Paul Saltman, Ph.D., Chairman, Shaklee Corporation Scientific Advisory Board, Professor of Biology, University of California, San Diego; Jeffrey B. Blumberg, Ph.D., Associate Director and Professor Chief, Antioxidants Research Laboratory USDA Human Nutrition Research Center of Aging, Tufts University; William Haskell, Ph.D., Professor of Medicine, Division of Cardiology, Stanford University School of Medicine; Peter Sacks, M.D., Director, Bariatric Program of the Division of General Internal Medicine, Scripps Clinical Medical Group, Inc.; Julian Spallholz, Ph.D., Professor, Texas Tech University and Texas Tech University Health Sciences Center; James Whittam, Ph.D., Senior Vice President, Science and Technology, Shaklee Corporation; and Myron Winick, M.D., Professor of Nutrition (Emeritus), Columbia University College of Physicians and Surgeons.

Carrying on Dr. Shaklee's research tradition, the 62,600-square foot Forrest C. Shaklee Research Center in Hayward, California, has been conducting research and developing products since it opened in 1971.

Charged with the development of specific analytical methods for testing the purity and efficacy of all products, the center's staff of over 60 specialists includes nutritionists, biochemists, dietitians, food scientists, microbiologists, engineers, chemists, packaging engineers, technicians, and a research librarian. The center utilizes such advanced instrumentation as a scanning electron microscope that magnifies images up to 100,000 times. Analytical instruments such as the atomic absorption spectrophotometer and the high-performance liquid chromatograph , allow exact measurements of minute compounds—and automated analytic instruments measure multiple samples simultaneously.

Though Shaklee performs as many as 63,000 laboratory tests for quality on nutritional products and their ingredients in a single year, the company conducts no animal testing.

All product label claims have documented substantiation. As many as 176 separate tests for purity, freshness, potency, and safety are performed on the raw ingredients for a single product, and products undergo as many as 262 separate quality assurance tests throughout the manufacturing process.

To confirm product stability, special environmental chambers can test product quality across a full range of environmental extremes: temperatures from 32 degrees Fahrenheit to 131 degrees Fahrenheit, and humidity levels from 30 percent or less to 85 percent or more.

Shaklee provides the nutritional expertise that makes the winning difference in many athletic accomplishments. Here are just a few:

The Voyager—the first nonstop, non-refueled flight around the world.

The Daedalus Project—the world record for human-powered flight: 72 miles between the Greek islands of Crete and Santorini

Team Shaklee—a top amateur cycling team, with riders who have set ten world records, and which placed four riders on the 1992 Olympic Team.

Trans-Antarctica Expedition—the first international explorer team to successfully cross Antarctica by dogsled

Mount Everest Expeditions—four expeditions, including the first American to reach the top without supplemental oxygen

U.S. Ski Team—the 1984 U.S. Olympic Ski Team won more medals in Sarajevo than any other competing country

U.S. Speed Skating and Luge Teams—the speed skating team won two gold medals during the 1992 Winter Olympic Games

Shaklee offers its members the opportunity to build their own businesses through multi-level marketing. Career opportunities are open to those who want to work independently at their own pace, choose their own hours, and attain financial security. Shaklee careers have attracted a wide variety of individuals—from business people wanting to break out of their nine-to-five routine, to the spouse wanting to earn extra family income at home, to couples who enjoy working together and are seeking a more flexible lifestyle.

Shaklee business people have achieved $50,000, $100,000, and $150,000 annually in just two or three years. Master Coordinators receive bonuses of between $50,000 and $500,000 a year.

In addition to profit from product sales, bonuses are paid for sales volume and leadership development. The following are the average 1990 monthly bonuses paid for the following levels: Supervisor and Senior Supervisor, $786; Coordinator and Senior Coordinator, $2,912; Key and Senior Key Coordinator, $7,195; and Master Coordinator, $14,659.

Each year, Shaklee rewards its top Sales Leaders with national and international conventions held in places such as Hong Kong, Vienna, Madrid, San Francisco, Hawaii, and Washington, D.C. Top Sales Leaders get paid transportation and accommodations for themselves and members of their families.

Shaklee also offers Sales Leaders the opportunity to qualify for a brand-new bonus car in as little as six months. Among the many choices are Ford Mustangs, Taurus, Thunderbirds, Mercury Sables, or Cougars. The most accomplished salespeople drive Cadillacs or Lincoln Continentals. To date, Sales Leaders have driven more than 30,000 bonus cars.

Most people come into Shaklee to use the products. They become members and buy at a discount.

Many people want to share the products with others. They can earn their products free.

Some people are looking for an opportunity to supplement their income. Many of them have become financially independent through building a lucrative full-time business. ∎

SHAPERITE CONCEPTS, Ltd.

2340 South 900 West, Salt Lake City, UT 84119
801-975-0811 Voice
801-975-0899 Fax
800-776-9898 Credit Card Orders

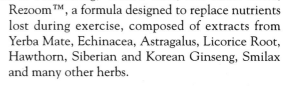

History
Founded 1989 by Donna, Scott, and Greg Martin

Financials *Not rated, privately held, incorporated NV*

General Statistics
Total 1993 Sales: *Not available; 1992 $15 Million*
Total Distributors: *35,000*
Foreign Countries: *N/A*

Method of Product Distribution *Deliver to distributor*

Association Membership *N/A*

Inventory Policy *First in/First Out*

Product Return Policy *100% in 30-days for distributors; customer 100%*

The Product Line: Product literature put out by Shaperite™ Concepts, Ltd. claims that Aloe Vera is a trademark of theirs, which is possibly an error. However, Shaperite™ Concepts, Ltd. does market a 100% pure cold-pressed version of Aloe Vera™ juice, as well as numerous nutritional products, some of which are described below.

The Straws™, Slim & Trim Straws™, Quick Energy Straws™, Stop Smoking Straws™, honey and herb straws; Shape-Fast™, an herbal catalyst composed of Ma Huang, Willow bark, and other herbs; Rezoom™, a formula designed to replace nutrients lost during exercise, composed of extracts from Yerba Mate, Echinacea, Astragalus, Licorice Root, Hawthorn, Siberian and Korean Ginseng, Smilax and many other herbs.

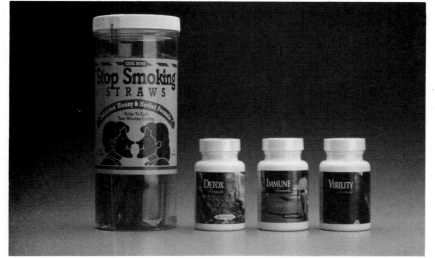

Shapelines™ is a line of nutritional supplements which seek to enhance the performance of specific body systems. The line includes Virility™, Female™, Stress™, Immune™, Cardio™, Detox™, Musculoskeletal™, Phytolax™, Multi-Plex™, and Effervescent C™, Catalyst™, Recall™, and Super Detox™.

Another line of Shaperite™ products is called The Trio™, a line of "metabolic equalizers" consisting of Metabo-Lite™, Gurmar™, and Yerba Mate™.

MARKETING/COMPENSATION PLAN

PLAN CATEGORY *Stairstep/Breakaway*
DISTRIBUTOR DISCOUNT OFF RETAIL *40% avg.*
QUALIFICATION PERIOD *Two Months*
COMPRESSION? *Modified*

MINIMUM QUALIFYING VOLUME *$100*
SUPPORT *Videos, Workshops, Literature, Newsletters, Broadcasts*
LEVELS LOCKED IN? *Yes*
INITIAL FEE *Not Available*

QUALIFICATION LEVELS

Advisor: *Purchase products wholesale (retained at all levels)*

Supervisor: *10% bonus on personal purchases and 1st level Advisors* **Qualification:** *purchase $200 volume as Advisor*

Manager: *15% bonus on personal and 1st level Advisors; 5% on 1st level Supervisors* **Qualification:** *$1,000 group volume in 2 months; $100 personal purchases*

Executive: *25% bonus on personal purchases and 1st level Advisors; 15% of 1st level Supervisors; 10% of 1st level Managers* **Qualification:** *$5,000 group volume in 2 months; $100 personal purchases*

1st Level Development Bonus: *Executive benefits; 5% override on 1st level Executives* **Qualification:** *Executive; 1 first level Executive; $100 personal purchases*

2nd Level Development Bonus: *Executive benefits; 5% override on 1st and 2nd level Executives* **Qualification:** *Executive; 2 first level Executives; $100 personal purchases*

3rd Level Development Bonus: *Executive benefits; 5% override on 1st, 2nd & 3rd level Executives* **Qualification:** *Executive; 3 first level Executives; $100 personal purchases*

Additional Levels (Contact Company For Details): *4th Level Development Bonus; 5th Level Development Bonus*

Other Bonuses *N/A*

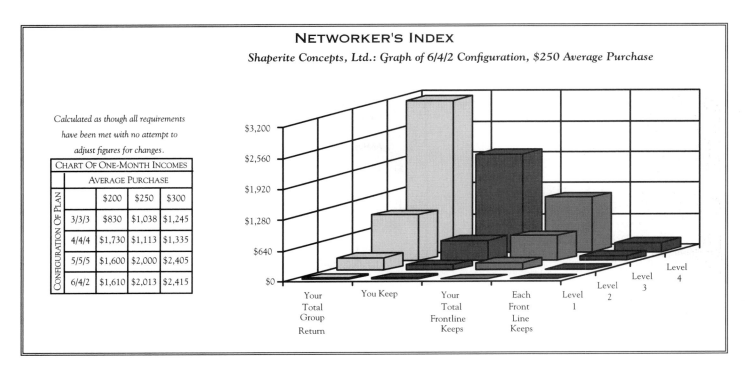

NETWORKER'S INDEX
Shaperite Concepts, Ltd.: Graph of 6/4/2 Configuration, $250 Average Purchase

Calculated as though all requirements have been met with no attempt to adjust figures for changes.

CHART OF ONE-MONTH INCOMES

CONFIGURATION OF PLAN	AVERAGE PURCHASE		
	$200	$250	$300
3/3/3	$830	$1,038	$1,245
4/4/4	$1,730	$1,113	$1,335
5/5/5	$1,600	$2,000	$2,405
6/4/2	$1,610	$2,013	$2,415

SUNRIDER INTERNATIONAL

3111 LOMITA BOULEVARD, TORRANCE, CA 90505-5109
310-534-4786 VOICE
310-326-3723 FAX

History
Founded December 1982 by Dr. Tei Fu Chen, whose research led him to rediscover the Chinese Philosophy of Regeneration. His interpretation, that health comes through balanced herbal nourishment of all the systems of the body, resulted in Sunrider.

Financials *Top rating; privately held; incorporated UT*

General Statistics
Total 1993 Sales: *$316,430; 1992 $260 Million*
Total Distributors: *300,000*
Foreign Countries: *Global (see pages 144-145)*

Method of Product Distribution *Picked up by distributor, delivered to distributor, delivered to customer*

Association Membership *MLMIA*

Inventory Policy *No requirement*

Product Return Policy *100% in 14 days to customer; 100% in 60 days to distributor*

The Product Line: Sunrider offers three lines of herbal foods and beverages: Sunergy, SunSport, and Vitalite; and line of herbal personal care, skin care, and cosmetics: Kandesn.

Sunergy, Sunrider's flagship product, is created to maintain the natural synergistic balance of *Quinary* (the relationship of the five principal systems of the body: circulatory, respiratory, digestive, endocrine, and immune). The Sunergy line is composed of a large number of herb food concentrates in packets, capsules and liquids; herb food beverages; balms, skin care, and essential oils.

SunSport is a sport and fitness herbal food and beverage line with a wide range of choices.

Vitalite is a light nutritional herbal food and beverage line seeks to keep the body's metabolism operating in balance during weight loss.

In addition to the various nutritional lines, Sunrider offers single herbs such as Dong Quai, Korean White Ginseng, and Goldenseal Root.

Kandesn products are formulates with ingredients such as herbs, squalane, Royal Jelly and essence of pearl. The products include a body and facial skin care line, a hair care set, a full line of cosmetics, and a color compact system.

MARKETING/COMPENSATION PLAN

PLAN CATEGORY *Stairstep/Breakaway*
DISTRIBUTOR DISCOUNT OFF RETAIL *25%-35%*
QUALIFICATION PERIOD *Level Dependent*
COMPRESSION? *Yes*

MINIMUM QUALIFYING VOLUME *$100*
SUPPORT *Videos, Workshops, Literature, Newsletters*
LEVELS LOCKED IN? *Yes*
INITIAL FEE *Not available*

QUALIFICATION LEVELS

Trainer: *Earn retail sales profit margin plus 5% rebate on personal sales volume (PSV)* **Qualification:** *$100 accumulated PSV*

Supervisor: *8% Direct Sales Rebate; 3% on Group Sales Volume (GSV)* **Qualification:** *$100 PSV; $1,500 GSV of which $400 is earned in qualifying month*

Manager: *11% Direct Sales Rebate; 3% on 1st level Supervisors; 6% of 1st level Trainers* **Qualification:** *$4,000 GSV of which $1,000 is earned in qualifying month*

Assistant Director: *15% rebate on PSV; 4% of 1st level Managers; 7% of 1st level Supervisors; 10% of 1st level Trainers;* **Qualification:** *$7,500 Group SV of which $2,000 is earned in qualifying month*

Director: *20% rebate on PSV; 5% of 1st level Assistant Directors; 9% of 1st level Managers; 12% of 1st level Supervisors; 15% of 1st level Trainers; Voice Mail Network (V-Net); Leadership Development Bonus 6% of 1st level Directors; 2% of 2nd level Directors; 1% of 3rd level Directors* **Qualification:** *$12,000 Group SV, of which $3,000 is earned in qualifying month (compression employed)*

Lead Director: *Director benefits; 6% of 1st level directors; 3% of 2nd level Directors; 2% of 3rd level Directors; 1% of 4th level Directors; one share lead Profit Sharing Fund* **Qualification:** *Director with two 1st level Directors (compression employed)*

Additional Levels (Contact Company For Details): *Group Director; Master Director; Silver Master; Golden Master; Executive Director; Silver Executive; Golden Executive; International Distributor*

Other Bonuses: *Group Profit Sharing; Master Profit Fund; Auto Fund Program; Home Fund Program; Qualified Director Achievement Bonus; Leadership Conference Trip Incentive Fund; Founder's Fund (U.S. Only)*

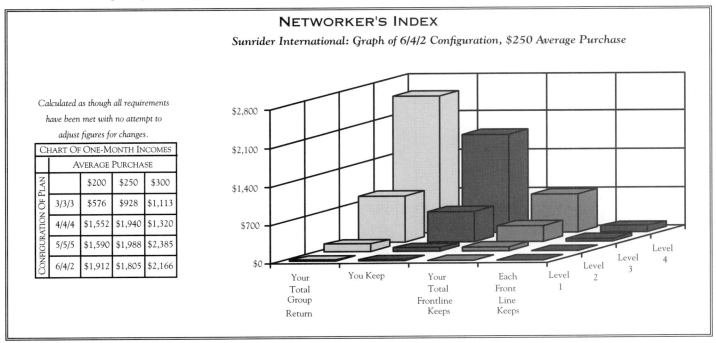

NETWORKER'S INDEX

Sunrider International: Graph of 6/4/2 Configuration, $250 Average Purchase

Calculated as though all requirements have been met with no attempt to adjust figures for changes.

CHART OF ONE-MONTH INCOMES			
	AVERAGE PURCHASE		
CONFIGURATION OF PLAN	$200	$250	$300
3/3/3	$576	$928	$1,113
4/4/4	$1,552	$1,940	$1,320
5/5/5	$1,590	$1,988	$2,385
6/4/2	$1,912	$1,805	$2,166

Uni-Vite USA (Vi-Tality Products)

2440 Impala Drive, Carlsbad, CA 92008
619-931-9942 Phone
619-931-0603 Fax

History
Uni-Vite USA was purchased from Uni-Vite in 1993 by Ken Winright, and the name changed to Vi-Tality Products near this book's press time.

Financials *Not rated, privately held, incorporated CA*

General Statistics
Total 1993 Sales: *Not Available*
Total Distributors: *Not Available.*
Foreign Countries: *N/A*

Method of Product Distribution *Delivered to Distributor, Delivered to Customer*

Association Membership *N/A*

Inventory Policy *No requirement*

Product Return Policy *100% within 30 days*

The Product Line: The Micro Diet is Uni-Vite's flagship product (a skin therapy program is slated for launch April 1993). The Micro Diet recommends that the dieter make meal selections totaling at least 800 calories per day, placing The Micro Diet in the category of a Low Calorie Diet.

The Uni-Vite product line falls mainly into four categories, Drinks, Soups, Entrees, and Meal Bars, each of which contain fewer than 300 calories.

The soup line consists of Split pea, chicken, and tomato.

Entrees include tetrazini, Spanish rice, chili, muesli cereal, and pasta.

Shakes come in chocolate, vanilla, and strawberry.

The Uni-Vite meal bars come in peanut, crunchy peanut, chocolate, yogurt-orange, muesli, and chocolate-caramel popcorn.

Uni-Vite stresses that personal support and behavioral modification are important factors in a successful weight loss program. Most of the consultants are "Micro Dieters" themselves. Uni-Vite also offers motivational and exercise programs.

PLAN CATEGORY *Stairstep/Breakaway*
DISTRIBUTOR DISCOUNT OFF RETAIL *N/A*
QUALIFICATION PERIOD *Level Dependent*
COMPRESSION? *Yes*

MINIMUM QUALIFYING VOLUME *$100*
SUPPORT *Videos, Workshops, Literature, Newsletters*
LEVELS LOCKED IN? *Yes*
INITIAL FEE *$100.00*

QUALIFICATION LEVELS

Affiliate: *Earn profit from markup on wholesale*

Advisor: *Earn profit from markup on wholesale, purchase product direct from company* **Qualification:** *Purchase $100 wholesale*

Senior Advisor: *5% on personal purchases and 1st level Advisors Personal Group Volume (PGV)* **Qualification:** *$500 PGV in month*

Coordinator: *10% on personal purchases and 1st level Advisors PGV; 5% on Senior Advisors* **Qualification:** *$1,000 PGV in month*

Senior Coordinator: *15% on personal purchases and 1st level Advisors; 10% on 1st level Senior Advisors; 5% on 1st level Coordinators* **Qualification:** *$2,000 PGV in one month*

Supervisor: *25% on personal purchases and 1st level Advisors; 20% on 1st level Senior Advisors; 15% on 1st level Coordinators; 10% on 1st level Senior Coordinators* **Qualification:** *$4,000 PGV within two consecutive months*

Director: *Supervisor benefits plus 5% on 1st and second level Directors* **Qualification:** *One 1st level Director; $500 PGV*

Additional Levels (Contact Company For Details): *Senior Director, Executive Director, Chief Executive Director, Presidential Director, paid 5% five levels deep, then up to 1% to infinity*

Other Bonuses: *Conference Bonus; Car Bonus*

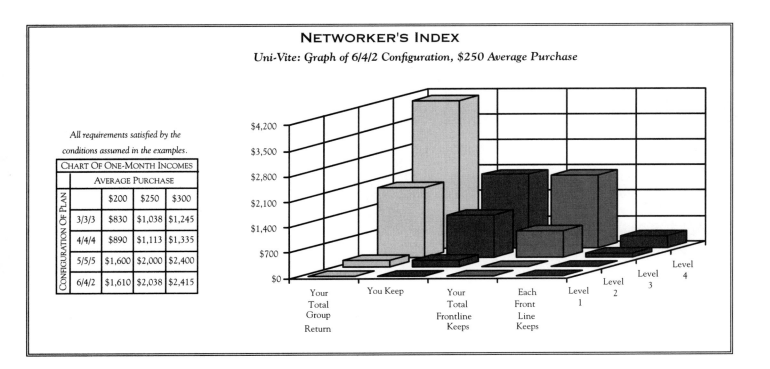

NETWORKER'S INDEX

Uni-Vite: Graph of 6/4/2 Configuration, $250 Average Purchase

All requirements satisfied by the conditions assumed in the examples.

CHART OF ONE-MONTH INCOMES			
	AVERAGE PURCHASE		
CONFIGURATION OF PLAN	$200	$250	$300
3/3/3	$830	$1,038	$1,245
4/4/4	$890	$1,113	$1,335
5/5/5	$1,600	$2,000	$2,400
6/4/2	$1,610	$2,038	$2,415

VITOL INTERNATIONAL

1201 SOUTH ELM SCHOOL ROAD, MESA, AZ 85210
602-892-8428 VOICE
800-488-4865 VOICE
602-497-2640 FAX

International

History
Founded 1987 by Hugh Vickers

Financials *Not rated, privately held, incorporated AZ*

General Statistics
Total 1993 Sales: *$2 Million*
Total Distributors: *2,000*
Foreign Countries: *Canada*

Method of Product Distribution *Picked up by distributor, delivered to distributor, delivered to customer*

Association Membership *N/A*

Inventory Policy *Strict rules against large inventories*

Product Return Policy *90 days 90% for distributors; 30 days 100% for customers.*

The Product Line: Vitol's product line consists of Vitol-27 Herbal Formula, Food Extract Wafers, and a line of skin care products, and a weight management system. Vitol-27 Herbal Formula contains the essence of no less than 27 complementary herbs. Vitol-27 supplies an array of natural substances complete in their biological structure verses the chemical isolation of ingredients. No claims are made for Vitol-27 beyond "the fact that centuries of human experience have shown that the many herbs contained in Vitol-27 act in total harmony with the human system."

Vitol's weight management system, "Natural Changes," is a combination of herbal weight reduction

products with an educational program designed to teach how to change physical, nutritional, and mental aspects of life to achieve proper weight, nutritional, and overall wellness. Food Extract Wafers are designed to be "a beneficial addition to the typical modern diet of fast, high-fat, and low-fibre foods." Ingredients include almonds, corn bran, wheat germ, lecithin, figs, papaya, watercress, dulse, Irish Moss, agar, mint leaves, licorice root, kelp, oat bran, bladderwrack, malto-dextrin, and parsley.

Vitol's skin-care system works in four steps, cleansing, toner, moisturizer, and refresher. It is recommended for all skin types.

Vital Skin Care products have no artificial dyes or color, are alcohol-free, and use no animal testing.

MARKETING/COMPENSATION PLAN

PLAN CATEGORY *Stairstep/Breakaway*
DISTRIBUTOR DISCOUNT OFF RETAIL *30% - 43%*
QUALIFICATION PERIOD *One Month*
COMPRESSION? *Yes*

MINIMUM QUALIFYING VOLUME *$100*
MAXIMUM QUALIFICATION PURCHASE *N/A*
SUPPORT *Videos, Workshops, Literature, Newsletters*
LEVELS LOCKED IN? *No*

QUALIFICATION LEVELS

Senior Distributor: *5% discount on personal purchases* **Qualification:** *$250 Accumulated Group Volume (AGV) in one month; $100 personal purchases*

Supervisor: *10% rebate on personal purchases; 5% bonus on 1st level Senior Distributors* **Qualification:** *$1,000 AGV*

Master Supervisor: *15% rebate on personal purchases; 5% on 1st level Supervisors; 10% on 1st level Senior Distributors* **Qualification:** *$2,500 AGV*

Director: *20% rebate on personal purchases; 5% on 1st level Master Supervisors; 10% on 1st level Supervisors; 15% on 1st level Senior Distributor; 7% Royalty Override Bonus on 1st and 2nd level Directors* **Qualification:** *$4,000 AGV, of which $2,000 must be in qualifying month; 1 1st level Director for Royalty Override Bonus. $100 personal purchase*

Executive Director: *Director benefits plus 7% royalty Override on 3rd level Directors* **Qualification:** *Director with 3 1st level Directors*

Senior Director: *Executive Director benefits plus 7% Royalty Override on 4th level Directors* **Qualification:** *Director with 5 1st level Directors*

Presidential Director: *Senior Director benefits plus 7% Royalty Override on 5th level Directors* **Qualification:** *Director with 10 1st level Directors*

Additional Levels (Contact Company For Details): *N/A*

Other Bonuses: *Production Bonus; Director Development Bonus*

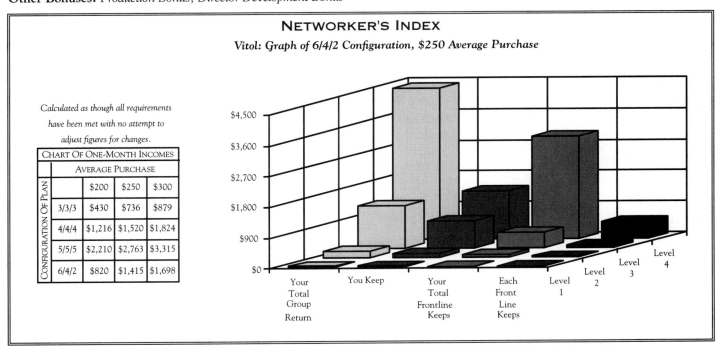

NETWORKER'S INDEX

Vitol: **Graph of 6/4/2 Configuration, $250 Average Purchase**

Calculated as though all requirements have been met with no attempt to adjust figures for changes.

CHART OF ONE-MONTH INCOMES			
	AVERAGE PURCHASE		
CONFIGURATION OF PLAN	$200	$250	$300
3/3/3	$430	$736	$879
4/4/4	$1,216	$1,520	$1,824
5/5/5	$2,210	$2,763	$3,315
6/4/2	$820	$1,415	$1,698

YOUNGER LIVING, INC.

PO BOX 1561, WATERTOWN, SD 57201
605-886-7203 VOICE
800-657-4346 VOICE ORDERS

History
Founded by Don Mussetter in 1961, incorporated in 1968, operating simultaneously as a service and retail business. Became an MLM company in 1974.

Financials *No rating*

General Statistics
Total 1993 Sales: *Not Available*
Total Distributors: *Not Available*
Foreign Countries: *N/A*

Method of Product Distribution *Delivered to distributor, delivered to customer*

Association Membership *N/A*

Inventory Policy *No requirement*

Product Return Policy *Not available*

The Product Line: Younger Living markets a variety of products, including car care, water treatment, homeopathic medicines, and vitamin and mineral supplements.

The Aqua-Fresh water filter is a three-stage water filter with a five-year unconditional guarantee on the housing and a two-year prorated guarantee on the cartridge. Younger Living also distributes the Vitalizer aerobic-rebound exerciser, Tuff-Lon Gear Treatment, Ultra-6 Fuel Treatment, and Tuff-Glo Paint Sealant

Younger Living nutritional supplements include Nu-Path, EPA-DHA,and Nature's formula, Detox Fiber, Miracle Fiber, Vital Mist, Mist-D-Lite, and the Perma-Trim System. Also available are Cheat Sweet fiber cookies.

The homeopathic Do-Drops distributed by Younger living include drops for Flu/Cold Symptoms, Cough, Sinus/Nasal Discharge, Intestinal Worms, Sore Throat/Inflammation, Ear Irritation, Allergy/Hay Fever, Trauma/Injuries, Skin Problems, Hemorrhoid, Headaches/Nerves, Joint/Rheumatism, Women/Painful Periods, Morning Sickness, Travel Sickness, Glandular Regulation (female and male), Diarrhea/Colic, Children/Teething, Digestion I-Stomach, Digestion II-Liver, and Smoking Withdrawal.

Marketing/Compensation Plan

PLAN CATEGORY *Stairstep/Breakaway*
DISTRIBUTOR DISCOUNT OFF RETAIL *15%*
QUALIFICATION PERIOD *Level Dependent*
COMPRESSION? *Yes*

MINIMUM QUALIFYING VOLUME *$30*
SUPPORT *Videos, Workshops, Literature, Newsletters*
LEVELS LOCKED IN? *Yes*
INITIAL FEE *$5.00*

QUALIFICATION LEVELS

Distributor: *Earn 15% profit margin on sales*

Senior Distributor: *25% on personal purchases; 10% on 1st level Distributor purchases* **Qualification:** *$250 volume in one month or $175 for two consecutive months*

Manager: *35% on personal purchases; 20% on 1st level Distributors; 10% on 1st level Senior Distributors* **Qualification:** *$500 in one month or $350 for two consecutive months*

Administrator: *45% on personal purchases; 30% on 1st level Distributors; 20% on 1st level Senior Distributors; 10% on 1st level Managers* **Qualification:** *$1,000 in one month or $700 for two consecutive months*

Career Breakaway Bonus 1: *5% on personally sponsored Administrators* **Qualification:** *1 Active personally sponsored Administrator*

Career Breakaway Bonus 2: *4% on 2nd Generation Administrators* **Qualification:** *2 Active personally sponsored Administrators*

Career Breakaway Bonus 3: *3% on 3rd Generation Administrators* **Qualification:** *3 Active personally sponsored Administrators*

Additional Levels (Contact Company For Details): *2% fourth Generation Administrator bonus*

Other Bonuses: *N/A*

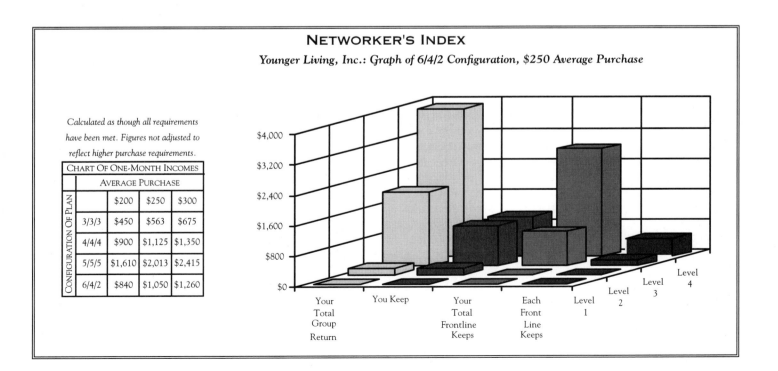

NETWORKER'S INDEX
Younger Living, Inc.: Graph of 6/4/2 Configuration, $250 Average Purchase

Calculated as though all requirements have been met. Figures not adjusted to reflect higher purchase requirements.

CHART OF ONE-MONTH INCOMES			
	AVERAGE PURCHASE		
	$200	$250	$300
3/3/3	$450	$563	$675
4/4/4	$900	$1,125	$1,350
5/5/5	$1,610	$2,013	$2,415
6/4/2	$840	$1,050	$1,260

INTRODUCTION TO CONVERSION PROFILES

BY DIRK JOHNSON

The following five companies have long and illustrious histories—but, with one exception, none was founded as an MLM company. And that exception, Jafra Cosmetics, Inc., though it was founded in 1956 as an MLM, was purchased by the Gillette company as a successful, mature network marketing company.

The other four companies are: ElySee Cosmetics, founded in 1926; The Fuller Brush Company, founded in 1906; Rexall Showcase International, a member of the Rexall Family of Companies which were founded in 1903, and the Watkins Company, founded in 1868.

Elysee and Fuller Brush became converted to network marketing in 1992; Rexall Showcase International was founded in 1990; Watkins converted to MLM in 1977; and $3.5 Billion Gillette's quiet involvement with network marketing began in 1973.

Elysee Cosmetics was a cosmetics manufacturer that marketed its products primarily through beauty salons; The Fuller Brush Company was a direct sales company, the well-known Fuller Brush Man operating primarily door-to-door; Rexall's history is that of an over-the-counter medicine manufacturer which operated a huge and well-known retail chain of drug store pharmacies; and Watkins Company was a direct sales company whose Watkins Man was a fixture in the rural mid-west for over one hundred years; Jafra Cosmetics was a small but successful cosmetics MLM company purchased by a gigantic personal care products manufacturer..

Studied as a group, these five companies are an excellent paradigm of the power of multi-level marketing to move products, and of the differences among MLM, point-of-purchase sales (Rexall, Elysee and, to some extent, Jafra Cosmetics), direct marketing (practiced by Rexall's new owner), and direct sales (Fuller Brush, and Watkins). And, since there is a popular misconception that multi-level marketing companies are the same as direct-sales companies, the conversions of Fuller Brush and Watkins are especially instructive.

Rexall was the first, and largest, national franchise in the United States, with nearly 25,000 drug stores carrying its name and products. Surveys indicate that the Rexall name is recognized by nearly 80% of the adult population in the U.S.

Rexall, as the first national franchise, has a tradition of market innovation—fortunately for Rexall. The marketplace has changed considerably in the ninety years since Rexall was founded. People as a rule no longer shop at the corner drug store, but go instead to "mega-stores." Though there are still about 7,000 stores bearing the Rexall name, the point-of-purchase aspect of Rexall's business is shrinking—and its network marketing segment is exploding.

Carl DeSantis, chairman and owner of S.D.V. Mail Order, Sundown Vitamins, and Thompson Vitamin Company, purchased Rexall in 1986. Though already the owner of a major direct marketing company, and now owner of a point-of-purchase marketing company with a billion dollar name and minimal market share, DeSantis' research led him to the conclusion that network marketing is the dynamic marketing trend for the •90s and beyond.

As DeSantis put it, "for the first time in network marketing history, a highly recognized and trusted name has openly and totally been committed to this industry."

Alfred C. Fuller started his company on $375 in 1906. He made brushes in the morning and sold them in the afternoon. When he realized that duplication of his effort would be needed to make his company grow, he began recruiting salespeople, Fuller Brush sales representatives. By 1946 The Fuller Brush Company was the largest direct sales company in the world.

In the late 1950's, the Fuller Brush Company and Avon were at the same sales levels. Sales declined steadily from the time of the company's purchase by Sarah Lee in 1968 until H. Lee Turner, a trial lawyer and investor, lead a group to acquire the company.

Fuller's new marketing team, including a former Mary Kay Vice President who later became an associate of Ochiltree's said to have been Ochiltree's sales and marketing architect in the successful turnaround at Avon, intend to use network marketing to catch back up to the $3.5 billion Avon. They got a head start when, simply by announcing their intention to "go MLM" in December of 1991 they were inundated with calls from prospective distributors.

This is another example of some of the country's most successful and innovative marketers selecting network marketing as the vehicle for turning around a traditional company which has fallen upon hard-times. We believe that during the next decade, there will be many, many, many more such examples as the retail markets continue to shrink, and alternatives to traditional and cumbersome distribution systems become more and more necessary to the survival of large companies.

Joseph R. Watkins began his company with liniment, which he mixed in the family kitchen, hand-bottled in the woodshed, and marketed from his horse-drawn buggy. By 1868, Mr. Watkins, with his market basket of liniment under his buggy seat, was a familiar sight.

Mr. Watkins soon branched out to include other products, and added a 100% money-back guarantee if contents didn't fall beneath the "trial mark" line on his bottles. Watkins still uses the same bottle for several products.

In 1885, Watkins incorporated. He recruited salespeople who drove red, yellow, and black buggies, and in 1912 built the first Watkins factory, which is still in use in Winona, MN.

As the result of a "Watkins Man" giving him a stick of gum when he was five years old, when Irwin Jacobs learned of Watkins impending bankruptcy thirty years later, in 1978, he cancelled a business trip to California in order to go to Minnesota and purchase Watkins for $4.1 million in cash.

Watkins had fallen from $25 million in sales and about 30,000 independent dealers in the mid-1940s to 9,000 dealers and about $8 million in sales. After two years and $7 million of experimentation, Jacobs began building the dealer force that had always been the backbone of Watkins, fine-tuning it along network marketing lines.

The company now has more than 50,000 dealers, and revenues estimated at approximately $100 million. And management intends to employ large-scale direct marketing campaigns to increase the visibility and size of the Watkins dealer network.

Elysee was founded in 1927 by Dr. Elizabeth Elysee Blumenthal in Frankfort, Germany, and brought to the U.S. in 1940. Blumenthal, an early pioneer in the development of skin treatment using botanicals, set up a salon in San Francisco which was a forerunner of full-service skin-care salons such as Georgette Klinger and Elizabeth Arden.

Blumenthal developed corrective skin care products, as well as skin therapy machines, including those used by Helena Rubenstein in her salons. In the fifties she was sent by the U.S. government to Guam and the Philippines to work with servicemen on skin care problems.

Blumenthal set up commissioned consultants around the country to market her skin care and fragrance lines through beauty salons and through private seminars.

But, during the twenty years following her death in 1965, the company stagnated and passed from Dr. Emil P. Salvotti, who had worked with Blumenthal, and Dr. Lucille Most in 1971 to a group of 32 shareholders of which Linda Marshall was president. In 1972, Elysee introduced color analysis. In 1985, Marshall captured 95 percent ownership, and kicked off an expansion campaign she had initiated years earlier to breathe new life into the firm.

In 1986, Elysee began marketing a fragrance line conceived and financed by Dionne Warwick, and marketed in Neiman-Marcus stores.

Marshall introduced network marketing to the company in 1992, and has plans for expansion into Thailand and Singapore in 1993. At this writing, the company has more than 1,000 distributors.

Each of these companies exemplifies the power of network marketing to achieve lasting effects in the marketplace. They also indicate a major marketing trend—multi-level marketing is acquiring a force in the economy of our country which is beginning to rival the major developments of the past, such as franchising, direct selling, direct marketing—and even retail. ■

ElySee Cosmetics

6804 SEYBOLD ROAD, MADISON, WI 53719
608-271-3664 VOICE
800-235-9733 VOICE

History
Founded 1926 by Dr. Elizabeth Blumenthal in Europe using Royal Jelly and herbs in original formulations; she brought ElySee to the U.S. in 1940; color analysis was introduced in 1972; under the Ownership and Presidency of Linda Marshall, converted to MLM in 1992

Financials *Not rated, privately held, incorporated WI*

General Statistics
Total 1993 Sales: *N/A*
Total Distributors: *1,000*
Foreign Countries: *Thailand, Singapore*

Method of Product Distribution *Picked up by distributor, delivered to distributor*

Association Membership *N/A*

Inventory Policy *No requirement; 70% of product sold or used before next purchase*

Product Return Policy *within 30 days of termination 90% to distributors, 60 days 90% to customers*

The Product Line:
According to the Mayo Clinic Health Letter "Alpha-hydroxy acids are applied as a cream or lotion. They reduce fine wrinkling and improve overall skin texture. They loosen dead cells from the surface of the skin, leaving a smoother, softer layer." Alpha-hydroxy acids have been an ingredient in ElySee products since 1926.

ElySee also manufactures a line of skin care products containing Nayad, an anti-ageing cream. Included in the list of Nayad enthusiasts are Ali MacGraw, Linda Evans, Veronica Hamel, Jamie Lee Curtis, and Barbara Eden, and are recommended by Louise Bianco, a Los Angeles-based "skin care specialist to the stars."

According to some immunologists and dermatologists, Nayad outperforms such dangerous prescription skin-care products as Retin-A, without harmful side effects. The reason for the lack of side-effects is that Nayad is not a drug, but a purified extract derived from baker's yeast—the same yeast used in food products. Yeast extracts have a GRAS (Generally Recognized As Safe) rating from the Food and Drug Administration.

ElySee markets a complete line of skin-care products, fragrances (for men and women), cosmetics, lipsticks, and nail polishes.

MARKETING/COMPENSATION PLAN

PLAN CATEGORY *Stairstep/Breakaway*
DISTRIBUTOR DISCOUNT OFF RETAIL *15%*
QUALIFICATION PERIOD *Level Dependent*
COMPRESSION? *Yes*

MINIMUM QUALIFYING PURCHASE *$100*
SUPPORT *Videos, Workshops, Literature, Newsletters*
LEVELS LOCKED IN? *Yes*
INITIAL FEE *???*

QUALIFICATION LEVELS

Associate: *Receive 15% discount on retail; earn 15% on retail sales*

Consultant: *Receive 30% discount on Personal Volume (PV); 5% rebate on PV; 2% Group Bonus* **Qualification:** *$100 Group Volume; $100 Personal Sales Volume (SV)*

Coordinator: *10% on PV; 5% on 1st level Consultants; 4% Group Bonus* **Qualification:** *$1,000 Group Volume ($250 in qualifying month); $100 Personal SV*

Supervisor: *15% on PV; 5% on 1st level Coordinator; 10% on 1st level Consultant; 6% on Group Volume* **Qualification:** *$3,000 Group Volume ($750 in Qualifying month); $100 Personal SV*

Manager: *20% on PV; 5% on 1st level Supervisor; 10% on 1st level Coordinator; 15% on 1st level consultants; 8% on Group Personal Volume* **Qualification:** *$5,000 Group Volume ($2,000 in qualifying month); $100 Personal SV*

Executive: *20% on PV; 5% on 1st level Manager; 10% on 1st level Supervisor; 15% on 1st level Coordinator; 20% on 1st level Consultants; 10% bonus on Group Personal Volume* **Qualification:** *$10,000 ($4,500 in qualifying month); $100 Personal SV*

Additional Levels (Contact Company For Details): *Silver Executive, Gold Executive, Diamond Executive, Presidential Diamond Executive*

Other Bonuses: *N/A*

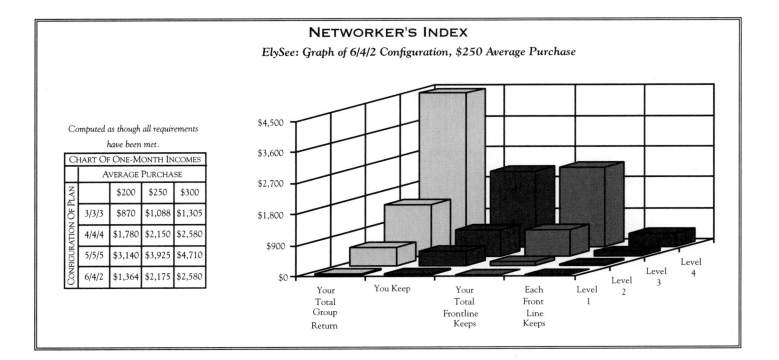

NETWORKER'S INDEX

ElySee: Graph of 6/4/2 Configuration, $250 Average Purchase

Computed as though all requirements have been met.

CHART OF ONE-MONTH INCOMES			
	AVERAGE PURCHASE		
CONFIGURATION OF PLAN	$200	$250	$300
3/3/3	$870	$1,088	$1,305
4/4/4	$1,780	$2,150	$2,580
5/5/5	$3,140	$3,925	$4,710
6/4/2	$1,364	$2,175	$2,580

THE FULLER BRUSH COMPANY

PO BOX 1247, ONE FULLER WAY, GREAT BEND, KS 67530
316-792-1711 VOICE
800-523-3794 VOICE
316-793-4523 FAX

History
Founded 1906 by Alfred C. Fuller on $375. By 1946 it was the largest direct sales organization in the world. Sara Lee purchased the company from the Fuller family in 1968. H. Lee Turner purchased it from Sarah Lee in 1990, and converted it to MLM in 1992.

Financials *Not rated; privately held; incorporated KS*

General Statistics
Total 1993 Sales: *est. $25.1 - $50 million*
Total Distributors: *12,000*
Foreign Countries: *Canada, Caribbean Islands, Guam, Japan*

Method of Product Distribution *Delivered to distributor, picked up by distributor, delivered to customer*

Association Membership *DSA*

Inventory Policy *No Requirement*

Product Return Policy *90% within one year*

The Product Line: A complete line of home and personal care products. The list of Fuller Brush products can be classified into eight categories: laundry, bathroom, kitchen, floor, all-house, outdoor seasonal, storage, and personal care.

Laundry products include Fuller Plus Powder, Pre-Laundry Stain Spray, Laundry Stain Remover Liquid, and others. Bathroom products include Toilet Bowl Swab, Tile & Grout Brush, Bent-Tip Bowl Brush, Toilet Bowl Brush Holder, and others. Kitchen products consist of Refrigerator Coil Brush, Fulsol Degreaser (decanter), Fusol Degreaser (34 oz.), Fusol Degreaser (gallon), Citrus Clean, and others.

Floor products include Sponge Mop, Wet Mop, Dry Mop, Kitchen Broom, Angle Broom, Formula 21 Spot Remover, and others. All-house products consist of Lambswool Duster, Reach Duster, Foam Clean, Lemon Furniture Oil, and more. Outdoor products are filled out with Indoor/Outdoor Broom, Window Brush, Ant & Roach Spray and Insecticide. Outdoor seasonal products are items such as Pro Tech Vinyl Polish. Storage items are those such as Belt Hangars and Vanilla Air Freshener. Personal Care products include Witch Hazel Lotion and brushes.

MARKETING/COMPENSATION PLAN

PLAN CATEGORY *Unilevel*
DISTRIBUTOR DISCOUNT OFF RETAIL *20-40%*
QUALIFICATION PERIOD *One Month*
COMPRESSION? *No*

MINIMUM QUALIFYING PURCHASE *$50/$100*
SUPPORT *Videos, Workshops, Literature, Newsletters*
LEVELS LOCKED IN? *No*
INITIAL FEE *$49.95*

QUALIFICATION LEVELS

Retailer: *5% Bonus on personal order of $200 - $499; 10% on Personal Order of more than $500. No override bonuses are paid to Retailers*

Supervisor: *5% Business Volume (BV) of 1st level distributors; 10% BV of 2nd level distributors* **Qualification** *$50 personal BV; one active level 1 Distributor; Fuller Institute Product Certification*

Manager: *Supervisor bonuses plus 10% of 3rd level distributors.* **Qualification** *$100 Personal BV; $300 combined 1st level BV; Career Program Manager Development Series 1 (correspondence or seminar)*

Director: *Manager bonuses plus 5% of 4th level and beyond down to "paid as" Directors* **Qualification:** *$100 Personal BV; $5,000 Group Volume; $500 outside volume; 3 active legs; Career Program Director Development Series II,(Correspondence or Seminar)*

Executive Director: *Director Bonus plus5% 1st level Directors and their groups* **Qualification:** *Director Qualification plus 1 "Paid-As" Director in your first three levels; 1500 BGV; 1000 outside volume;*

Senior Director: *Executive Director Benefits plus 5% 2nd Generation Directors* **Qualification:** *Director plus 3 "Paid-As" Directors in 1st 3 levels; $1250 BGV; $2000 outside volume; $20,000 downline volume*

District Director: *Executive Director Benefits plus 5% 3rd Generation Directors* **Qualification:** *Director plus 5 "Paid-As" Directors in 1st 3 levels; $1000 BGV; $3,000 outside volume; $30,000 downline volume*

Additional Levels (Contact Company For Details): *Region Director; National Director*

Other Bonuses: *Overlapping bonuses*

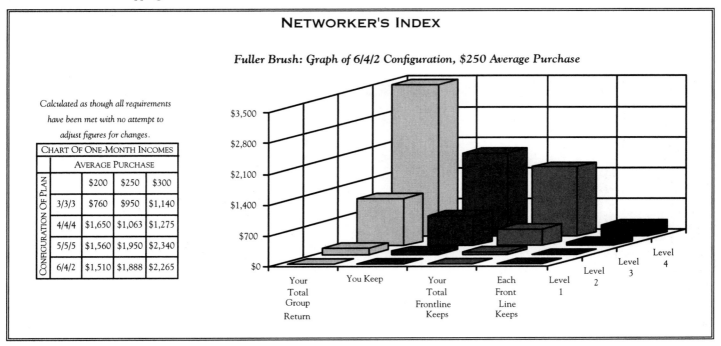

NETWORKER'S INDEX

Fuller Brush: Graph of 6/4/2 Configuration, $250 Average Purchase

Calculated as though all requirements have been met with no attempt to adjust figures for changes.

CHART OF ONE-MONTH INCOMES			
	AVERAGE PURCHASE		
CONFIGURATION OF PLAN	$200	$250	$300
3/3/3	$760	$950	$1,140
4/4/4	$1,650	$1,063	$1,275
5/5/5	$1,560	$1,950	$2,340
6/4/2	$1,510	$1,888	$2,265

JAFRA COSMETICS, INC.

2451 TOWNSGATE ROAD, THOUSAND OAKS, CA 91361
805-496-1911 VOICE
800-551-2345 VOICE

Jafra
Cosmetics International

History
Founded 1956 by Jan and Frank Day in their Malibu, California home as a direct sales cosmetics company, Jafra Cosmetics has been a subsidiary of the Gillette Company since 1973. Jafra's official position is that they are not an MLM.

Financials *Not rated; publicly held subsidiary of the Gillette Company; incorporated CA*

General Statistics
Total 1993 Sales: *Est. $100.1 - $500 Million*
Total Distributors: *65,000*
Foreign Countries: *Global (see pages 144-145)*

Method of Product Distribution *Delivered to distributor, delivered to customer*

Association Membership *DSA*

Inventory Policy *Personal inventory recommended for fulfilling orders; none required*

Product Return Policy *N/A*

The Product Line: Jafra markets a complete line of skin care, color care, nail and hand care, body and sun care, personal care and fragrance products under the concept of the "art of total beauty."

Central to the Jafra skin care program is Royal Jelly Milk Balm Moisturizer Lotion, a lotion that blends royal jelly with an emulsiondesigned to soften skin for up to 24 hours. Jafra considers this lotion to be the foundation of the company's success. All other Jafra products prepare the skin for this lotion, and they all revolve around it. Among these other products are two skin formulas for different skin types, each designed for use in a three-step process: cleansing, moisturizing, and protecting.

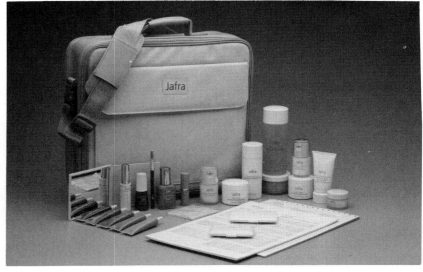

Jafra color care includes Supertone Makeup SPF 6, Light Protective Color SPF 6, cream concealer, White Soufflé Highlighter, Moisturizing Translucent Face Poweder, and Powder Blush Duo, to name just a few. Also included are lipsticks, lip pencils, eye make-up, mascara, and eyebrow products.

Amounting to a complete home manicure system, Jafra's Nail and Hand care line includes base coats, protein wraps and nail lacquers.

Also available from Jafra are personal care items ranging from shampoo to vitamin supplements to men's fragrances.

MARKETING/COMPENSATION PLAN

PLAN CATEGORY *Stairstep/Breakaway*
DISTRIBUTOR DISCOUNT OFF RETAIL *15% - 40%*
QUALIFICATION PERIOD *Level Dependent*
COMPRESSION? *Yes*

MINIMUM QUALIFYING PURCHASE *$150/$300*
SUPPORT *Videos, Workshops, Literature, Newsletters*
LEVELS LOCKED IN? *Yes*
INITIAL FEE *$95.00*

QUALIFICATION LEVELS

Consultant: *40% Profit Mar gin; Additional 10% profit margin opportunity* **Qualification:** *Accumulate $1,200 invoiced resale sales within 4month period*

Manager Candidate: *personally sponsor five activated consultants for a total of eight; submit Manager Candidate Application 2 weeks before qualifying month*

Manager: *10% on Central Branch Cash-In* **Qualification:** *Manager Candidate; $4,000 invoiced Resale Sales in month; orders from Manager Candidate and eight Consultants in qualifying month*

District Manager I: *12% on Central Branch Cash-In; 4% on 1st level Manager (Branch)* **Qualification:** *One 1st level Branch*

District Manager II: *15% on Central Branch Cash-In; 5% on 1st level Branches; 1% on 2nd level Branch* **Qualification:** *two 1st level Branches*

District Manager III: *16% on Central Branch Cash-In; 5% on 1st level Branches; 1% on 2nd level and 3rd level Branches* **Qualification:** *three 1st level Branches*

Additional Levels (Contact Company For Details): *Director Levels I-V*

Other Bonuses: *Action Pak; Success Start; Pacesetter; Founder's Circle; Monthly Leadership Bonus; Quarterly Sponsoring Dividend; New Manager Promotion Bonus; New Manager Promotion Bonus; Sales Awards; Sharing Awards; Sponsoring Consistency Awards; District Director Jewelry; District Director Car Allowance; Company Awards*

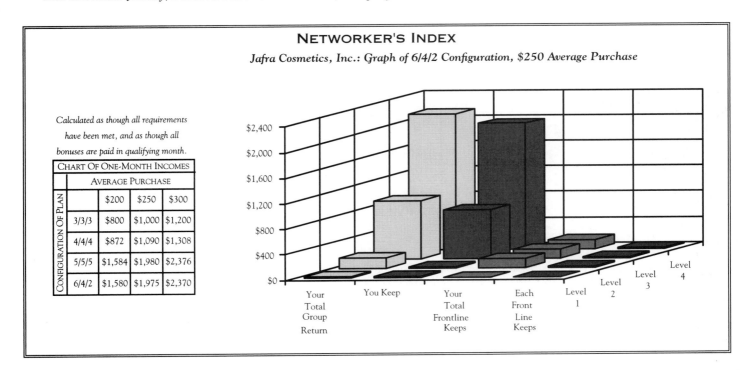

NETWORKER'S INDEX

Jafra Cosmetics, Inc.: Graph of 6/4/2 Configuration, $250 Average Purchase

Calculated as though all requirements have been met, and as though all bonuses are paid in qualifying month.

CHART OF ONE-MONTH INCOMES

CONFIGURATION OF PLAN	AVERAGE PURCHASE		
	$200	$250	$300
3/3/3	$800	$1,000	$1,200
4/4/4	$872	$1,090	$1,308
5/5/5	$1,584	$1,980	$2,376
6/4/2	$1,580	$1,975	$2,370

ORIFLAME USA

76 Treble Cove Road, North Billerica, MA 01862
508-663-2700 Voice
508-663-0254 Fax

ORIFLAME INTERNATIONAL

History
Founded in Stockholm, Sweden in 1967. Founded in the United States in 1981. Historically a party-plan organization, Oriflame USA instituted MLM in 1993. A discussion of Oriflame's history is not included in the "Introduction to Conversion Profiles" because Oriflame was added to the book during an information update between reprintings.

Financials *Not rated; Publicly held*

General Statistics
Total 1993 Sales: *$150 Million worldwide*
Total Distributors: *(Advisors) 100,000*
Foreign Countries: *Global*

Method of Product Distribution *Delivered to Distributor; Delivered to Customer*

Association Membership *DSA*

Inventory Policy *No requirement*

Product Return Policy *90% for Distributors for one year; 100% for customers*

The Product Line:
Oriflame manufactures and markets a complete line of cosmetics, fragrances, hair and skin care products combining traditional Scandanavian and Swiss beauty secrets with modern scientific research.

The Oriflame Basic Skin Care System is a four-step care plan with separate lines for combination, dry, and oily skin types. There are also systems for delicate, sensitive skin and very oily skin, as well as aloe vera basics, cleansers, masques, and special care.

The Royal Velvet line consists of special skin care and body care for aging skin. Oriflame also markets the Swedish Body Care system of in-bath and after bath products.

In addition, Oriflame offers Marine Therapy Body Care System of ocean and ivy extracts; a tender skin line, Sun Care, Foot Care, and Jojoba hair and body care.

Oriflame also offers a complete line of cosmetics from foundations, blushers, bronzers, eyecolor, lip color, to the Giordani Makeup Collection.

International Fragrances include Italian, French and Asian scents and combinations for both women and men.

MARKETING/COMPENSATION PLAN

PLAN CATEGORY *Stairstep/Breakaway*
DISTRIBUTOR DISCOUNT OFF RETAIL *30%*
QUALIFICATION PERIOD *Variable*
COMPRESSION *Yes*

MINIMUM QUALIFYING VOLUME *$100*
SUPPORT *Workshops, Literature, Newsletter*
LEVELS LOCKED IN? *No*
INITIAL FEE *$30.00*

QUALIFICATION LEVELS

Advisor: *Earn 30% profit on retail sales*

Team Bonus Level I: *Advisor benefits plus 5% bonus on personal sales and 2.5% on Personal Recruit Sales (PRS)* **Qualification:** *$500 combined personal and PRS, of which at least $100 is personal*

Team Bonus Level II: *Advisor benefits plus 10% bonus on personal sales and 5% on PRS* **Qualification:** *$1,000 combined personal and PRS of which at least $200 is personal*

Group Director: *24% bonus on personal sales; 9% on Personal Recruit sales; 4% on downline Advisors; 5% on 1st level groups* **Qualification:** *Personally sponsor 5 or more, and in two consecutive months achieve Team Bonus Level II with $3,000 Total Downline Retail Sales in one month or sponsor 5 or more and team bonus Level II with $6,000 in one month*

Area Director: *Group Director Benefits Plus up to 4% on Central Area sales; up to 5% on 1st level Area sales* **Qualification:** *In two consecutive months: $3,000 Central Group Sales with $9,000 total downline Retail Sales*

District Director: *Area Director Benefits Plus up to 2.5% on Central Area sales; up to 3% on 1st level District sales; up to 2% on 2nd level District sales; up to 1% on 3rd level District sales* **Qualification:** *In three consecutive months: $9,000 Central Group Sales with $27,000 total downline Retail Sales*

Additional Levels (Contact Company For Details): *N/A*

Other: *Commissions paid on Suggested Retail Price; Pacesetter Bonus*

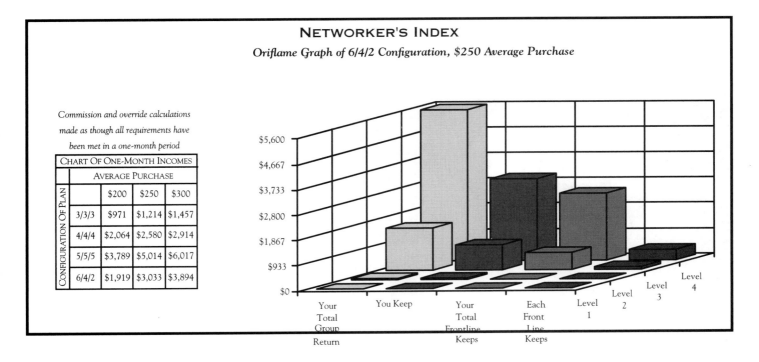

NETWORKER'S INDEX
Oriflame Graph of 6/4/2 Configuration, $250 Average Purchase

Commission and override calculations made as though all requirements have been met in a one-month period

CHART OF ONE-MONTH INCOMES

CONFIGURATION OF PLAN	AVERAGE PURCHASE		
	$200	$250	$300
3/3/3	$971	$1,214	$1,457
4/4/4	$2,064	$2,580	$2,914
5/5/5	$3,789	$5,014	$6,017
6/4/2	$1,919	$3,033	$3,894

REXALL SHOWCASE INTERNATIONAL

6600 NORTH ANDREWS AVENUE, FORT LAUDERDALE, FL 33309
305-771-1446 VOICE

History
A member of the Rexall Family of companies; founded by Carl DeSantis in July, 1990 and launched August 1990 with a single patented product, the Bios Life Diet.

Financials *Not rated, privately held, incorporated FL*

General Statistics
Total 1993 Sales: *$10.1 - $25 million*
Total Distributors: *15,000*
Foreign Countries: *N/A*

Method of Product Distribution *Delivered to distributor, delivered to customer.*

Association Membership *DSA, MLMIA*

Inventory Policy *No requirement*

Product Return Policy *100% for customers, 90% for one year for distributors.*

The Product Line:
The Rexall Showcase International product line can be classified under five headings: Bios Life Diet, nutritional supplements, water filtration devices, homeopathic remedies, and traditional remedies.

Bios Life Diet consists of a Bios Life Diet drink mix, Diet Essential vitamin/mineral supplement, Essential Enzymes supplement, Bios Life Diet fruit bars, *Showcase Nutritionals* booklet, *The Bios Life Diet Weight Management Program* Booklet, and the *You and the Bios Life Diet* audio cassette.

RSI individually markets 12 nutritional supplements: Daily Essentials, Essential Bodyguard, Diet Essentials, Energy Essentials, The Ultimate Plenamins, Senior Essentials, Teen Essentials, Essential B Concentrate, Essential E Concentrate High Potency, Essential-C 6+6 Formula, Workout Essentials, and Essential Fish Oil Concentrate 3000/300.

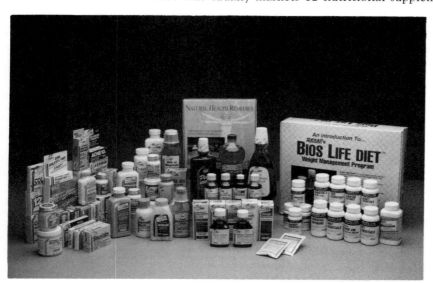

RSI's natural health remedies include Protect•ol Calmplex•2000, and In•vigor•ol homeopathic remedies.

A nine-stage activated carbon with Halogen Reduction Media water filtration system comes in countertop, undercounter, whole-house, in-line, and shower unit sizes.

RSI's Traditional Remedies Line includes Rexall's version of most popular over-the-counter drugs.

MARKETING/COMPENSATION PLAN

PLAN CATEGORY *Stairstep/Breakaway*
DISTRIBUTOR DISCOUNT OFF RETAIL *33%*
QUALIFICATION PERIOD *Level Dependent*
COMPRESSION? *Yes*

MINIMUM QUALIFYING PURCHASE *$100*
SUPPORT *Videos, Workshops, Newsletters, Training Manuals*
LEVELS LOCKED IN? *Yes*
INITIAL FEE *$35.00*

QUALIFICATION LEVELS

Distributor: *Earns up to 50% retail profit margin*

Associate: *5% on personal comissionable volume (CV) and on 1st level Distributors' CV* **Qualification:** *$300 group CV in one month; $100 personal CV*

Supervisor: *10% on personal CVs; 5% on 1st level Associates; 10% on 1st level Distributors* **Qualification:** *$1,000 group CV in one month; $100 personal CV*

Manager: *10% on personal CV; 5% on 1st level Supervisors; 10% on 1st level Associates; 15% on 1st level Distributors;* **Qualification:** *$2,500 group CV in one month; $100 personal CV*

Director: *20% on personal CV; 5% on 1st level Managers; 10% on 1st level Supervisors; 15% on 1st level Associates; 20% on 1st level Distributors* **Qualification:** *$4,000 group CV in one month, at least $1,000 on which is not under another Director OR $5,000 group CV in two months, at least $1,000 on which is not under another Director; $100 personal CV*

One Star Director: *Director benefits; 5% on 1st level Directors; for the first 6 months, One Star Directors will be paid as a Three Star Directors (i.e, 5% on Directors to the 3rd level)* **Qualification:** *Director; $1,000 group CV; $100 personal CV*

Additional Levels (Contact Company For Details): *Four Star Director; Five Star Director; Six Star Director; 10 Star Presidential Director;*

Other Bonuses: *One Star and Two Star Director Head Start; Star Director Bonus Pool; 10-Star Presidential Bonus Pool; Trips, Cruises*

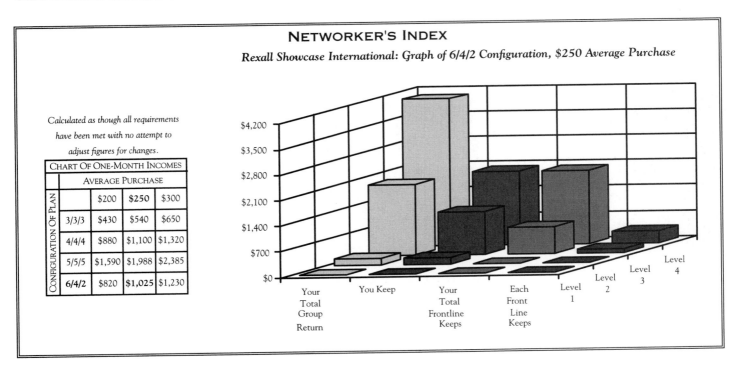

NETWORKER'S INDEX

Rexall Showcase International: Graph of 6/4/2 Configuration, $250 Average Purchase

Calculated as though all requirements have been met with no attempt to adjust figures for changes.

CHART OF ONE-MONTH INCOMES

CONFIGURATION OF PLAN	AVERAGE PURCHASE		
	$200	$250	$300
3/3/3	$430	$540	$650
4/4/4	$880	$1,100	$1,320
5/5/5	$1,590	$1,988	$2,385
6/4/2	$820	$1,025	$1,230

WATKINS

150 LIBERTY STREET, WINONA, MN 55987
800-533-8018 CREDIT CARD ORDERS

History
Founded 1868 by J.R. Watkins, converted to MLM in 1977, purchased by Irwin Jacobs in 1978.

Financials *Not rated, privately held, incorporated MN*

General Statistics
Total 1993 Sales: *est. $100 million*
Total Distributors: *800 Directors, 50,000 Representatives*
Foreign Countries: *Canada*

Method of Product Distribution *Delivered to Representatives, Delivered to Directors, Delivered to Customers*

Association Membership *DSA*

Inventory Policy *No requirement*

Product Return Policy *100% to customers*

The Product Line: Well known for its Imitation Vanilla Extract, ground cinnamon and pepper, Watkins product line consists of over 350 products in its main line catalog, plus approximately 50 seasonal products introduced for the field's fall selling season. Every four weeks, two to five new products are added to the regular line items. Below is a very partial list of items in a Watkins catalog.

Spices, flavorings, and condiments—including gourmet extracts and flavors, concentrated soup and gravy mixes, and meat sauces, seasonings, dry and liquid spice blends, mustards and more... and this part of the catalog is generously peppered with complete recipes for home-made foods.

Desserts and cream beverage mixes, unsweetened punch concentrates—, and several cookbooks are also available.

Nutritional supplements and foods range from Aloe Vera Juice to meal replacement products to vitamins, fiber, and mineral supplements.

There are also over-the-counter medicines, liniments, salves and balms; shampoos, soaps, lotions, creams, fragrances, disinfectants, room fresheners, window cleaner, detergent, furniture polish, and car-care items, all with the Watkins imprint.

MARKETING/COMPENSATION PLAN

PLAN CATEGORY *Stairstep/Breakaway*
DISTRIBUTOR DISCOUNT OFF RETAIL *25% - 61%*
QUALIFICATION PERIOD *Four Weeks*
COMPRESSION? *Yes*

MINIMUM QUALIFYING PURCHASE *N/A*
SUPPORT *Videos, Workshops, Literature, Newsletters*
LEVELS LOCKED IN? *Yes*
INITIAL FEE *$73.00*

QUALIFICATION LEVELS

Representative: *Earns income based on percent paid out difference between total group volume and individual downline volumes, percentages and dollar amounts as follows: $40-$139/25%; $140-$369/30%; $370-$739/35%; $740-$1,119/38%; $1,120-$1,819/40%; $1,820-$2,629/42%; $2,630-$3,699/44%*

Director: *5% on 1st level Directors; 3% of 2nd level Directors; 2% of 3rd level Directors; personal and downline percentages as follows: $40-$3,699/44%; $3,700-$5,499/48%; $5,500-$6,949/50%; $6,950-8,699/52%; $8,700-$10,449/53%; $10,450-12,199/54%; $12,200-13,949/55%; $13,950-$17,199/56%; $17,200-$22,099/57%; $22,100-$31,049/58%; $31,050-$41,999/59%; $42,000-54,229/60%; $54,300 and over 61%* **Qualification:** *a 4-campaign process, at the beginning: 9 personally sponsored active Representatives, and 15 Representatives in downline; $3,700 sales at retail each four campaigns; in final campaign: 12 personally sponsored active Representatives.*

4th Level Breakaway Bonus: *Director benefits plus 1% of 4th level Directors* **Qualification:** *Director with $100,000 volume in year*

Additional Levels (Contact Company For Details) *Executive Director; Master Director; $100,000 Club Director; $250,000 Club Director; $400,000 Club Director; Presidents Club Director; Silver Master Director; Gold Master Director; Grand Master Director*

Other Bonuses *Key Representative; Group Builder, Unit Leader, Garnet Leader, Double Garnet Leader, President's Honor Guild and Council, "52" Club, 2% Rebuilder Bonus, Senior Director Benefit Plan.*

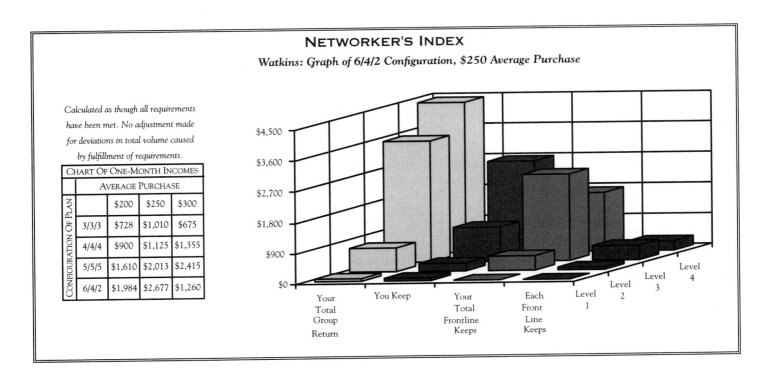

NETWORKER'S INDEX

Watkins: Graph of 6/4/2 Configuration, $250 Average Purchase

Calculated as though all requirements have been met. No adjustment made for deviations in total volume caused by fulfillment of requirements.

CHART OF ONE-MONTH INCOMES			
	AVERAGE PURCHASE		
	$200	$250	$300
3/3/3	$728	$1,010	$675
4/4/4	$900	$1,125	$1,355
5/5/5	$1,610	$2,013	$2,415
6/4/2	$1,984	$2,677	$1,260

MLM DISCOUNT BUYING SERVICES

BY DIRK JOHNSON

Virtually everyone has heard of buying clubs, or discount buying services. Due to their tremendous purchasing power and low overhead, these services are able to extend significant discounts to members, who pay an annual fee for the privilege of participating in the services. Though buying clubs are a recent marketing phenomenon, major players, such as banking giant National Westminster, have entered the field.

Generally, membership in a buying club is a relatively easy sale. The difficulty lies in reaching large numbers of consumers in a cost-effective way. For this purpose, buying clubs utilize direct mail, telephone solicitation, point-of-purchase displays, and direct response advertising.

And within the newfangled realm of buying clubs, an even more recent phenomenon is the buying club promoted through the medium of network marketing. Even when compared to the relatively youthful network marketing industry, buying clubs are in their infancy. Only one of them, AMS, Inc., with 50,000 distributors and founded in 1988, is of sufficient age and stability to be included in the company profiles beginning on page 52.

One of the difficulties buying clubs have is that they generally do not themselves manufacture or distribute any product, but are simply entities that arrange for the possibility of the movement of other companies' products by means of marketing memberships. This places them into a grey area of the law, since buying clubs don't have the advantage of legal precedents, such as those established for multi-level marketing by Amway Corporation, to guide them in conducting their businesses.

In an excellent February, 1992 article in Downline News, MLM lawyer Jeffrey A. Babener says that "...various states have chosen different regulating agencies to monitor this area. In some states, buying organizations are regulated by consumer protection divisions, and in others by corporation commissioners, and even one state regulates this area through the insurance commissioner's office."

Potential legal tangles exist for all buying clubs, but especially for those promoted through network marketing.

The best example we're aware of is Consumer's Buyline, Inc. (CBI) which, according to *Marketwave*, November 1992, the state of Virginia declared to be a pyramid scheme, and prohibited from selling memberships on a multi-level basis. And, according to the same article, the state of Arkansas will still allow downline commissions to be paid on multiple levels, but only on the sale of a membership (i.e., not on monthly dues; part of the total annual cost of CBI is a $15 monthly charge).

But CBI wasn't charged with fraudulent activity, and is still able to sell memberships in both states. Problems arose simply because movement of product was not directly linked to the fees charged. CBI's difficulties in this regard highlight the stringency of laws and regulators concerning multi-level marketing. It is also a lesson in just how far above reproach a relatively large network marketing buying club must be to survive for longer than five years, as AMS, Inc. has.

Although there are many other multi-level buying clubs, this article will compare only three (for a useful grid comparison, the reader is referred to *Downline News*, August-September, 1992): Consumers' Buyline, Inc; American Benefits Plus; and The Mainstreet Alliance.

American Benefits Plus: For an annual fee of $129, American Benefits Plus offers residual override income; toll-free telephone ordering; 250,000 items with automatic extended warrantee; a double-the-difference price guarantee; amusement park discounts at 50% off retail; Books at 30% off retail; a quotation and selling service for both new and used automobiles; a 25% discount off car rentals from most major companies; a college financial aid service; 50% off retail on condo rentals (for an additional $19.95 annual fee); credit card protection; a 12.99% annual interest credit card and/or secured card; 15% off retail dental charges; flowers; gift baskets; 40% off at 1,400 golf courses (for an additional $29.95 annual fee); grocery coupons (for an additional $4.50 annual fee); 10% off for in-home health care; 50%

off at 1,400 hotels; 25% off legal services plus three free half-hour sessions; long distance telephone services through Metromedia; magazines; a mortgage accelerator service (for an additional $141.95); 50% off movie tickets; moving company services; 50% off optical wear; personal care products; pet insurance ($99.00 per year); prescription discounts; real estate referral service; roadside automobile services ($19.95 per year); recreational vehicle rentals; skiing at 300 resorts ($24.95 annual fee); short-notice preferred travel rates, 5% airfare rebate; vacation spas; and voice mail.

Consumers' Buyline, Inc.: For an annual fee of $262, Consumers' Buyline, Inc. offers toll-free telephone ordering; 600,000 items with automatic extended warrantee; a double-the-difference price guarantee; business and corporate start-up plans (fees from $250); quotation and selling service for new automobiles ($10 fee for quotation); 25% off car rentals from most major companies; a college financial aid service; a community merchant shopping card giving 5% to 30% discounts; condo rentals starting at $500 per week; a debit and debt disclosure service ($125 fee); 20% to 60% of retail dental charge; $96 pre-paid dental service; grocery coupons; 5,000 dry-goods shopping items; hearing aids; 50% off 4,500 hotels; 25% off legal services plus 3 free half-hour sessions ($3.00 annual fee); AT&T long distance telephone service; magazines; 50% off movie tickets; moving company services; 45% off optical wear; personal care products; personal financial analysis service ($100 additional fee); 30% to 50% off prescriptions ($3.00 annual fee); a real estate referral service; records, tapes, and compact disks; 40% off roadside automobile services; recreational vehicle rentals; a tax audit service; short-notice preferred travel rates, 5% airfare rebate; and vacation spas.

The Mainstreet Alliance: For an annual fee of $190, The Mainstreet Alliance offers company toll-free access; residual override income; toll-free telephone ordering; 250,000 items with an automatic extended warranty (additional fee of $69-$295.00); a quotation and selling service for both new and used automobiles ($25 for the first three quotations, $10.00 per quotation thereafter); 25% off car rentals from most major companies; college financial aid services ($89.00 additional fee); a community merchant shopping card giving 5% to 50% discounts; condo rentals from $249 to $350 per week; an 8.5% annual rate credit card ($20 annual fee); a secured credit card; 20% to 60% off dental ($38.40 annual fee); a financial consultant service; grocery coupons; 50% off 1,600 hotels; insurance services; U.S. Sprint long distances telephone service; a mortgage accelerator service ($4.80 per transaction); 25% off optical wear; Airborne Express overnight delivery service; Franklin Time Management systems; personal financial management services; 10% to 25% off prescriptions ($28.80 annual fee); roadside automobile services ($33.60 annual fee); skiing at 300 resorts ($24.00 annual fee); Sybervision products; short-notice preferred travel rates; 5% airline ticket rebate ($7.00 per transaction ticketing fee); vacation spas; and voice mail.

These companies can be contacted as follows:

American Benefits Plus
4701 Columbus Street
Virginia Beach, VA 23462
804-456-0443

Consumers' Buyline, Inc.
100 Sitterly Road
Clifton Park, NY 12065
518-383-5950

The Mainstreet Alliance
4457 Willow Road
Suite 200
Pleasanton, CA 94588
510-463-3223

■

A check mark (✔) indicates a company's operations in the country identified	Aim International	AMS	Amway Corporation	Brite International	Cambridge	Carco	Cell Tech	Diamite	Discovery Toys	Ely See	Enrich International	Fuller Brush Company	Herbalife International	Jafra Cosmetics	Japan Life International	Karla Jordan International	Light Force	Lite & Rite
ARGENTINA														✔				
AUSTRIA			✔															
AUSTRALIA	✔		✔						✔				✔					
BAHAMAS			✔					✔										
BELGIUM			✔															
BRAZIL			✔										✔					
CANADA	✔		✔	✔			✔	✔	✔		✔		✔		✔			
COLUMBIA													✔					
FRANCE			✔										✔					
GERMANY													✔	✔				
GUATEMALA			✔															
HONG KONG	✔		✔												✔			
HUNGARY			✔										✔					
INDONESIA			✔															
ITALY			✔										✔					
JAPAN			✔					✔	✔				✔		✔			
MALAYSIA			✔								✔				✔			
MEXICO	✔		✔				✔			✔			✔	✔				
NETHERLANDS			✔										✔					
NEW ZEALAND	✔		✔										✔					
PANAMA			✔															
PHILLIPINES			✔															
POLAND			✔															
PORTUGAL													✔	✔				
SPAIN			✔										✔	✔				
SINGAPORE			✔							✔	✔				✔			
SOUTH KOREA			✔												✔			
SWITZERLAND			✔															
TAIWAN	✔		✔												✔			
THAILAND			✔						✔									
UNITED KINGDOM			✔										✔	✔				
VENEZUELA													✔					

Mary Kay	Matol Botannical	Melaleuca	Multi-Pure	Nanci Corp	NSA	Neways	Nikken	Noevir	NonScents	Nu Skin	Nutrition For Life	Oriflame	Oxyfresh	Reliv	Rexall Showcase Int'l	Shaklee	Shaperite Concepts	Sunrider International	Uni-Vite (Vi-Tality)	Vitol International	Watkins	Younger Living
✔			✔																✔			
			✔																✔			
✔			✔			✔			✔	✔		✔		✔				✔	✔			
																			✔			
			✔									✔										
			✔				✔												✔			
✔	✔	✔	✔	✔	✔	✔	✔	✔	✔	✔	✔			✔		✔		✔	✔	✔	✔	
			✔									✔						✔	✔			
✔			✔	✔				✔				✔							✔			
			✔			✔	✔		✔	✔								✔	✔			
			✔									✔										
			✔									✔						✔	✔			
			✔									✔										
			✔	✔			✔	✔		✔						✔		✔	✔			
			✔			✔		✔			✔	✔				✔		✔	✔			
✔	✔		✔	✔		✔						✔						✔	✔			
			✔									✔						✔	✔			
			✔			✔			✔	✔				✔				✔				
			✔									✔										
			✔								✔	✔										
			✔				✔					✔							✔			
			✔				✔					✔							✔			
			✔			✔						✔				✔		✔	✔			
			✔					✔			✔	✔						✔	✔			
			✔									✔							✔			
✔			✔			✔	✔			✔						✔		✔	✔			
			✔			✔	✔					✔						✔	✔			
			✔			✔	✔					✔						✔	✔			

THE OPPORTUNITY MEETING

BY J. MICHAEL PALKA

J. MICHAEL PALKA IS A TRAINER, MARKETING CONSULTANT, AND CO-FOUNDER OF MILLIONAIRES IN MOTION, AN INTERNATIONAL MLM TRAINING COMPANY. HIS LATEST TRAINING MANUALS ARE THE MLM SUCCESS GUIDE AND LEADERSHIP WORKBOOK.

You've been invited to an opportunity meeting and you're not sure what to expect. Let me give you some insights to what can be an experience you'll never forget.

First, the settings of opportunity meetings can vary greatly. They can be held in someone's living room, a banquet room at a four star-hotel, or anything in between. Likewise, the decor can be from simple to elaborate. Over the years (and opportunity meetings have been going on for many years) the culture of the opportunity meeting hasn't changed much.

The purpose of the opportunity meeting has always been to recruit new people into an organization. This is done by presenting the company, the products, and the opportunity in such a positive manner that you can hardly wait to write your check and get started.

Usually you'll be accompanied by the person who invited you, or at least that person will meet you there. When you first enter the room, you begin to notice that everyone seems to be in business dress. This can be a little intimidating at first, but soon you'll notice how friendly and happy everyone is, people coming up and introducing themselves, welcoming you, and making you feel right at home.

They know that when you are relaxed you will be more receptive to what they have to say. After a few introductions and a little social time, the meeting begins.

Some opportunity meetings are quite elaborate productions. It's all with the intent of getting you excited about the opportunity being presented to you.

You will usually hear about the credibility of the company and its founders. Then someone will present you with the product line and all the benefits that go along with using them.

You'll want to pay particular attention here. You'll discover many new and useful products that never would have made it into the marketplace, had it not been for MLM. Introducing a product into the marketplace via MLM costs considerably less than through conventional channels.

At this point there will be people there who will get up and give their testimonial as to how the product has helped them. A word of caution: this is where a lot of MLM companies get into grey areas.

When overzealous distributors start making claims as to the curative powers of their product, the government can and will step in; but if the persons who actually experienced the effect of the product just share their personal stories, they are pretty safe. It's when others start using and embellishing the story that problems crop up.

Throughout the presentations, it's up to you to ask questions if you don't understand or if you need clarification.

After they get you all excited about their fabulous product line, it's time to talk about the money making possibilities. You will be told how easy it is to make your life's fortune as a distributor. Another word of caution: MLM is a people business. It's not necessarily an easy business.

When they have completed the marketing plan presentation, it is natural to be a bit dazed, glazed, and amazed. See the plan again, several times if necessary, and ask questions.

You have seen all these prosperous people, with their fancy cars and wardrobes.

You have been befriended by everyone you have met.

You have discovered products that are impressive, and you have been shown how you might make a fortune.

You might think, "If these people can do it, it will be a snap for me."

This could be very true. Many independently wealthy people started right where you are today. They understood the power of the mind to create whatever was wanted.

It's your future, so make sure you have all the necessary information to make an intelligent decision. ∎

THE LIES OF MLM

BY JOHN MILTON FOGG

JOHN MILTON FOGG IS
EDITOR OF UPLINE™,
THE JOURNAL FOR
NETWORK MARKETING
LEADERS AND AUTHOR
OF THE GREATEST
NETWORKER IN THE
WORLD. HE CONDUCTS
SEMINARS FOR NETWORK-
ING PROFESSIONALS AND
PRODUCES THE THE
UPLINE™ MASTERS
SEMINAR TAPES.

I don't know if you share my experience with lies, but I'm guessing you do. Every single one I can ever remember telling has come back to haunt me. Part of growing up (a process I am, at age forty-three, more than ever actively engaged in) is setting straight those lies of the past. It seems they act as blocks that inhibit my growth and development.

Lies limit the future.

The lies that limit the future of MLM network marketing began as so many untruths do. They were initially told to bolster up our insecurity. In this instance, the perceived lack of self-esteem of the industry—the lies were harmless little white (meaning okay) ones to make us seem bigger and better than we really thought we were.

As always, they back-fired.

Now, when people ask us about this or that "false fact" and we have to admit to their fabrication, we come up looking smaller and worse than we are. What follows are the most common lies in the MLM community:

• The *Wall Street Journal* says that by the year 2000, 60 to 70 percent of all goods and services will be sold through network marketing.

• MLM is taught at Harvard and Stanford business schools and in numerous other leading colleges and universities.

• Some 20 percent of all millionaires in America were created through network marketing.

• John Naisbitt, in his bestselling book, *Megatrends*, says network marketing is the wave of the future.

There are others. These are the leading offenders. I have yet to speak to any group of people about network marketing—from established multi-level marketers to the general public—and not be asked about the truth of one or all of these statements.

THE WALL STREET JOURNAL

According to more than a dozen reporters and staffers, *The Wall Street Journal* never said that by the year 2000, 60 to 70 percent of all goods and services will be sold through network marketing.

They're not stupid.

The U.S. currently sells $5.5 trillion worth of goods and services per year—give or take one or two billion dollars. By the most aggressive accounts, MLM (which, for the sake of quoting big numbers, must include the direct selling industry) accounts for forty billion dollars in sales annually. More conservative estimates put that figure at a max of ten to fifteen billion dollars worldwide. Super conservative folks say MLM is about five billion dollars.

No matter which figures you favor, follow this: one percent of all the goods and services in the U.S. would amount to fifty-five billion dollars. 50 percent—10 to 20 percent less than the *Journal* was falsely quoted as saying—would be $2.75 trillion. Not bad growth for seven years!

One trillion is one million million. Get out your calculator. This is a lie of the lowest order, i.e. not even creative just stupid.

If someone tried to sponsor you into the business boastfully claiming he or she made $30,000 per month and you discovered that he or she really made one percent of that (which is what $55 billion is of $5.5 trillion) or $300, what would you think of that person? Enough said.

HARVARD, STANFORD, AND THE REST

Network marketing is not taught at Harvard and Stanford business schools and in numerous other leading colleges and universities throughout the country.

Truth is, most of them detest MLM. They don't understand MLM and do not care to.

As Harvard "B" School Professor Thomas Bonoma recently said in an article in *Marketing News*, "We do not teach such methods (MLM) at the Harvard Business School; they are not part of the curriculum; to my knowledge, they are not taught at this or any other reputable business school in the country..."

And he continued, "Multi-level marketing schemes, like chain letters and other devices, sometimes are at the borderline of what is legal—and over the borderline of what is ethical..."

He concluded by saying that examples of legitimate MLM's are few and far between. Not a glowing endorsement for such valuable subject matter.

Harvard has, twice that we know of, reviewed a case study of Mary Kay Cosmetics, but that's all. Stanford seemingly refuses to discuss it.

MLM Millionaires

"Twenty percent of all the millionaires in America" were *not* created through network marketing. By most accounts, 90 percent were created through real estate. 90 plus 20 equals 110, and that kind of math would get an "F" in any school—even Harvard "B."

We've got men and women who make a million dollars a year in this business. Many more who've made one million dollars in their networking careers. But 20 percent of all the millionaires in the United States?

Please, use some common sense.

John Naisbitt

John Naisbitt never mentioned network marketing in *Megatrends*, *Megatrends 2000*, or anywhere else for that matter.

I can't even discover a mention in his far more liberal *Trend Letter*. If you can, please let me know.

I called him and asked him for his opinion on MLM and he said—well, his people told me—he didn't have one.

There is no listing of network marketing or multi-level marketing in any index of a Naisbitt book. The references Naisbitt makes to networking are many. The use of them by multi-level marketers are convoluted misquotes and rubbery stretches of the truth.

So What's The Problem?

A good friend of mine, a man who is an acknowledged expert in our business and a leading network marketing trainer, recently sent me a generic prospecting product he was very proud of. Sadly, I can't offer it to you because it includes every one of the above lies.

If this misinformation works its way into my friend's repertoire (a man who has talent, experience, and integrity and who is depended upon by many people as a source of "how-to truths" about

this business), how many others are running around saying this stuff?

We've got to paper-train this industry.

The point—the problem, difficulty, challenge—is that you can't build lasting relationships with people (or regulators and the press) with lies.

You will be found out and your stock and the stock of the entire industry will go way down.

There is so much positive stuff—facts, not opinion, much less lies—to be shared about network marketing that it is foolish to say anything less. It's manipulation, not MLM. You may make a sale with it, but you won't create a customer and certainly can't build a successful network of distributors. That's a house built on get-rich-quicksand.

Please, do not say false and misleading things about network marketing to anyone. If you are insecure about the legitimacy of this business and feel the need to bolster up your courage and confidence, resist until you bone up and grow up.

If you need credible stuff to say about MLM, read newsletters and books, listen to tapes, get good brochures.

I urge each of you to squash the lies you find out there. Tell the truth. Honesty is and always will be the very best of policies. For my part I will continue to set the record straight every chance I get. Integrity is our most precious asset. Like our bodies, it requires a proper diet (the truth) and exercise (telling it) to become healthy and prosper. ∎

Eight Habits for MLM Success

By John Milton Fogg

John Milton Fogg is editor of Upline™, The Journal For Network Marketing Leaders and author of The Greatest Networker in the World. He conducts seminars for networking professionals and produces the The Upline™ Masters Seminar Tapes. There is no connection between Upline™ and this publication.

Habits are a fact of life and work. There are bad habits, ones which undermine and disable you, and there are good ones, habits which empower you and assure on-going positive action and achievement.

The following is a list of eight habits you can acquire for daily action. They're not the only good ones, but they are proven practices that, if you develop until they are second nature, will contribute to your MLM success.

1. Write Down Your Goals and Review Them Daily.

Successful people in all walks of life and work not only have goals, they also write them down and review them daily.

Making written goals keeps the "why" of the business up in front of your face. Written goals assist in keeping you focused, help you get through difficult times, and are more "real" and concrete than daydreams and wishes.

Where you want to go transforms a "Sunday drive" into a purposeful journey. It is the key to creating success by design, the design you want, and not by luck or accident.

2. Listen.

How often are you more interested in knowing what you have to say than in what the person you're speaking with is saying?

Do you have more answers than questions?

Do you approach conversations with an agenda you want the other person to see or agree with?

Listening is a powerful ingredient for success, yet many people are not good listeners.

The key to listening is this: notice when you're thinking about your answer instead of hearing the question. Stop. Focus on what the other person is saying and ask more questions.

Kahlil Gibran said that the flute teacher does not bring you to the storehouse of his or her wisdom, but rather leads you to the threshold of your own.

Giving people the right information is important, even empowering. Helping them discover what's right empowers them one hundred times more.

3. Acknowledge Your Actions Instead of the Results.

Although many people have been taught that results are what count, a focus on results may actually be counterproductive. What if, instead, you focused on your actions and let the results take care of themselves?

For one thing, it's your actions that create results. So it makes sense that continuous action—what is called being "pro-active"—will generate the greatest results. By acknowledging your actions, you give yourself and others positive reinforcement. You build a pattern of success.

Focusing on results tends to encourage people to "do it right," rather than to just do it. That's a sure set up for failure. Remember, Thomas Edison took 9,999 times (actions) to make a light bulb (the result). If he'd been preoccupied with the result, we might still be in the dark.

Consistent action—each action completed—generates momentum, the on-going power you need to accomplish your goals.

4. Say Only Things That Champion People.

If you can't say anything nice, keep quiet.

There's more than enough negativity and criticism in the world. For every three good things being said on any subject, there are thirty-three bad comments whispering down the lane. Saying only those things that champion people, companies, and causes generates positive word-of-mouth.

In a predominantly negative world, this will attract people to you like a powerful magnet.

When you find yourself engaging in negative talk, notice what you're saying. Stop. Make a positive observation instead or be quiet.

Being known as a man or woman of your good word is something you can put right in the bank. The interest it earns is both "residual" and powerful.

5. Fulfill Your Agreements.

"Those people never return phone calls; they must simply not care."

"Tom said he'd send literature, but it never came. He's not serious about this business."

"We had an appointment at 3:00, but she never showed up. She never even called. I just can't count on her."

These conclusions may not be the truth, but that's how people feel when you don't return their calls, follow through, and keep your appointments.

Keeping your agreements in a timely manner is both professional and duplicatable. It's the kind of action you want to encourage your distributors to model. Imagine how powerful your organization would be if everyone in it could be counted on to do what they said they would?

Most calls don't get returned, letters don't get mailed, and appointments aren't kept because of "not enough time" or "not being organized."

The fact is, it's really a lack of commitment to keep our agreements. Making that commitment alone is a powerful action. Honoring your intention to make and keep your promises is an almost 100 percent guarantee of success.

6. SET A LIMIT ON YOUR PHONE TIME.

Placing a time limit on calls increases your effectiveness and reduces your phone bill, too—a classic win-win.

Communications experts estimate that more than 80 percent of what we say is not to the point. Even if you saved only 50 percent of your telephone time by making time limit agreements, you'd have time for twice as many calls. Busy people appreciate your being concise and to the point. It's a habit they have.

The telephone may be the most powerful business tool you have, but only if you're actually using it to do business.

7. SAY "NO" THREE TIMES A DAY.

Building your network marketing business can be a very busy enterprise. Many of us have a tendency to overcommit. One problem is saying yes too often.

Being all things to all people is a crazy goal. It can't be done. However, most people want to be well thought of, and they want to be there for their people as well. Learning to say "no" and when to say it isn't a self-indulgent limitation. It is a solid expression of what it takes to run your business in the most efficient and effective manner.

It will also help to promote your people, who will rise up to take responsibility for their own success.

Set a simple goal of saying "no" three times each day. Don't make it arbitrary. Choose times and subjects where saying "yes" doesn't serve you or your enterprise.

Say "no" when you really mean it.

Say "no" when it serves everyone involved.

8. DO ONE THING AT A TIME.

Focus is vital for your success.

Many people split their focus: writing notes or organizing while on a phone conversation, having two conversations at once, and the frequent trap of the home-based business person, which is being torn between family and work.

"Jack of all trades" is truly master of none.

You've got to concentrate on the task at hand and give it your full attention in order to succeed. Otherwise, you're selling yourself and others short. From paying full attention to the person on the other end of the phone to scheduling your time so that you're not torn between two concerns, the one thing at a time approach is the one that works best.

If you find yourself looking up a phone number while writing a note to someone, stop. Make a choice of one or the other and complete one task before moving on to the next.

Choice is the key. It leaves your mind free to be fully engaged in your action.

Distraction saps your energy and leads to fatigue and a lack of productivity. Remember, producing predictable results is what you're after. The ability to focus on one thing at a time will increase the number of wins in your day and in your MLM career as well. ■

1. **WRITE DOWN YOUR GOALS AND REVIEW THEM DAILY.**

2. **LISTEN.**

3. **ACKNOWLEDGE YOUR ACTIONS INSTEAD OF YOUR RESULTS.**

4. **SAY ONLY THINGS THAT CHAMPION PEOPLE.**

5. **FULFILL YOUR AGREEMENTS.**

6. **SET A LIMIT ON YOUR PHONE TIME.**

7. **JUST SAY "NO" THREE TIMES A DAY.**

8. **DO ONE THING AT A TIME.**

How to Sell Without Seeming To

By Gini Graham Scott, Ph.D.

GINI GRAHAM SCOTT, PH.D., J.D., IS A CONSULTANT, SPEAKER, AND WORKSHOP/SEMINAR LEADER. SHE HAS PUBLISHED OVER 20 BOOKS, INCLUDING: GET RICH THROUGH MULTI-LEVEL SELLING, SUCCESS IN MULTI-LEVEL MARKETING, STRIKE IT RICH IN PERSONAL SELLING, BUILDING A WINNING SALES TEAM, AND MIND POWER.

A powerful tool to use in any kind of selling is the technique of selling without seeming to, or promoting your product as you do what you normally do everyday.

This strategy works so well because you talk about your product in a very informal, natural way, so that people see you not as a salesperson trying to sell them something, but as a friend or adviser who has some important, interesting information to convey.

As a result, they are especially eager to hear about it and are particularly open to trusting what you tell them. You are not selling, you're allowing them to buy.

Consider your own reactions.

For example, you see a new line of hats advertised at your local department store and the copy reads something like: "The latest fashion. Now available at..." If you're like many readers, that ad will register along with the hundreds of others you see in a day, and you'll probably give it relatively little weight.

But then, your business associate, Sam, whose opinion you really respect, shows up at work with one of these hats, shows it to you, and says something like: "It's the latest fashion." You'll probably be more likely to want one, too.

The same process applies when you are promoting a product. By harnessing the power of "word of mouth" advertising, you can make people really pay attention to your product.

There are three major steps in the process:

1. Find ways to talk about your product or service as you go about your daily activities.

2. Be prepared to follow-up after you have opened the door through conversation.

3. Follow-up later.

Next, we'll talk about the first two steps.

How to Talk About Your Product or Service During Everyday Activities

The key to this strategy of everyday promotion is to find appropriate opportunities to talk about your product or service as you go about your ordinary activities and to do so in a way that is helpful without creating pressure and informative, offering tips on the latest trends.

Initially, you may have to carefully plan what to say under various circumstances. But after awhile, your comments will become second nature and you'll naturally bring up your product or service, when appropriate, everyday.

For example, you are promoting a convenience food product. Look for openings in any conversation that allow you to talk about convenience foods. There are dozens of such opportunities. For instance, Aunt Mary mentions she is tired because she has so much to do. You helpfully suggest that you used to be overwhelmed by household chores too, until you found this great way to save time. Then, you briefly mention the virtues of the product. Probably, Aunt Mary will want to hear more, so you offer to send her a sample or stop by tomorrow to show her the product. The idea is not to make the sale on the spot because then you suddenly shift from being helpful to being a salesperson. Mainly, your intention should be to open the door, then follow through at an appropriate time.

You can also steer a conversation to a desired topic so you can talk about your product. After all, you don't want to drop hints about your product out of the blue, making it obvious you are trying to promote it. If the course of conversation doesn't lead in the proper direction, step in and steer it accordingly. For example, say you have a car product that increases gas mileage and people are talking about sales at department stores. One natural bridge might be to shift the conversation to some car sales you have heard about. Then, once the conversation has shifted to cars, you can mention your product.

The situations in which you can bring up your product are virtually limitless. Besides talking to friends and business associates, you can initiate conversations with just about everyone you encounter, as long as you do it in a comfortable, natural way, so that people see you as a helpful, friendly person, instead of a pushy, brash stranger with a product to sell.

With people you have just met, start off with some casual small-talk to break the ice and build rapport and trust. Then, gradually shift the conversation.

For example, if you commute regularly on a bus, you might start a conversation with your seat mate about something, such as: "You know, I've been taking this same bus like you every morning, and I was just noticing this unique pin you're wearing, and I had to ask you something about it."

Then, after you've gotten the conversation going for awhile about something neutral, you can subtly refer to your product. "You know, it's funny. I don't usually feel like talking to people in the morning when I get on this bus. But lately, I've had so much energy. It's because of this new product I've been using."

Remember, keep your promotion low key and informal and don't move into a heavy sales pitch. Offer a sample or literature if appropriate, or offer to send the person something or call with more information. The idea is to get the door open, not to close the sale right now.

You can start these conversations almost anywhere, the gas station, a supermarket line, your post office, or with the salesperson at a department store. Wherever you are, you can usually find a way to throw in a remark about your product that fits or shift the conversation so your remarks become relevant. Then, with the door open, you can lay the groundwork to follow up.

TOOLS FOR FOLLOWING UP

Following through once you have the door open is crucial. To do so, you usually need a little bit of advance preparation. Have a business card, flyer, or sample to hand out if the person you talk to seems interested in hearing more.

You can, of course, always ask the person for a business card and use that to follow through if you don't have anything to give out yourself. But it's always better to leave the person with something, so they are more likely to think about your conversation. If you can leave them with something they can try, like a sample or exercise to perform, so much the better. You now have a reason to follow up almost immediately to find out how they liked what they tried. Participating gets your prospect immediately involved in your product, setting up the sale.

Another technique is to use your business card as a mini-advertisement and reminder about what you do. For example, print on the front or stamp on the back of your card a line or two of advertising copy that emphasizes the benefits of your product. Besides being a reminder, that line of copy can also generate some interest in your product if you haven't had a chance to mention it

in conversation. As an example, a line for a health product might state: "Feel more energy than you ever had in your life."

Flyers or brochures also make an excellent hand-out after you've opened the door. I always carry a few of these in my pocketbook or attache case and hand one out as soon as someone indicates he or she wants further information. I do this just about everywhere.

Sometimes I leave these around if appropriate, so I can pass on information to people I might not be able to speak with personally. It's much more effective, of course, to talk to someone before they get a flyer or brochure. But if you can't do this, realize that the setting in which a person picks up your flyer or brochure can affect their reaction to it. For example, if someone gets this information at a private party or dinner, they will give it extra credibility and attention because they associate it with the event they are attending. In contrast, people are much less likely to notice or take as seriously a flyer they pick up on the street or at a public event. When you do use flyers or brochures, be sure your name and phone number are prominently featured, so people can readily contact you.

Giving out samples is another good approach if you meet someone who seems especially interested. For example, if you are marketing a line of vitamin supplements, you might make up a small packet of vitamins and staple these to the back of your business card. Then, invite the person to try these for two days, and call to find out if the person feels any differently.

In short, use your own creativity to adapt your promotional techniques to your everyday activities. Don't expect to sell your product on the spot. Rather, see each day as a chance to advertise and promote your product, helping you identify a group of qualified prospects who want to know more. Use a subtle, natural approach to get the person interested. Then, after the door is open, set up a future meeting or give out a business card, brochure, or sample. Finally, follow up.

With practice you'll find this approach will soon become second-nature to you. And best of all—it's easy, effective, and fun. ■

MLM FAILURES: WHO'S RESPONSIBLE?

By Leonard W. Clements

LEONARD CLEMENTS IS THE PUBLISHER OF MARKETWAVE, AN OPPORTUNITY ANALYSIS NEWSLETTER FOCUSING ON THE MLM INDUSTRY. MARKETWAVE FEATURES IN-DEPTH REVIEWS OF POPULAR PROGRAMS, AS WELL AS EXPOSÉS ON THE LATEST SCHEMES, SCAMS AND MONEY-GAMES. AS A SPEAKER AND TRAINER, CLEMENTS CONDUCTS FACTS & MYTHS OF MULTI-LEVEL MARKETING SEMINARS.

I was recently asked at one of our Facts & Myths seminars what I thought the top five reasons were for people failing in MLM.

When I opened that question up to the group, I heard, again and again, stories of those they'd heard about who were front-end loaded, who had to stockpile tons of product to meet quotas, who were deceived into believing in a worthless product or opportunity, who were duped into believing there was little or no work involved, or who simply got involved with a failed company.

Not one time during this rather lengthy exchange did anyone suggest that perhaps the individual distributor was at fault.

More importantly, in any discussion in the media as to why ex-MLM distributors failed, never does anyone ever put the responsibility on the distributor. It was always the company or the MLM concept that was to blame.

In no particular order, here is a list of what I've found to be the top five reasons for distributor failures.

Take note, as you make your way through each point, of who is really responsible.

LACK OF KNOWLEDGE

Many people just don't seem to take their business seriously. Heck, many won't even acknowledge it as a business. It's just this plaything they take out once in a while to try to get rich with. Then, of course, they toss it in the dump when it doesn't perform.

Any legitimate MLM opportunity is a business opportunity no less genuine than any other. But they don't teach this type of free-enterprise in school. No, not in Harvard, Stanford, or anywhere else. Yet, you do have to learn how to do it, and this educational process is worthy of much more than a quick flip through your distributor manual.

If you want to make a comfortable living out of MLM, you must go to school. Read MLM books, listen to motivational and training tapes, go to training meetings, read as many of the MLM publications as you can, and learn everything you can about your product line or service.

Call up your upline and ask questions.

Do your homework first.

THE JUNKIE SYNDROME

There is no basis for this figure, but I would guess that less than 10 percent of all MLM distributors who have been actively pursuing this business for more than one year, are still with their first company. Probably most have been with several.

Of course, this is not always the sign of a junkie. I, personally, have been involved with five, but they kept going out of business (this was years ago when I didn't do my homework).

I believe MLM junkies fall into two categories. First, there are those that believe, "If I can make one thousand dollars doing one program, I can make ten thousand dollars doing ten!" These are the folks who are distributors in ten programs simultaneously.

Then there are those who believe, "The cash is always greener on the other side of the fence." These people are in whatever program was presented at the last opportunity meeting they attended. They're in ten companies in ten months.

I know a gentleman who used to brag about his "expertise" regarding the MLM industry. He was quite proud of the fact that he had been involved with twenty-one companies over the last fifteen years. Of course, he hadn't made any money in any of them, but the one he'd just signed up for was going to make him rich. Again.

PUMPING UP THE VOLUME

I'm referring to the act of artificially meeting group and personal volume quotas by stockpiling product with money out of your own pocket. This also includes the act of front-end loading your new recruits.

From all the feedback I get from the field and from all the press MLM receives, it seems obvious that this is a major killer of MLM success, not only for the recruits who are victims, but the experienced distributors as well.

And, in some cases, even the company itself is ruined by it.

Last year, while investigating a company, I went to an opportunity meeting and later met with one of the representatives. She strongly encouraged me to sign up for five hundred dollars worth of product since that was the program's personal monthly volume requirement for advancement.

Of course, I also needed two thousand dollars monthly group volume and five active front line distributors, and it was the twenty-fifth of the month.

But that wasn't discussed.

There was absolutely no excuse for her to suggest that kind of purchase, other than to increase her bonus check. By doing this, she runs the risk of either blowing out her prospect's budget the first month, turning the prospect off completely, or losing trust and credibility not only in her but in the MLM company she represents.

And, besides, front-end loading is illegal.

Sure, this company didn't require a product purchase at start-up, but these people were actually being taught by their upline not to sign anyone up unless they bought product. Otherwise, they rationalized the people who wouldn't front-load would "poison" their downline.

I agree, a new distributor should buy some amount they are comfortable with, not by force. Which would you rather have, a distributor do one thousand dollars in volume and quit in a month or two, or one hundred dollars in volume for the rest of his/her life?

What I think is even worse than front-end loading, as far as cause for failure, is stockpiling.

There are many people out there who are either over-anxious, lazy, desperate, or just plain ignorant when it comes to this practice. They think if they take money out of their own pocket and meet all the monthly volume quotas, they won't have to retail or perhaps believe they'll sell it all later.

Or they may not want to wait to naturally meet the criteria for higher bonuses by building a retail base or downline, so they buy in at some huge amount of inventory.

Of course, sometimes they do this out of desperation. Their downline is dwindling fast or maybe they had a lot of people break away all at once. This might be a fair excuse for a month or two, maybe, but doubtful.

I've heard of people who do this every month.

There's a popular story going around about a guy in a well-known break-away program who purchased three thousand dollars worth of product one month to maintain his status level because all his eight front-line people broke away. He claims to have quit this business with over five thousand

dollars worth of product rotting in his garage.

Here's a thought. He could have set up ten of his friends in the business with five hundred dollars worth of free product each.

Who knows, maybe two or three might want to continue. Or, better yet, he could do whatever he did to get eight front-line break-aways and build his front line back up.

Okay, maybe he couldn't wait.

Maybe he quit his job to do this full time and couldn't afford the lower bonuses in the meantime. My suggestion: don't quit your job until your income is secured.

I'm not trying to be sarcastic here. I'm simply trying to suggest that these situations all stem from bad business decisions on the part of individual distributors.

Another motivation to practice loading and stockpiling probably comes from the idea that MLM is a get-rich-quick or get-rich-easy scheme.

When the naive distributors discover you actually have to work to make MLM work, they try to circumvent the rules. They attempt to make it a get-rich-easy scheme anyway.

Some less reputable companies even try to design their programs to meet this end. It never works in the long run.

The worst thing about this practice is that once the disgruntled distributor gives up and quits with this mountain of stock they've accumulated, they bad-mouth the company, their sponsors, and the industry in general. They file class-action suits, go on TV, get interviewed by USA Today, and every MLM distributor suffers because of it.

DISTRIBUTOR APATHY

Probably the most obvious reason for failure in anything is lack of action, especially in MLM.

So many distributors are convinced that to be successful in this industry, you get other people to sell for you. And in many programs, they even believe their upline will build their downline for them as well.

And, of course, some distributors are just not very motivated or are simply lazy. They want all those wonderful benefits they heard could be achieved in MLM, but they don't want to do what is necessary to achieve them.

The more companies or their distributors continue to promote their opportunities as ones that require little work or that can provide success "easily," the more they are going to attract people who don't want to work; who are going to take it easy.

When they fill their downline with these people, they wonder why nothing happens.

During seminars, I like to tell the story of a man who is looking for a chisel (an MLM opportunity), a tool he can use to carve out a sculpture (carve out a living).

He does his homework.

He shops around and looks over several chisels.

After studying each one thoroughly, he excitedly makes the purchase (signs up).

Then, he goes home and puts the chisel away.

Days go by. The block of wood stands ready but untouched.

Occasionally, he takes the chisel out and ponders it. He fantasizes about what he could create with it.

He keeps hearing great things about this brand of chisel. It's sharp, accurate, straight, and very comfortable to hold.

Once in a while, he takes a stab at it, literally. He makes a few scratches here and there. A few shavings fall to the floor.

Weeks go by.

The block of wood is still shapeless. Spider webs begin to form at its base.

The man begins to notice what little effect this chisel has had on his carving.

"It's just not taking shape," he says.

"Damn chisel! I've been had," he thinks.

"My family was right all along. These chisels are nothing but junk. They never work, not just this brand, but all chisels," he assumes.

He throws the chisel into the trash can out back. Then, at work the next day, his co-workers ask him how his carving is doing.

"Terrible," he says. "Those chisels are nothing but junk. Don't ever buy any of them. It's not my fault. I didn't have the right tools. But I'm going to the hardware store tomorrow. I'll find something that works."

I QUIT

MLM is the one form of business about which one could accurately state, "If you fail long enough, you will succeed."

I've heard many times that, in MLM, you can not fail, you can only quit. I believe this is, in fact, 99 percent accurate.

After a seminar one night, I met a woman who informed me that she was going to quit her MLM opportunity because, after four months at it, she was "failing miserably."

I asked her what that meant in numbers.

She replied that she had signed up "only" two people her first month, none the second and third, and two more her fourth month. Four in four months.

I asked her what she felt she would need, as far as total frontline distributors (inactives considered) to realistically expect a full-time income in her particular MLM opportunity.

She said that about fifty would surely do it.

I then explained to her that if she did nothing more than continue her current pace (continue to fail miserably), an average of one recruit a month, she would have sixty in five years. Roughly half would be active and ten to fifteen would probably be working the business to some extent. In fact, she would have much more income than necessary to replace her current salary, even considering inflation.

But five years!

"They told me one or two," she replied.

I asked her how long it would take to earn her current salary, working less than part-time in her current job.

"Well, never," she responded.

Five years is a lot less time than that.

Multi-level marketing works. The concept is sound. Good, legitimate opportunities are everywhere.

Everything you will ever need to succeed in this industry is out there right now. The only ingredients that still need to be added to the mix are hard work, patience, knowledge, honesty, and commitment. These are things we must provide, all of us. We are responsible. ∎

In any discussions in the media as to why MLM distributors fail, never does anyone ever put the responsibility on the distributor.

COMPUTERS AND YOUR MLM BUSINESS

BY TOM WILLIAMS

TOM WILLIAMS IS VICE PRESIDENT OF MILLIONAIRES IN MOTION, AN INTERNATIONAL TRAINING COMPANY. HIS RESPONSIBILITIES INCLUDE THE DESIGN AND DEVELOPMENT OF ALL COLLATERAL MATERIALS AND THE MAINTENANCE OF MIM'S DATABASE.

In today's fast paced world where you want more time for yourself, efficiency and effectiveness are major factors to be considered. In fact, running your business efficiently and effectively not only gives you more time for yourself, it also increases profitability. And everyone would like more profits.

An important part of efficiency can be accuracy, making sure everything is where it is supposed to be. For an effective use of the information you have so efficiently stored, speed of access is important. So how do we accomplish this?

The computer is an excellent solution.

A computer can help make your MLM business run efficiently and effectively, performing many operations in a fraction of the time they would require without one.

The following are a few distinct areas in which a computer can help you to increase your productivity.

INVENTORY CONTROL

If you stock product for retail sales or for sales to your downline, knowing what you have on hand, what needs to be ordered, and what is on backorder is very important.

No one likes to wait for product.

What about all the samples you give anyway? That can add up to a tidy sum at tax time.

There are many integrated programs (four or five programs in one package) that can help you to maintain your inventory, as well as all the financial aspects of your business.

FAX AND MODEM

Information is king. Your ability to send and receive information in a timely manner is key to the degree of success of your business experiences.

With the fax and modem technology that is currently available, you can send and receive any type of document or graphic in a matter of minutes to and from anywhere in the world.

The cost of a fax-modem board for your computer can be as little as two hundred dollars. With the modem you will also be able to access databases like Prodigy or Access America. These databases can open up a whole new world of instant information to you, from making your own airline reservations to gathering the names of potential customers.

Some local libraries are even offering modem access to their card catalog.

DESKTOP PUBLISHING

Not long ago creating a camera-ready flyer or brochure required a lot of expensive and sophisticated equipment. Depending on the complexity of the piece, it may have even required an experienced technician and a graphics designer. As if that weren't enough, it could have taken three to five days and end up costing hundreds of dollars.

Now, with the proliferation of Desktop Publishing (DTP) and word processing software, you can do much the same job in a matter of hours, once you become familiar with the software (usually four to eight hours for the basics).

The software itself can be purchased from under one hundred dollars to eight hundred dollars and up. DTP software can give you the ability to produce a variety of graphics, charts, letters, newsletters, and much more.

CONTACT MANAGEMENT

In the people business, which MLM is, the three most important aspects are follow up, follow up, follow up.

With a contact management program on your computer, you can be in command of all your prospect and distributor contacting and follow up. It has the capability to help you arrange your schedule, remember important impending events, make mass mailings, and generate reports, among a host of other functions.

If you did nothing with your computer other than use it for contact management, it could more than benefit you and revolutionize your business.

WHICH COMPUTER?

People have different tastes. Some prefer DOS-based computers, also known as IBM compatible, while others prefer MacIntosh computers.

Do some homework and decide which is best for you. Either type, properly configured, can provide you with all of the benefits stated above. ∎

The Conquering Force Within You

By Jack Zufelt

JACK ZUFELT WAS SELECTED AS ONE OF THE TWO TOP SPEAKERS OF 1988 BY WINNER'S DIGEST, A PUBLICATION FOR FORTUNE 500 EXECUTIVES. IN 1989, PRESIDENT GEORGE BUSH AWARDED THE PRESIDENT'S MEDAL OF MERIT TO MR. ZUFELT IN RECOGNITION OF HIS TEACHING ABOUT HOW TO USE THE CONQUERING FORCE.

There is a conquering force within each of us. Everything we achieve is a result of that conquering force.

A dictionary defines conquering as "overcoming physical, mental or moral forces...getting what one seeks."

It defines force as "the power of a person to act effectively."

If you put those two words together, conquering force, it simply means "the power of a person to act effectively, to get what one seeks by overcoming any obstacles in the way."

The conquering force is the only reason that things get accomplished with any measure of satisfaction. The conquering force is an inherent motivation to do or have something.

Nothing Can Stop You

When you are driven from within, nothing can stop you. That drive is the conquering force in action. It unleashes incredible energy and creativity and brings with it enthusiasm.

A core desire is a genuine, clearly defined want or need that causes you to be willing to put forth the effort necessary to make the desire become reality, even when it means overcoming seemingly insurmountable obstacles. The core desire is not just a wish or a hope or a dream.

I have found that most people, regardless of their age or experience, do not know what they really want or what their core desires are. They draw a blank when asked to clearly define what they truly want in each area of their lives.

Genuine Core Desires

How can you determine what your core desires are which will unleash this conquering force within you?

First, you must list everything you'd really like to have or do, not your "should's" or "ought to's." Do not list what someone else wants for you or those things that "would be nice" to have or do.

Second, you must clearly define what you have to do to get or accomplish that which you have listed. This is not easy because you won't always know how to get or accomplish what you want.

Some inquiry and study will be necessary at this point. If you are not willing to do this on any of the items on your list, then it is not a genuine core desire, and the conquering force will not be there.

So, take it off your list.

But, be careful not to be too hasty in deleting an item just because the "how to" isn't easy to come by. If you act too hastily, you may rob yourself. If you can't find the "how to" easily or quickly, do not assume that it is not a core desire–unless you are willing to quit and give up on it.

Now comes the most interesting part.

It's even fun. This is the only way to really find out if an item on your list is a core desire or want. You must act as a barometer measuring your feelings and responses about each item on your list.

Imagine yourself as a machine like the seismograph, which measures the intensity of an earthquake. You are to measure the intensity of your feelings about each item, on a scale from zero to one hundred. Zero means that you would never do it. One hundred represents the greatest interest: an absolute, ultimate want.

The power of your conquering force is many, many times greater for an item measured at one hundred on the scale than at seventy-five. It is only when you are focusing on those items registering one hundred that you will get the thing you want. Anything less than one hundred reduces the power of the conquering force dramatically.

That is why it is so critical to determine exactly and clearly which of your core desires are at one hundred. With practice you will be able to do this kind of measuring quickly. This exercise is important because it helps you see and feel what is really exciting to you.

The benefit of learning to use the conquering force within you is that, when you have learned to use it, you are able to enjoy a life in which you achieve a high level of harmony and satisfaction.

Anyone can have a satisfying life, but few attain it because most people do not know how to use the conquering force inside them.

SUCCESS ATTITUDE

How do you apply this powerful conquering force to your unique situation? Use the following step-by-step formula.

SA=(D+D) x PA+P

"SA" stands for Success Attitude. The success attitude always works. It never fails. The definition of the success attitude is that frame of mind which allows you to accomplish whatever you want because you know that you can create the opportunity, and then make it happen.

Please note. It does not say that you know how to make it happen, rather that you know that you can make it happen.

Many people think opportunity only knocks once. Actually opportunity is like a door.

You knock.

When you are driven by the conquering force, you don't knock lightly or timidly.

You are anxious to get that door open, so you knock determinedly. You'll pick the lock, take off the hinges, get a battering ram. You'll do whatever it takes to make the opportunity open up to you.

In the next two elements of the formula, (D + D), the first "D" stands for desire. That "core desire" measuring one hundred, which has been explained. This is extremely important.

The second "D" is for direction. The shortest distance between two points is a straight line. It makes sense to go as straight as possible toward the desired end result, the core desire.

This is where most people get bogged down. It's a simple matter to buy a map of the United States to get clear directions to where you want to go. It is not always so simple to map out exactly how to get some core desires. You need to figure out a specific step-by-step plan to get what you want.

The third part of the formula is "PA." This stands for Proper Action. Without proper action you will never attain your core desires. The conquering force is the driving force that causes you to take proper action no matter what the risk or how many obstacles appear to be in your way.

Remember, all action taken must be proper action. Duplicate success. Follow the advice of mentors, those who are already successful at what you want. Going down the wrong paths, spinning wheels, being busy without getting satisfactory results, and halfhearted efforts won't get you what you want.

Don't confuse hard work with proper action. Millions of people are hard workers yet don't focus their work energy on their core desires.

The final part of the formula is "P." This stands for Persistence.

Calvin Coolidge said it well, "Nothing in the world can take the place of persistence. Talent will not; nothing is more common than unsuccessful men with talent. Genius will not; unrewarded genius is almost a proverb. Education will not; the world is full of educated derelicts. Persistence and determination alone are omnipotent."

As you persist in doing a difficult thing, your ability to do it increases.

When you identify a core desire, apply proper action and persist in the right direction, and you'll eventually obtain your core desire. It's not a matter of if, but when.

I am absolutely convinced that when a person clearly defines a genuine core desire at one hundred on the scale, a powerful, unstoppable force is unleashed.

Alexander Graham Bell said, "What this power is, I cannot say. All I know is that it exists and it becomes available only when a man is in that state of mind in which he knows exactly what he wants and is fully determined not to quit until he finds it."

Using the power of the conquering force that is within you produces tremendous and often immediate results. It is my belief that it never fails. ∎

Share the Fame & Plan for Profit

By Kathy Mathews

Kathy Mathews is a freelance writer and publisher. Her major publication is The Stepping Stones Towards Becoming Healthy, Wealthy, and Wise.

Some multi-level marketers work with their spouses. If you can come up with such a relationship, great. Perhaps more work against their spouse's wishes though, especially if they are trying to be a "heavy hitter." Not everyone is tolerant of the constant telephoning necessary. So, it's probably best to find a partner outside your household.

Don't look for partners with the wrong attributes. A lot of people talk a good line about wanting to have their own business someday. Most of them don't want to invest the time or money to make their business secure. They are content to spend hours developing ideas, which they have only vague ideas about turning from fantasy into reality.

Such a person might make a good partner if they can come up with some concrete ideas. Here you'd be looking for a complementary person if you're the one with the hard, common-sense approach. If you're both dreamers, make sure you both know when to roll up your sleeves and get your hands dirty with all the details of running a business, such as mailings, recordkeeping, follow-ups, inventory, and decisions about what to sell and when.

In short, look for a partner with skills you lack. Someone you know from work or a committee might be an ideal candidate to recruit as a partner. You will have observed their work habits over time. You'll know if they are inclined to dodge responsibility or not. A couple of friendly lunches should lay the groundwork for the possibility of working together on building a business.

One word of caution: avoid big talkers. You want someone who'll share responsibility rather than hog the glory or pass the buck.

Some people prefer silent partners who contribute money to the business. This is nice if more capital is your only consideration. But a working partner will help with all the things that have to be done every day. If you have a regular nine to five job, having help may be more important than having money.

If you are dealing with a friend, you probably won't have to do much of a background check on the person. On the other hand, if your prospective partner is a relative stranger, you might want to do a credit check and talk to some people not given as references. The more money you are putting up, the deeper should you dig into a prospective partner's background.

Get all the details down on paper. Writing up the details of a partnership agreement is important to avoid later disagreements. You don't have to get a lawyer to draw up the papers like you do when you incorporate. Once you get your agreement settled, you can have a public notary witness it, probably for free. Most banks supply a notary free for their customers.

Partnerships can be as simple or as complicated as you want to make them. Some items you should consider including are:

1. Agree on the percentage of capital each partner is going to put into the business and on what terms. This would include your initial investment to get your business started and any monthly investments you plan to make until your cash flow (income) covers expenses.

2. Agree on how profits and losses will be distributed. The first year or so, most cash flow should be invested back into the business. Distribution of losses is important for tax purposes. Make sure you know what you are doing here even if you have to pay an accountant for advice.

3. Agree on how decisions will be made. You can decide to manage by committee or one partner can be designated the managing partner who is responsible for making the day-to-day decisions. To avoid arguments, include a time commitment if you chose a working partner. All major decisions should be joint ones.

4. Agree on how the partnership will be disbanded and how the assets or losses will be distributed. In addition, you need to cover transfer of interests in case your partner wants to sell. You want some say in who your new partner will be or have the first option in buying your partner out. You will also have to cover such contingencies as a death, moving, disability, bankruptcy, and retirement.

Double check your own working style. Your own temperament, working style, energy, and ability to share will be an important part of working with a partner. If you want total control of your business, an equal partnership isn't for you. In this case, each person should go with their strengths.

RESOLUTIONS

After the partnership is in place, make the following resolutions:

#1. Set aside time to read and study about network marketing every week. The more you know about business management, the more likely your business is to be an eventual success.

Take a page from all the motivational books. Don't give up. So what if you've fallen on your face ten times. Review your previous failures. Find the common threads that made your efforts go no-where. Then, plan to avoid the failure factors that torpedoed your previous efforts.

Build on the successful things you did. Read a good sample of what your local library has to offer about running a business. It may take a while. You need to develop a business plan, then act on it. You don't know how to write a business plan? Go buy a book about business plans or a computer program that can help you write one.

Most important, create a business orientation. Too many people treat their MLM efforts as a hobby. MLM is a business like any other business.

#2. Shop around. Don't take the first upline that pops through your mail box. Take the time to do a little market research. Call the person who sends you a promising program. Find out what kind of support they offer to help you build your downline. Avoid the people who give you a flyer and say, "Go ye forth and succeed."

Be wary of promises to recruit for you and your downlines. The help is nice and may get you into a paying position faster; however, your success is based on how much effort you put into a program.

Don't let anyone ever tell you that MLM is easy. To make significant dollars in MLM, you have to work hours and hours and hours, all in your "spare-time," until you make enough to go full-time. Then, you have to work more hours.

While you are doing your market research, spend a little time finding out about the company which supplies the product you are going to sell. Are they stable? Will they provide your organization with good customer service when they have problems? How fast do they process orders?

Research the product too. Ask for samples. Do you like them? Is there a local market for the products? Don't get involved with a company unless you like their products. If you can't be enthusiastic about the product, no one else will be either. All of us have built-in sensors to reject sales pitches. As a sales person for a product, you have to be enthusiastic enough to make the closes that will convince people to buy your products.

#3. Don't overspend. Only spend what you can afford. This is easy to say, but hard to live up to. Make sure you evaluate your expenses once a month so you can determine what is profitable and what doesn't work.

#4. Use your time and talents wisely. Do you have a special talent or knowledge you can make money with if you market it right? Are you making the most of the equipment you already own?

Take the time to identify what resources you already have and make a conscious effort to maximize the benefits they offer.

You are the one making the map for your own business growth. Being an entrepreneur gives you the freedom to travel your own path to success.

If you are new to the MLM business, don't get discouraged if you haven't made a fortune your first year or even your second year. You have a lot of skills you need to develop. ■

Uncle Sam Owes You

By James B. Lawrence

JIM LAWRENCE, A CPA FOR TWENTY-ONE YEARS, HAS PRACTICD AS A CERTIFIED MANAGEMENT CONSULTANT FOR SMALL BUSINESSES, FORTUNE 500 COMPANIES, AND THE GOVERNMENT. HE IS PRODUCER OF THE VIDEO TAPE UNCLE SAM OWES YOU, A PERSONAL CHECKBOOK-SIZED SIMPLE TAX RECORD-KEEPING SYSTEM, AND A MONTHLY BUSINESS TRANSACTION PROCESSING SERVICE.

As an independent network marketer, you have your own business and therefore have available to you one of the real tax shelters provided by the IRS.

Many expenditures, which are not deductible as a personal deduction on your 1040, are deductible as a legitimate business expense, even if these deductions result in a business loss, because the loss can be used to reduce your other personal taxable income.

If you legitimately started the business, not as a hobby, but with the intent of making a profit, from a tax viewpoint it's okay if you don't make a profit.

Here we are exploring some of the kinds of potential tax advantages available to you which can help you keep more of your earnings by having Uncle Sam pay his legal and rightful share of your business expenses.

I have also included some basic record-keeping hints. Under the law, Uncle Sam owes you, but it's up to you to ask for it.

It is impossible to cover all the tax advantages to you, but we can at least discuss some of the more beneficial ones. Even these are only highlighted.

The tax code is voluminous and is constantly changing. In addition, it is subject to interpretation.

To maximize your business tax savings, you need to consult a professional.

Remember, as important as the gross income from your business will be, even more important is what you get to keep after taxes.

MAJOR AREAS OF TAX SAVINGS

Hundreds or even thousands of dollars can be saved in car expenses alone. Every time you travel in your car for a business purpose, you can deduct on your 1992 return, 28 cents per business mile.

For example, if in 1992 you used your car for 15,000 business miles, you could deduct $4,200, regardless of how much it actually cost you to operate your car for those miles. This is just one option available to you.

You could choose instead to keep track of your total business miles for the tax year and apply the percent of business miles to the sum of all of the actual expenses you incurred during the year, adding depreciation on the car to the pro-rated actual expenses.

For example, if your business use was 75 percent, you could deduct 75 percent of all your expenses for gas, oil, maintenance, service, tires, car washes, and insurance for the entire year, plus depreciation on your car.

Interest paid is fully deductible as a business expense. Personal interest is not deductible.

So don't borrow for personal purposes. Pay cash. Just borrow for business purposes. This way, the interest will be fully deductible.

Another area of tax savings is travel expenses. Generally you can recruit anywhere in the U.S. and often overseas in network marketing.

If your travel is for business purposes, even if you do some personal activities while on the trip, most of the trip cost is deductible. Travel costs include transportation, laundry, hotel bills, tips, car rentals, and cab fares.

You can deduct 80 percent of meals and entertainment expenses if they were made for a legitimate business reason and if they were incurred during an out-of-town business trip. This includes not only your expenses, but that of your spouse's, if the spouse works in the business with you.

Business meals and entertainment even in your home base are 80 percent deductible as long as you have a business guest, the purpose of the event is for a business reason, and you pick up the tab.

House expenses can be partially deducted when you use your home as your only place of business and you use a portion of the house exclusively for business purposes.

If 20 percent of your home meets the business use criteria, then you could deduct 20 percent of your mortgage or rental costs, utilities, insurance, repairs, maintenance, and property taxes, as well as taking depreciation on your home.

These are just a few of the many tax advantages of being self-employed.

BASIC RECORD-KEEPING HINTS

The key to getting Uncle Sam to pick up what he owes you for his share of your business expenses is simple: keep good records of your business transactions. You'd be amazed how much is lost because people don't document what they do, and they later forget. Not bothering to document will cost you. Here's some important hints.

1. Get a receipt for every business transaction you have. When not possible, make one for yourself; it's OK.

2. Record your check number on your copy of the document you're paying.

3. Record the deposit date on the sales slip for all monies received.

4. Pay by check or credit card whenever possible. I suggest that you have a separate checking account and a separate credit card to use just for business activity. It's not a legal requirement, but it will save you a lot of time and aggravation compared to trying to separate both personal and business activity when tax time comes.

5. For every business trip you make in your car, make a record of it indicating your starting mileage, where you went, and for what business purpose. You need this to claim a deduction for the car expenses.

6. Keep a business diary of the basic business activities you performed each day. An annual business diary or appointment book is ideal for this purpose. Either of these is available at an office supply store.

7. If your office is in the home and you conduct meetings or do business entertaining there, keep a list of guests attending. Doing this will help you in being able to take home expenses as a deduction, including grocery bills for food and drink provided.

8. Prepare sales slips for each sale you make, whether retail or to your downline.

9. Organize your documentation. There are many different ways you can file documents. You can file alphabetically by person or company or in check number sequence.

The method I use is to organize them by the tax categories that I will be required to summarize and report on for Schedule C of my tax return, since I am operating my business as a Sole Proprietorship. Doing it this way will save a lot of time.

If you have your return professionally prepared, it can save you tax preparation fees. Accountants usually get paid for time spent. Schedule C is the IRS form for reporting your profit or loss from business as a Sole Proprietorship. Set up a file for each of the categories.

If you do all these things right, it can mean a lot of money to you. ■

MLM GOVERNMENT COALITION CREATED

BY DEBBIE A BALLARD

DEBBIE BALLARD IS FOUNDER AND PRESIDENT OF INTERNATIONAL MULTI-LEVEL MARKETING CONSULTANTS, INC. (IMLMC). SHE SITS ON THE BOARD OF DIRECTORS FOR THE MLMIA, IS THE AUTHOR OF HOW TO SUCCEED IN YOUR OWN NETWORK MARKETING BUSINESS, AND HAS A RADIO SHOW CARRIED NATIONWIDE ON BUSINESS NETWORKS.

It can be difficult for a multi-level company and independent distributor to be in compliance with an array of regulations which can be interpreted in various ways by each of the fifty states. That same difficulty applies to any regulator trying to properly enforce regulations affecting an industry such as MLM when issues pertaining to a company's program are uniquely complex and often vulnerable to misinterpretation.

The rights of the consumer, the independent distributor, and the company will never be fully protected unless government and industry work together to overcome these problems. Each party must educate the other, paving the way for clarification and understanding. In addition, both parties must act to better inform and protect the public from those companies which pose as legitimate MLM companies but which, in reality, are not.

To this end, I am pleased to announce confirmation from three regulators who will participate in ongoing quarterly meetings with the MLMIA.

Fair and even handed regulation and enforcement is impossible to achieve without ongoing communication between network marketers and those who make and enforce the laws. The consumer, the independent distributor, and the MLM company itself must all be represented when legal matters are addressed.

This coalition between industry and government is long overdue. Conscientious regulators know that they cannot properly regulate that which they do not understand. Likewise, conscientious business people know that unless they comprehend the laws within which they must operate their businesses, it is difficult for them to stay within compliance. This is especially true when the regulations are relatively new and part of a growing body of law.

The government exists to serve and protect us all. However, the MLM industry must take the responsibility to assist government whenever possible.

To begin with, there will be three regulators participating. These will include people representing state securities administrators and office of the states' Attorney Generals. The offices involved are:

Attorney General's Office, State of New Mexico

Assistant Director of Securities for Enforcement, Arizona Corporation Commission

Director, Utah Securities Division.

This group will develop an action plan that will delineate:

1) What the two parties can do to better inform and educate each other as to their respective concerns.

2) What both parties view as positive steps that should be taken to address those concerns.

3) How these steps will facilitate both parties functioning in a manner that better serves and protects the public. ■

THE FIRST ANNUAL
MLM AWARDS

AWARDS

FOR

CORPORATE

EXCELLENCE

Environmental Responsibility Award

Public recognition given to the company that has demonstrated the most outstanding environmental record. Areas examined and evaluated include the environmental impact of manufacturing, distribution, promotion, and support of legislation activities that truly make a difference. The litmus test for this award is effect, not appearance.

Community Service Award

Presented to the MLM who has shown the most commitment to the betterment of the community. Areas examined and evaluated include employee and distributor relations, support of local, state, national, and international charities dedicated to improving life on earth for all.

Outstanding Newcomer Award

Presented to two companies under five years old who show phenomenal strength and growth, or growth potential, while upholding the highest standards in the following areas—employee and distributor relations, financial soundness, strong customer service, innovative marketing plans, and support of the MLM Revolution by promoting their benefits while refraining from engaging in negative attacks upon competitors.

Lifetime Achievement Award

Recognizes the achievements of an individual distributor who has blazed a trail so wide that the size of his/her organization and the number of successful distributors it has is so large and established that they have earned the honor of being identified as one of the world's greatest network marketers.

Leadership Award

Recognition for strong leadership: helping people to become successful network marketers. This award pays homage to a leader among leaders who is especially notable for helping men and women become leaders in their own right. Areas examined will include the development of training seminars, innovative teaching aids and materials, and leadership by example.

Free Enterprise Award

Recognition for contributions to the furtherance of the free enterprise system, exemplified by the MLM process.

Amway Corporation

"Proper use and management of the world's limited resources and the environment are the responsibility of industry and individuals alike."

Amway Corporation believes that the proper use and management of the world's limited resources and the environment are the responsibility of industry and individuals alike. As a leading manufacturer of consumer goods with a direct sales network of more than two million independent distributors worldwide, Amway recognizes its responsibility and role in both fostering and promoting sound environmental stewardship," says Amway Corporation's Environmental Mission Statement.

It is in recognition of the deed as well as the word of this statement that we present Amway Corporation with the Environmental Responsibility Award.

The first product marketed by Amway, L.O.C., has always contained only biodegradable surfactants and no phosphates, solvents, or caustic material. Today, surfactants used in all of Amway's cleaning products are biodegradable.

As a result of product concentration and reduced packaging, any Amway products produce from 50 to 75 percent less solid waste than similar products available in the marketplace.

Amway was the first company to purchase resin made from recycled soda pop bottles from Johnson Controls. Two of Amway's products are being packaged in bottles containing 90 percent recycled plastic. A new process will enable Amway to use recycled H.D.P.E. resin in its liter containers. Their Water Treatment System is packaged in a protective cushion made from 100 percent scrap paper and materials that in turn can be recycled. SA8 containers are made from recycled material.

The Amway Personal Shoppers Catalog features tissues, napkins, garbage bags, and other products manufactured from recycled materials, as well as recycling aids and other products that create an end-use for recycled products and encourage environmental awareness through source reduction, recycling, and conservation.

Before the international ban on CFC's, Amway reformulated all Ada-manufactured aerosol products to CFC-free alternative propellants, which the company distributed worldwide.

Amway is a participant in the EPA's pollution prevention initiative that asks industry to voluntarily reduce releases and transfers of seventeen toxic chemicals by 50 percent by 1995.

The Amway Environmental Foundation is the main sponsor Masters of the Arctic™—Art in the Service of the Earth™, an international travelling exhibition of contemporary Inuit and circumpolar artworks illustrating the artists' coexistence with nature. Other sponsors include the Government of the Northwest Territories, the United Nations Environment Programme, the Greenland Home Rule Government, Canadian Airlines International, the Inuit Circumpolar Conference, the Northwest Alaskan Native Association (NANA) Regional Corporation, NANA Museum of the arctic, the Russian Chukotka Republic, and the Department of External Affairs and International Trade, Canada, The exhibit was the cultural centerpiece for the 1992 U.N. Conference on Environment and Development. Future venues include the Field Museum in Chicago.

With an annual fifty thousand dollar donation to the United Negro College Fund, Amway sponsors the Amway/Ebony Environmental Scholarship Fund, which awards ten scholarships to students of environmental sciences and related subjects.

Amway is one of the founding corporate sponsors of the Aspen Global Change Institute, which was formed in 1990 to study global change and develop educational materials and outreach programs to inform the public about environmental issues. Other founders include NASA and the U.N. Environment Programme.

As well as being a major sponsor of the U.S. Pavilion at Genoa Expo '92, the focus of which was the importance of waterways in the United States and the need to protect them, Amway sponsored "Windows on a Fragile Planet," an exhibit highlighting Amway's environmental projects.

In conjunction with *Newsweek* magazine, Amway sponsors the annual "Class Act" Environmental Competition, which awards cash prizes throughout the United States. to the best environmental projects by middle-school students.

With *Time* magazine Amway sponsors an

"Earth Teachers" contest. Environmentally active teachers are featured in advertorials, and their schools are awarded supplies and equipment.

Proceeds from the sale of Amway's "Life on Earth" note cards, based on its endangered species advertising campaign in *Life* magazine, helped support National Wildlife Federation educational projects.

Amway was the major sponsor of a ten-man expedition to climb Mt. Everest. The team brought its solid waste, and that left behind by others, back down the mountain after attempting to reach the 29,028-foot summit.

In 1989, Amway sponsored a 500-mile walk to the North Pole featuring eight world-class explorers from seven countries. Beyond the goal of becoming the first team to walk to the North Pole, Icewalk: The International North Pole Expedition's goal was to focus the world's attention on the need to protect the environment. It also dramatized the need for international cooperation and individual initiative in making the environment a priority concern. In conjunction with Icewalk, Amway sponsored a Student Expedition of twenty-two youths from fifteen countries. They went to the Arctic to study its nature and culture, start "Icewalk Clubs," learn survival skills, and conduct scientific experiments.

Amway affiliates in Asia and Europe also sponsor foundations that support environmental education and preservation.

Amway Corporation is the recipient of many other environmental awards, including: United Nations Environment Programme Achievement Award for promoting environmental protection and awareness and encouraging youth to make the environment a concern (Amway was only the second corporation to receive this award); UNESCO Transpolar Medal; National Environmental Development Association Honor Roll; and the National Wildlife Federation National Conservation Achievement Award for outstanding contributions to the conservation of our nation's environment and natural resources. ∎

THE SHAKLEE CORPORATION

The company has always recognized its social responsibility.

We are operating in a complex world where technological changes take place at a breathtaking pace. The world is rapidly shrinking as worldwide communications become almost instantaneous.

But people still need personal connections with others and desire to find meaning in their lives.

People are worried about economic security and what the future holds for both themselves and their children.

From the beginning, Shaklee operated with the golden rule—treat others as you want to be treated—as the foundation of its business philosophy.

The company has always recognized its social responsibility and has a real concern for people, for the sales force, the employees, the customers, and for the world at large.

Shaklee has established standards of excellence in all phases of operations, in the quality of products, accuracy of labeling, truth in literature, and a sales plan that makes upward mobility available to anyone, regardless of cultural, religious, or economic background.

In the long run, the success of any corporation is dependent on the caliber and integrity of its people. Those corporations that act in a socially responsible way attract people of integrity and will be the companies that grow and prosper in the years ahead.

When Shaklee Corporation was founded in 1956, Dr. Forrest C. Shaklee, Sr. dedicated himself to improving the world we live in. He said, "You keep what you give away," and encouraged all distributors to share both the products and the philosophy.

Today, the company actively follows this philosophy and has devoted continuous efforts to improve the quality of life and help protect and preserve the environment. The following groups and programs are examples of those Shaklee has supported.

Shaklee was one of only seven national corporate sponsors for the 20th anniversary of Earth Day in 1990. The sales force and employees gathered "green pledges" and participated in community programs that educated and informed people about environmental protection.

Each Earth Day since then, Shaklee has continued this commitment with events such as tree planting with partner adopted schools.

In 1992, the company initiated a nationwide "make time to make a difference" program, where distributors were again involved in the communities with grass-roots programs to improve the environment.

Projects ranged from recycling batteries to cleaning up the shores of local lakes and rivers. All those who gathered fifty or more hours of volunteer pledges of time to environmental causes were eligible for a drawing to win a seat on Earth Train.

As founding sponsor of the Earth Train project, Shaklee was instrumental in launching this ten-year campaign focussed on youth leaders inspiring others to commit to work to insure the future health of the planet.

In 1990, Shaklee received *Family Circle* magazine's "Green Chip" award as one of America's ten most environmentally conscious companies.

The Americares group sends food and medicine to all parts of the world, particularly when there is a disaster such as the earthquake in the Philippines, floods, famine, or drought—anywhere help is needed.

Donations of medical supplies and equipment, as well as food, are made by American companies like Shaklee and flown quickly to be handed over to the local groups who best know how to get them immediately to where they are most needed.

In the aftermath of hurricane Andrew, Shaklee established Shaklee Cares, a program for their local distributors to become involved in the rebuilding efforts.

In addition to cash contributions to those sales leaders suffering major losses, over $50,000 worth of products were made available to local groups working to restore their communities.

Teams of local distributors determined where the products would be given and remained involved with those groups to provide continuing assistance for those rebuilding their lives after what was called the worst national disaster in recent history.

For over ten years Shaklee sponsored the winter games program for the San Francisco Special Olympics.

In fact, they helped to start this program, which serves as a model for other Special Olympics groups. Employees play active roles as volunteers and have organized local games and events such as soccer and basketball tournaments.

In an on-going partnership with the Cousteau Society, Shaklee has helped to reinforce the importance of educating children so that they can make valid and better decisions about preserving our precious resources.

Shaklee employees and distributors are helping gather signatures on petitions for the "Campaign for the rights of future generations," which the Cousteau Society has launched to present as demonstrating that citizens everywhere want action to be taken to protect and preserve the planet for the future.

Other Shaklee community-oriented contributions also include active support of organizations such as The United Way, Boys' and Girls' clubs,

and YMCA and YWCA's.

The company also supports nutrition education and scholarship programs at various colleges and universities.

In addition, the Shaklee Corporation supports the arts in communities where it has headquarters and facilities and for schools with partnership programs where employees volunteer through the Serve program.

The company's environmental task force reviews all new packaging materials for environmental impact, making specific recommendations based upon their findings.

The Shaklee Corporation has committed to improving the quality of life for others and has supported groups that are looking at problems that extend beyond borders, global issues. Shaklee has responded to the challenge of remaining a concerned and caring company while growing their business in turbulent and changing times. ■

BODY WISE INTERNATIONAL

The United States is still only 12th in longevity and a shocking 16th in infant mortality among industrialized nations.

Since its inception in 1989, Body Wise International has gone from a six-month sales figure of $469,096 to well over $7 million.

And in three short years, Body Wise already has distributors at the top levels of its compensation plan.

Attractive promotional materials, advertising which includes high quality photos of athletic young adults, and celebrity athlete Consultants including NFL quarterback Bruce Mathison, Mr. Missouri 1990 Mark Matthews, and road racing champion Marriane Berglund have undoubtedly added to the momentum of the Body Wise rise to success.

But that is by no means the whole story.

There's Dan Riley, a retired Army Lt. Colonel, who joined Body Wise International in November 1990 to make a little extra money to pay the bills his military pension didn't cover. Today he's making more than thirteen thousand dollars a month as a Five Star Manager, the top level of the Body Wise compensation plan.

Then there's Mary Oswald. She sold $41,000 of Body Wise products in her first 120 days in the business, earning a total of $12,000 for the period. Her three young daughters and her husband seem very proud of her.

Both of these examples are taken from a single Body Wise monthly newsletter. Each article had a picture associated with it. And there are many more testimonials besides these.

Body Wise International manufactures and distributes products for weight management, health enhancement, and athletic performance.

Right Choice AM is designed for energy required during daytime activity and Right Choice PM is designed to replenish the skeletal matrix and provide nutrients for cell repair as the body rests; ingredients include Beta Carotene, Esterified Vitamin C, and Boron.

The Future Perfect Formula drink mix consisting of complex carbohydrates, protein, and Inulin Analog, used to promote long-term carbohydrate availability for energy production. Oxy-G^2 is designed to assist the body's use of oxygen to possibly reduce tissue aging and immune system degradation.

Ingredients of this product include Ginko Biloba, L-Glutathione, and Cyhtochrome C Oxidase.

Cardio Wise includes Niacin (Body Wise advises us to ask our doctor about Niacin's ability to lower serum cholesterol.), L-Carnitine, which assists in transforming fat into energy, and silymarin, a detoxifier.

The Reshape Formula is created to help control hunger by reducing cravings for fat-promoting foods while sustaining energy and supporting muscle definition.

Ingredients of this product include Chromium, a nutrient related to insulin regulation, and ammonia scavengers, to assist in processing of ketones, by-products of protein metabolism which diminish strength and stamina.

Body Wise's Advanced Nutrition System includes, besides Future Perfect, Righ Choice AM and PM, and Cardio Wise Caplets, a product information cassette, a weight management system video, a fat gram counter, and a product sales brochure.

The Weight Management System includes the same products but drops Cardio Wise and adds The Reshape Formula and a "Reshaping America" leaflet.

The newest addition to the Body Wise line of products is Beta-C, a combination of beta carotene, vitamin C in the form of Protamine Ascorbate, cruciferous vegetable concentrate, bilberry extract, and Vitamin C facilitators.

This product grew from Chairman Thomas T. Tierney's brief encounter with Nobel Laureate and vitamin C advocate Dr. Linus Pauling and subsequent study of the contemporary research on the subject.

Following is a letter from Chairman Tierney dated April 1992 sent to health professionals along with many testimonials, detailed Body Wise Product information, and bibliography made up of nearly fifty entries:

Responsible nutrition can positively impact health status; however, in the United States of America, limited access to a proper diet puts the majority of our population at health risk due to lack of essential nutrients. This fact was clearly established in 1982 when the United States Department of Agriculture National Food Consumption survey revealed <u>not one person</u> of the population surveyed received all of the recommended daily allowance (RDA) for 10 essential nutrients. Subsequent surveys continue to validate this. Shortage of these minimum reference nutrients is of special consequence when taken in the context of longevity, vitality, and biological capacity for disease resistance. Further insight is needed to educate the total population as to alternatives for better health. Body Wise Internatinal, Inc. was founded on the premise that good health should start with education, not surgery.

Obesity, heart disease, and some cancers can be characterized as primarily manufactured diseases. They are diseases of affluence: they are created by a diet of excess sugar and saturated fat while acquiescing to environmental insults such as polluted air and water. These conditions can be changed.

Money does not buy health or longevity: for all our health care expenditures, (over 12% of GNP), we still are only 12th in longevity and a shocking 16th in infant mortality among industrialized nations. Citizens of Japan, Sweden, and Iceland enjoy longer life. As a highly developed nation we have significant room for improvement in health enhancement.

The experience foundation for Body Wise International is based on over 37 years of product formulation, the advice and counsel of a distinguished Scientific and Medical Advisory Board, and a profound desire to uphold individual dignity and personal self-esteem...

Health professionals have experienced Body Wise in all four areas of concentration: Health Enhancement, Cholesterol Control, Weight Management, and Athletic Performance. Several of your colleagues have given permission to reproduce their letters. Hundreds more testimonials testify to

very personal life changing experiences with Body Wise products.

I invite you to share in this rewarding endeavor. Body Wise is not for everyone. It is only for those of us who want positive change in our lives. ■

NATURAL WORLD INCORPORATED

This company will be known for its environmentally responsible products, innovative marketing, and warm, friendly people.

Ask Janice DeLong, President of Natural World Incorporated, and she'll tell you there are four trends for this decade, "environmental concern, entrepreneurial spirit, catalog shopping, and network marketing."

"Natural World," says DeLong, "is riding the wave of all four trends and will be a multi-million dollar company in a few years time." DeLong continued with confidence, "We are a company that focuses on building a strong foundation, a foundation that will support this company far into the future."

Just over a year old, this Connecticut company has combined environmentally responsible products people use everyday with an innovative and powerful combination of catalog and network marketing.

Ms. DeLong brings to Natural World her seven plus years of experience as an executive in the venture capital industry, working with many start-up and fast-growth companies. The majority of her tenure in venture capital was spent with Oxford Partners, a Stamford, Connecticut-based venture capital firm which specializes in start-ups with over $100 million under management. Ms. DeLong holds an MBA in marketing and finance from the University of Connecticut.

Austin O. Furst, Jr., Founder and Chief Executive Officer, is a successful entrepreneur in his own right. Prior to establishing Natural World, Mr. Furst was founder and chairman of Vestron, Inc., a film and video production company that went from $0 to $350 million in five years. Previously, he held a number of executive positions with Time, Inc., including President, Time-Life Films; Executive Vice President, Home Box Office; and Circulation Director at the launch of *People* Magazine. Furst is committed to having that same success with Natural World.

"This business is the opportunity for individuals to set their own goals, choose their own hours, and select their own rewards." Furst continued,

"We offer people the opportunity to start their own business, to control their own destinies, and to be proud every step of the way."

Natural World unveiled its new marketing plan October 1, 1992. The plan offers three ways to build income and reach personal financial goals: Weekly Fast Start Bonuses, retail profits up to 33%, and 5% to 25% Personal Order Rebates, which offer new Independent Representatives immediate income opportunities.

By helping others develop their own groups, a Representative can earn 5% overrides on as many as six generations, monthly Car Bonuses from $250 to $750, Infinity Bonuses of an additional 2% plus an unusual Floating 5% Bonus.

The company's Convenience Shopping Plan employs the concept of transfer buying. The plan allows Representatives and consumers to receive preselected or customized product packages delivered to their home on a monthly basis. These are products they would be purchasing on a regular basis. By purchasing them from Natural World, each organization builds volume month after month, insuring residual income.

Natural World has a mission beyond providing people the opportunity for financial growth. They, as well as their products, are environmentally responsible. Natural World markets over one hundred environmentally responsible products in five categories: household and pet care, personal, skin, child, and nutritional care. The company's non-toxic household cleaners are formulas based on seaweed, cereal and citrus enzymes, and fruit extracts such as coconut and lemon. Their naturally-based skin care items contain cold-pressed herbs, nut oils, and other like ingredients. The child and baby care lines are chemical free.

The Natural World Board of Advisors includes Thomas Donnelly, who has over 25 successful years in direct sales and network marketing, and has managed both domestic and foreign companies with over $400 million in sales volume. He has directed international expansion of high-growth companies in 18 foreign countries, with over $100 million annual sales in three years.

Ed McCrea serves as Director of Development and Planning for the North American Association for Environmental Education (NAAEE). He is slated to become the Executive Director of NAAEE. He holds a Masters Degree in Environmental Education and a Bachelors Degree in Zoology.

Joan A. Friedrich, Ph.D. is a researcher, writer, and counselor specializing in nutrition wellness and stress management. She is the author of *Be Well...Stay Well* and *Lifetime Wellness*. She holds a masters degree in counseling psychology, and a Doctorate in clinical nutrition.

Ashley F. Yankowski, Director of Product Development for Natural World says, "Being environmentally responsible is insuring a product's creation, usage, and disposal is kind to our world and all its inhabitants. It means never animal testing. It also means products that are well crafted and effective because the consumer's immediate environment matters too."

Natural World is committed to providing products people use every day that are safe for us, our children, and our world. DeLong stated, "According to the United States Poison Control Center, last year 4.7 million poisonings occured in the home due to household products—two-thirds of the victims were children under six. Our non-toxic household cleaners can help change that."

Natural World is a member of the Direct Marketing Association (DMA), the Humane society, the Better Business Bureau, and the DSA.

Though they make every effort to use minimal packaging with recyclable materials, the company finances a creative recycling program: "You collect 10 or more empty containers of Natural World products, then contact either your Natural World Representative or the company, and we will arrange to have them picked up."

Natural World uses no harsh chemicals and does no animal testing. The Natural World catalog is printed on recycled paper using soy-based inks and carries the explanation that "The use of soybean based inks is an environmentally superior choice because it decreases the emissions of volatile organic compounds (VOC's) by 80% or more. They are totally biodegradable under land fill conditions. If all printing companies used only soy inks, we could decrease our oil imports by 5-6%—about the amount of oil we used to import from Iraq." ∎

Dexter and Birdie Yager

Success is the progressive realization of a worthwhile dream.

"Opportunity comes to each one of us several times in our lifetime, but it's our choice what we do and what decisions we make about these opportunities," said Amway Crown Ambassador Birdie Yager before an audience of several thousand cheering distributors. "You have to believe that what you're doing is right."

In 1964 the Yagers were supported by Dexter's ninety-five dollar job as a brewery salesman. The first couple of times he was approached about Amway Dexter rejected the offer. "He just dropped by, without an appointment, talked about the business in very general terms, and nonchalantly answered my questions," Dexter says. "He didn't sit down and really explain it to me. I still thought it was a door-to-door type of deal, and I didn't want to get involved."

Birdie had just quit her job as a secretary at a military base and hoped that she might not have to return to work. Without asking Dexter, she arranged for him to see the business.

Later that evening, when Birdie walked in the door, she heard Dexter say, "How do I get started? What do I do next?" That same night, Dexter went out with his sponsor and helped him sponsor someone else.

Not long afterwards, Dexter approached his boss at the brewery for some time off for a network marketing-related activity. When his boss refused, "I quit my job and made up my mind I was in Amway for life. I got into this business to be free. I was sick and tired of someone owning me."

A few years later, the Yagers left Dexter's hometown of Rome, New York, a mill town about two hundred miles north of New York City. Today their rambling southern estate, their majestic estate on the lake, and their majestic primary residence on a waterway in Florida (complete with tennis courts, boats, coach, pool, numerous Rolls Royces, and a large office building) are showplaces for the potentials of network marketing and a trib-ute to the Yagers' achievement.

Exactly how large Dexter and Birdie's organization is we don't know for certain. *Forbes* estimated one hundred thousand distributors, but *Forbes* is well-known for its antagonism toward network marketing, tending to underplay the positive and overemphasize the negative. Sources place the organization of just one of the Yagers' twenty personally sponsored Direct Distributors at forty thousand.

The *Forbes* estimate pales before such reports. Rumor has it that the Yagers' worldwide organization is composed of over eight hundred thousand distributors. The actual number is probably somewhere in between, but one thing is for certain: the Yagers have more active distributors in their downline than the total number of active distributors in many successful networking companies combined.

Though *Forbes* attempts to estimate the Yager income from network marketing as "in excess of ten million dollars per year," we will only say that they're rich by just about anyone's standards.

How did they get that way?

On the last page of his book *Millionaire Mentality*, Dexter lists what he calls the "Five keys to success: 1) dreams 2) attitude 3) work 4) proper vehicle 5) duplication."

Elsewhere, he has cited reading David Schwartz's book *The Magic of Thinking Big* as a major stepping-stone to his success as an Amway Distributor. Not only did he read it for himself, but he also gave copies of it to distributors and suggested that they read it. "I give positive thinking books to people who aren't even in Amway, because I know it can change their life."

"There's some point in your business when you've got to get it all together," says Dexter, "where it is more than just a pin and some dollars, but it represents the heart of America, the dream of America, until it represents the American people. It represents someone else's life that you're out there striving to help make it, instead of just you making it."

Acting out of love and concern for others is a major part of Mr. Yager's philosophy. "Today, when people don't trust people, you and I can show them that we're trustworthy. Today, when love is needed more than ever, we've got a chance to say 'I love you.' People need people. And those that fill that need get paid well. But you got to look at something beyond the money. You got to look at the excitement of helping somebody else."

Known as the master dream-builder, Dexter frequently underlines the need for each of us to build a meaningful dream which we can believe in. "Get your dream tank filled," he says. "Spend an afternoon looking at the most beautiful homes around; go look at the nice cars; look at the minks. When you've got a dream, you can give it. There's an old song that says 'If you don't have a dream, how ya' gonna have a dream come true?' And you've got to believe in your dream."

On the subject of whether a degree is necessary to be successful in network marketing, Dexter says, "I went through high school. That's it."

Could a degree in, say, economics be of more value to the attainment of wealth than his "Five Keys to Success" above? Dexter answers, "I love economics professors. I think they should all be rich. But, you know, if they're not rich, how can they teach economics? Lots of people say, 'but he's an economics professor—he disagrees with you.' I say, 'I'm a rich man. I disagree with him.' He hasn't gotten the rewards of his profession. We're not that kind of expert. We're performers in this business. We pay people to perform."

Dexter is the author of many books, including *Millionaire Mentality, Don't Let Anybody Steal Your Dream, A Millionaire's Common Sense Approach to Wealth,* and *Everything I Know at the Top I Learned on the Bottom,* and *Ordinary Men, Extraordinary Heroes.* Birdie authored *The Secret of Living is Giving.*

What is success? According to Dexter, "Success is the progressive realization of a worthwhile dream. Real success is not to be taken for granted. The achievement of our goals, if of any value to begin with, is no minor undertaking. If you do not have to work to accomplish a goal,

then probably there was no validity to it in the first place. Anything of value is worth exerting the effort to obtain. One underlying fact always must remain: a dream unrealized is a dream imprisoned by that enemy of all enemies—the fear of failure. Set that dream free by determining that you will make it happen." ■

MARK AND RENE REID YARNELL

"Survival of the fittest" has been replaced by the concept "Survival of the most cooperative"

Mark and Rene Reid Yarnell have built a 30,000 person downline as independent distributors for Nu Skin International, received the American Dream Award from Howard Ruff Company, and have published two books and numerous audio tapes on the subject of Network Marketing. The couple resides in Reno, Nevada where Rene serves as a county commissioner and Mark serves on the board of directors for several major corporations, including The National De Tocqueville Society of The United Way. Both are founders of the International Green Cross (Mikael Gorbachev, President), and their own corporation. They deliver over 100 lectures a year in the United States and Canada.

The following is excerpted from an article written by Mark Yarnell, and published in the February 1992 issue of *MLM Success* (now *Upline*), entitled "A Goal Bigger Than You Are."

It was a belief that one person can make a difference in this world that led me into the seminary in 1976, and subsequently into a decade of service as a Christian minister. After ten frustrating years in that field, I finally determined that in America, wealth tends to be an adult's "report card," and I exited the ministry to begin a new career in MLM.

While I was still motivated by a sense of altruism, I had come to the conclusion that I could do more good as a spiritual person with vast sums of money than I could as an impoverished minister.

My assumption has proven accurate.

My real motive in writing this article is to suggest an impractical way to succeed in MLM.

I use the term "impractical" because the entire notion of applying altruistic and spiritual principles to a business/scientific pursuit reeks with contradiction. That is, until one firmly understands that we live in a cosmos based almost entirely on spiritual "deal making."

Virtually everything that ever happens does so because someone or something stands to benefit from the action. Even the Darwinian evolution concept of dog-eat-dog, "survival of the fittest" brought about by genetic mutation and resulting in natural selection has recently been debated by scientists who suggest that we have evolved through *symbiotic cooperation*. Survival of the fittest has now been replaced in the minds of numerous anthropologists with the concept of *survival of the most cooperative*. What I'm leading up to is this: one of the greatest parts of charity is the "payoff."

By creating goals bigger than ourselves, such as succeeding at MLM in order to fund a project for street people, we are setting in motion some very quantifiable principles.

First, when we do give our money or time for the purpose of helping others, we are recognized as decent people by our peers, and that makes us feel wonderful. When we feel wonderful, our lives seem to work much better than when we do not. When our lives work better, we work better—and are hence compensated better for our work.

In 1972 it took me four months to raise $5,000 to start my own company. In 1991 it took me four days to raise $185,000 for a lady in Michigan who needed a bone marrow transplant.

And there's another payoff. Six months after donating another $150,000 to the United Way in Reno, I stood before 300 of the most prominent people in the Pacific Northwest and received a plaque for being the "Philanthropist of the Year" in Northern Nevada. That night I felt like a million dollars!

Equally significant is the fact that a prominent banker who happened to be at the meeting approached me about my occupation—and is now a significant part of my MLM organization. In 1992 alone, her efforts could easily net me more than the entire $150,000 I donated to the United Way.

Here's the bottom line: if you want to succeed dramatically in MLM, create a goal bigger than yourself. As A.L. Williams points out in his epic book, *All You Can Do*, "We all need to be crusaders. We must have a significant purpose."

Among members of my downline, I've observed these principles applied very successfully.

There's the former college student from Texas, who was earning $800 per month as a student teacher when I recruited him into my organization. He wasted no time creating a goal to establish a trust account for indigent parents whose children need testing for various allergies, some of which had plagued his own son. Last year, he paid taxes on substantially more than a million dollars of MLM income.

There's the maid from Colorado who, upon seeing the income potential in MLM, immediately began to project how much she would use to fund a health/retirement home for elderly, homeless citizens. Motivated by that altruistic objective, it took her less than two years to create a monthly income in excess of $20,000. When I recruited her, her annual income was less than that.

If you aren't already partial to one specific charity, begin to look around for one which might have particular significance to you, and write down a specific percentage of your check which you would be willing to give to them, assuming that your monthly income were to exceed $100,000.

Then, begin immediately to donate that percentage each month, irrespective of how small it might be initially. That activity is very important, because if you wait until a future date to begin systematic giving, you will probably never give away anything.

As your income increases, so too must your giving, in direct proportion to your initial percentage. Above all else, never cut that percentage back, regardless of how large your monthly check becomes. Do not back out on your original deal, for to do so could seriously jeopardize future earnings.

If all this seems like the deluded ramblings of an ex-pastor, don't be fooled. Most people in the business world would give anything to earn just five percent of what I earn, and I can, without

reservation, go on record as stating that I owe it primarily to hard work and this process of altruistic goal setting.

That should be reason enough for you to give it a shot. ■

RICHARD BLISS BROOKE

The key is residual income. Residual means you can step away from it.

Richard Brooke went to Oxyfresh in 1985 as a consultant, bringing with him vast experience from the field, having been at various times distributor, founder, and manager for another network marketing company.

Oxyfresh was on the verge of closing its doors for good. Brooke came in as part of a management team that "scrapped everything and basically just started over."

In 1985, its second year, Oxyfresh sales had reached the $3 million mark and had quickly begun to decline. According to Brooke, they managed to turn the company around by December of 1986. Oxyfresh grew by 65 percent in 1987, and by 1991 had surpassed the $9 million mark.

At the start, Brooke wasn't optimistic about the company's chances for survival. But, he says, "we stayed committed to the people. Ninety-nine point nine percent of the distributors in the field had no idea the company was in trouble, so we stayed focused on not letting them down. We stayed focused on possibility thinking, "sure, it might go down, but what are we supposed to do about that, quit now? Then it for sure goes down!" We focused on the up side. We knew we had an opportunity to have a great company, one that we designed ourselves from the inside out, that had all the things we wanted in it... so we simply stayed focused on what we wanted it to look like, how that made us feel, and why that was important to us.

"I didn't allow myself the luxury of sitting around having expectations that this company was ever going to go out of business, or wallowing in that projection of sorrow and guilt. What I did, and still do, was constantly analyze the risks. Where are this company's risk areas, where could this company take a hit and fall apart?

"Then I focus on solutions: how do you plug those holes. How do you steer around those risks? I don't view that as negative thinking—it's embracing the liabilities in a way that solves things, that's solution oriented and not worry oriented.

At the age of 37, Richard Brooke knows a lot about solution oriented thinking. There was a time he worked 60 hour weeks cutting chickens on a "production line" for chicken feed wages, with no apparent way out.

After attending an MLM opportunity meeting for a company marketing a gasoline additive, he quit his job and staked everything on success in network marketing.

After three years, he was in debt, making only $4,000 per year through his opportunity, living on credit cards, and hearing from friends and relatives that he was a sucker and should quit.

After four years, he was making over $100,000 a year, and suddenly found sponsoring achievers a natural activity. "Before," he says, people would say they didn't have time or they didn't think it would work. What they really meant was they didn't believe in *me*."

When Brooke arrived at Oxyfresh, the company needed a man who wouldn't fold up his tent and move on. But besides following through with his quality of not letting go of the job until it gets done, what did Brooke do to turn Oxyfresh into the healthy company it is today?

"We created basic, solid, proven systems—and stuck with them. You start with fundamentals... Exceptional customer service is an essential, and in our business, our "customers" are our distributors. So we made, and continue to make, a very strong effort to make our people feel as good as possible, as needed as possible, as important as possible. A 'they're always right' sort of attitude.

"Multi-level marketing, by definition, is a lot of people, each doing a little bit. Most everyone in MLM is part time, or at least they start that way. They're independent distributors, so they don't have to sell a certain amount; and most don't even see themselves as salespeople—they get involved because they're attracted to a product, not because they're looking for a sales opportunity.

"Now, if each individual distributor is only going to sell a small amount of product, then, by definition, the way you succeed as a multi-level marketing company is to get a lot of 'em!

"We don't teach anybody how to make a lot of money now. We only teach one thing: how to generate residual income. We give our people a proven systematic business plan through which they can have a residual income of 'X' dollars per month four or five years from now. The 'X' is determined by your effort over that four or five years.

"The key is residual income. Most people don't understand what 'residual' means. 'Residual' means that you can step away from it; it survives your efforts. $5,000 monthly residual income has ten times the value of an opportunity where you need to continue generating $5,000 a month, every month.

"In having a long -term business plan based on a permanent income, we're trying to emulate Shaklee and Amway—which is atypical and very unpopular, but that's exactly what we're trying to do. You can count on two hands the number of companies that have been in business ten years. But if you took all day, you still couldn't count all the deals you've *heard* about in the last ten years. Are we interested in emulating those other deals? No way, shape, or form—'cause I don't want to start over, and I know our distributors don't want to start over. We want to build another Amway. A better one.

"Here's one of our corporate purposes: Ten years from now, when somebody says to the public, 'multi-level marketing,' we want the public to respond, not like they do today, 'Oh, you mean like Amway?' but, 'Oh, you mean like Oxyfresh.' So when we pursue Amway, we do it with a great deal of respect and admiration for what they've achieved. ...When we approach people with the Oxyfresh opportunity, one goal is that if they don't get involved, we want them to walk away respecting and admiring the process. 'Oh yes, somebody talked to me about that last year. Nice people, looks like a great product line, just not something I'm interested in.'"

I think network marketing is going through the same kind of evolution that franchising went

through. At first it was heavily promoted and heavily abused, then it began to be heavily regulated, and now franchising is the preeminent, the best, the most sure-fire business expansion methodology there is. And I think network marketing is going to go through that same process. ■

FLYING HIGH IN RETIREMENT

Spotlight is on: Roy and Bonnie Myers

Company: Advantage Marketing Systems, Inc.

When Joined: 1991

Level of Achievement: Crown Ambassadors

Size of Organization: 2,561

Roy and his wife Bonnie are not new to multi-level marketing. For nineteen years, they were distributors for another major company while Roy was an Air Force officer. "We didn't really work at that opportunity, but it gave us a good feeling about networking. And when I finally retired, I decided to look into networking full-time," explains Roy.

In true military fashion, Roy had a plan for his retirement career. He says, "I chose AMS for the services they offer. In three weeks, I decided to work the business and in three months I went to the top. In fourteen months, I've gone where I'd never gone before, even in the Air Force. Now I earn more in two weeks than a whole year's retirement pay."

Giving his advice to those looking into network marketing, Roy offers, "When you join a company, I think it is important to investigate the top people and check out the stability of the company."

Bonnie mostly likes the way AMS keeps their representatives informed and keeps members renewing. She says, "We feel very connected to the company."

According to the AMS spokesperson who nominated them: "Roy and Bonnie followed the AMS marketing system to the letter. The Myers recruited six new member-associates the first ten days after joining. He then worked with his new recruits to get them to Senior Partner status.

"When any of their recruits reached Senior Partner level, they would get another first level person. The couple now has eighteen personally sponsored First Level Associates."

The downline numbers are growing faster now that fifty-seven of his organization have qualified to become Crown Ambassadors.

Roy was recently appointed vice president of Oklahoma, Kansas, and Missouri. He receives a bonus on all new members joining in the three state area.. ■

SYNERGISTIC PARADIGM

Spotlight is on: Gilles Arbour and Guylaine Nadeau

Company: Cell Tech

When Joined: 1988

Level of Achievement: Double Diamond

Size of Organization: 4,813

Typical of their openness and willingness to share, a phone conversation and follow up letter from Gilles just bursts with enthusiasm for network marketing in general and Cell Tech specifically.

Just four short years into networking, this team has established a very successful business and is financially independent, while helping others to become the same.

According to Cell Tech: "Gilles Arbour and Guylaine Nadeau have consistently exemplified the best of Cell Tech. They have achieved Double Diamond status, the top of our compensation plan, in record time."

"It was during the first year that I recognized that we would be successful, that this would work for us. After that it was not hard to stay motivated," recalls Gilles.

Cell Tech again: "Their success is understandable only when you factor in their level of commitment to their downline. Through regular meetings and creative ideas in networking and communications, they have provided the sort of leadership that provides support for others to excel."

When asked about these techniques, Gilles said, "you must create fun relationships. You must make every relationship quality, interesting, and yes, fun. Then you have a win-win situation."

About the place that network marketing will assume in the minds of the entrepreneurial class, Gilles predicts that the potential is just beginning to unfold. "I see this type of marketing taking more and more space. It will become very common. As this happens, the distribution of money will be very different. Ordinary people will have the means to do extraordinary things."

Cell Tech's last comment: " By working together they demonstrated the synergistic potential of the new male/female paradigm."

Gilles and Guylaine live in Mont St-Hilaire, Quebec. Their personalized and telling letterhead is emblazoned: Teamworking For Planetary Impact. ■

MASTERS OF RECRUITING

Spotlight is on: Shirley and Delmar Carmack

Company: Diamite Corporation

When Joined: 1985

Level of Achievement: Triple Diamond Directors

Size of Organization: 8,000

From Diamite: "If our distributors are living a full life of adventure, then Shirley and Delmar are the most adventurous people we know."

Since joining Diamite, the Carmacks have become the ultimate "jet setters," living a life full of adventure in places like Tahiti, Canada, China, the Bahamas, Acapulco, and Maui.

With eight thousand distributors in their downline, the Carmacks are prime examples of distributors who make recruiting a top priority. Their organization has grown so much, they've taken their business out of the home and moved into a center devoted to "helping men and women grow into greatness."

Greatness can't always be measured in terms of income, but earning in the neighborhood of $500,000 a year (over $70,000 in just one month) does allow a person to do many things. This income has allowed them to invest in a new home, countless cars, real estate, and make charitable contributions.

According to Shirley, "Working our distributorship and helping others to achieve their goals has become our life's mission. I really feel like God has placed a guiding hand over this company. If all the people of the world adopted Diamite's caring and sharing philosophy, there would be peace on earth."

They both agree, "We just love this business and appreciate all the people involved. We give thanks to our leaders, friends, and mentors. Of course, our team The Pacesetters is the greatest, finest team in the world."

Delmar's message to anyone trying to achieve the dream is: "Hang in there. With network marketing, you are going to have the time of your life." ∎

POUR YOURSELF A CUP OF AMBITION

Spotlight is on: Jan Ruhe

Company: Discovery Toys, Inc.

When Joined: 1980

Level of Achievement: Diamond Sales Director

Size of Organization: 6,500+

Jan Ruhe turned a part-time job for a little extra income into a dynamic career which now pays her more than $150,000 per year. The self-made business woman likes her work and has mastered the art of selling and building a productive MLM organization. "I play for a living," says the energetic entrepreneur, who is the number one distributor in the South for Discovery Toys.

When she first started networking, the five-foot, two-inch housewife only wanted to earn enough extra money to buy soccer and ballet supplies and uniforms for her son and daughter. She also planned to earn enough to pay a weekly housekeeper, since Jan had a new baby at the time.

"I wanted a change in my life," says Jan. An acquaintance invited her to a home party to see a demonstration on children's playthings. She decided to become a distributor in 1980. "I also became my own best customer," explains Jan. "It is important for all multi-level marketers, no matter what the product line, to become their own best customers."

Three months after beginning her toy sales, Jan started recruiting. She recruited thirteen people during the next six weeks and finished the year with twenty-four people in her downline and a newborn baby. During the year, the dynamic Mom sold ten thousand dollars worth of toys and the company named her top manager.

Jan began educating herself by reading sales, motivational, and training books. She attended meetings and seminars featuring professional speakers, trainers, and salesmen. "I listened and listened to those persons who had proven themselves in the marketplace. And I turned a deaf ear to those who offered advice, yet had no proof that they had succeeded with anything substantial."

"Multi-level marketing provides the catalyst for tremendous change in a person's life. And a person must be prepared to change and then change again, if the need arises."

Today, Jan has an organization that numbers more than 6,500 distributors but she insists, "You cannot motivate people. You can only lead by example." ■

LOVE AND SERVICE MAKE A MASTERPIECE

Spotlight is on: Tola and Hy Newman

Company: ElySee Cosmetics

When Joined: 1945

Level of Achievement: Silver Executive

Size of Organization: Not Available

Tola Newman was the first person trained by Dr. Elizabeth Blumenthal, the founder of Elysee Cosmetics, who was not a part of her Scientific Skin Care Salon in San Francisco, California.

Tola had come to see Dr. Blumenthal about a serious brown pigmentation problem.

Elysee products provided the help Tola needed. And today at seventy-eight her skin doesn't have one brown pigmentation.

She was so impressed with the results that she began selling. Dr. Blumenthal insisted that she have additional training.

That training was the basis for a lifelong pursuit.

Tola, who is blind, originally sponsored over 90 percent of the Elysee representatives and is still very active today.

During her telephone interview, she explained proudly, "I do my skin evaluations by touch."

Her husband Hy, recently eighty-five, is her eyes. He takes orders and fills them.

They work as a team. After sixty-two years of marriage, they have their system down pat.

Tola feels very strongly that multi-level marketing gives people with disabilities every chance to have a successful career.

She has been involved with Elysee for forty-seven years.

Concerning Tola, Elysee remarks, "Where else could you be seventy-eight years old, totally blind, and living in a retirement home, and earn over forty thousand dollars per year?"

Tola's motto is: "When love and service work together, expect a masterpiece." ■

WIN WITH TEN

Spotlight is on: Barry Borthistle

Company: Enrich International

When Joined: 1992

Level of Achievement: Presidential

Size of Organization: 800

Barry Borthistle's genuine, people-loving disposition has helped him to become a very successful Enrich Distributor. Barry has been shaking things up in his neck of the woods—Vancouver, British Columbia.

Although a veteran of network marketing, Barry started his Enrich organization from scratch. In just eight short months, Barry created an organization of over eight hundred people.

Barry said three things attracted him to Enrich: first, the company had been in business sixteen years, demonstrating strong corporate stability; second, the compensation plan was the best he'd ever seen; and third, Enrich sold consumable products that worked.

Barry's tremendous success and the example he has set for other distributors is based on a business philosophy that promotes long-term stability and growth, not only for him but for his organization as well. Barry puts in the time to make sure that others—not just members of his own organization—succeed.

According to the Borthistle Philosophy, the networking business is, first and foremost, a retail business. "The products have to be retailed."

"We have developed a strategy called 'win with ten,' and that is if a distributor establishes ten retail customers and just one of those ten retail customers becomes a distributor within a month, then you replace the one. And if that new distributor goes out and does what you've done and gets ten customers and one of those ten becomes a distributor, then they replace one. Well, if that process is carried out to the end of a year, you would have 2,048 Distributors serving 20,480 customers. That's how you deal with network marketing."

So far, Borthistle's strategy is right on target. He has experienced steady growth of between 20 and 25 percent each month since he began, and he anticipates the same for years to come. Enrich is proud to have distributors like Barry Borthistle representing it in the field. ■

KEEP BUSINESS IN FLOW WITH LIFE

Spotlight is on: **Jarman Massie**

Company: **Light Force**

When Joined: **1982**

Level of Achievement: **Master Diamond Director**

Size of Organization: **4,037**

Before his career with Light Force, Jarman Massie was a professional dancer and before that a pro tennis player. When asked why he turned to network marketing, Jarman shared his feelings freely.

"I'm involved in network marketing because it's in alignment with my purpose in life, which is to be the best I can be and help others to be the same, in terms of mind, body, and spirit, in terms of health and prosperity.

"This business allows me a total and complete expression of who I am–who I want to be for the rest of my life. I get to do, and to be, and to have everything I want through network marketing."

According to Jarman, the biggest challenge for capable people is being successful enough early on. Many people leave before they realize the fruits of their efforts.

"For me personally, you have to be doing this business for a higher purpose. When you're approaching it that way, you're sustained. You're successful from day one. My father and sister died of cancer, so health is part of my purpose. Light Force is enabling me to do my work in health. I am successful because I am working and living my purpose."

When asked about his key to success Jarman responded, "This business is in flow with my life. I don't do my life through the business. I do the business through my life. I'm a very physical person. I like to have fun. I think of the things I want to do most in my life and I go out there and do them. I meet people who are already having fun–like-minded people. I attract people who are on that same level.

"My success isn't tied up in financial goals. And I'm not saying the money isn't welcome or useful. I'm saying that the money came as a result of living and working the way I wanted, not the other way around.

"I've learned to sponsor fewer people and spend more time with them, work with them more intensely, more completely. I move in with them.

"Most of all, I have fun." ■

MORE OF A PLEASURE THAN A JOB

Spotlight is on: Sylvia Westrom

Company: Lite & Rite

When Joined: 1988

Level of Achievement: Ruby Director

Size of Organization: 716

In the four years since she began networking, Sylvia has shown the endurance, stability, and concern for the individuals in her organization which is indicative of a pure motive. She has proven time and again her interest is helping the other person be successful–even at personal expense.

When asked when she first knew that she would succeed with the business, Sylvia remembers, "I wasn't really working the plan, but I received a check from the sales of one of my downline and wondered what might happen if I really pursued the opportunity. Now I look at it as more of a pleasure than a job."

No one ever becomes an orphan in Sylvia's group. She sets out an immediate network of communication with each new distributor sponsored into her organization. She accepts it as her responsibility to make sure they know the marketing plan and how to build their own personal group. She equips her new business associates with the tools they need to be successful–developing ideas beyond what is even provided by the company–with monthly newsletters and in-depth essays describing the products and program.

Sylvia also supplies product through the company's transfer program and instructs each new Director how to assume leadership for his/her own group.

Finally, Sylvia is always in touch with the company and is knowledgeable with all the latest pertinent information. She has her own 800 information and ordering hotline, so her organization members call her first when they have questions or needs.

It is easy to see how Sylvia Westrom and other distributors like her have formed a true alliance with the Lite & Rite company. Sylvia has taken the Lite & Rite Mission as her own.

Endurance, stability, and concern are qualities to emulate for success. "I hope the concept of network marketing spreads and grows so people like me can make a living. I'm a single mother and once thought I'd need food stamps to survive." ■

COMMITMENT FOR THE LONG TERM

Spotlight is on: Robert and Roberta Alston

Company: Melaleuca, Inc.

When Joined: 1991

Level of Achievement: 6-Star Diamond

Size of Organization: 4,765

Robert and Roberta are Melaleuca's 1992 Marketing Executives of the Year and are the only 6-Star Diamond Executives in Melaleuca. From their home in Winter Park, Florida, they are tremendous leaders for Melaleuca in the South and have personally enrolled three Diamond Executives. They currently have more than four thousand people in their downline.

The Alstons earned more than one hundred thousand dollars in their first twelve months and have received many of the top honors available, including a trip to Hawaii as part of the businesses comprising the 1991 President's Club. They have also been part of Melaleuca's prestigious Executive Leadership Council six times.

Robert was a stock broker for seventeen years and was used to analyzing business opportunities. About five years ago, he looked into another multi-level company, but was turned off by some difficulties imposed by their structure. He says, "Then my brother-in-law showed us the Melaleuca opportunity, and we were very impressed by many things. First, he had taken two weeks to prepare a very professional presentation. My interest and confidence in the program was piqued, and his continued help presenting to prospects after I signed up got us off to a very quick, strong start."

"Secondly, we appreciated the fact that the

initial investment was very low and no inventory was required. If you tell someone that they can start their own business for twenty dollars and the paperwork is taken care of, why wouldn't anyone do it?

"I was immediately impressed by the all natural products, the reasonable prices, and the marketing plan which did not require deliveries or paperwork," states Roberta. "But now that we are both full-time networkers, I see many other wonderful benefits. For instance, it is very exciting and rewarding to know that anyone that comes into our organization has the ability to do much better than we have. Everyone can achieve whatever level of success that they want. It just takes a commitment for the long term." ∎

OVERCOME YOUR FEAR

Spotlight is on: Lawrence and Mary Lou Booker

Company: The Nanci Corporation

When Joined: 1989

Level of Achievement: Diamonds

Size of Organization: Minimum of 12 Qualified Legs

Lawrence and Mary Lou Booker, from Moundridge, Kansas, think that being distributors for The Nanci Corporation has turned their lives around. Only a few short years ago, Lawrence suffered a heart attack and lost his company at the same time. Shortly after that, they heard about Nanci's opportunity and joined.

From Nanci: "This couple signed up in the Nanci business and promptly went through the experience of having their upline and downline quit the business.

"Finding themselves on their own, they decided to come to a convention, like the one we have every year, to find out if the Nanci business was for real.

"For over two years, they floundered around with no direction or real prospects for success. Then, in January of this year ('92), they made some quality decisions, and their lives changed."

They started in February as Ambassadors, but by the end of February they were Bronze. They went Silver in March, Gold in April, qualified the second month as Gold in May, and the third month as Gold in June.

Now they are Diamonds and reached 100 percent qualification for the cruise, plus a day and night at the Doral Saturnia Spa.

Their fantastic achievement in such a brief period of time–overwhelming enthusiasm, positive spirit, diligence, and organizational ability certainly qualify them for this spotlight on success.

When asked about their success and advice to others, Mary Lou credited "keeping in touch with people and letting them know you care. Of course we have weekly meetings for the overall group and monthly meetings for Ambassadors and up."

According to Lawrence, "The biggest challenge is overcoming your fear of talking to people, particularly strangers. The old saying is: Inch by inch it's a cinch, yard by yard it's hard."

Both of them, commenting on networking, said, "It's the way to go!" ∎

ONE PERSON CAN MAKE A DIFFERENCE

Spotlight is on: Mark and Rene Reid Yarnell

Company: Nu Skin International

When Joined: 1986

Level of Achievement: Blue Diamond

Size of Organization: 35,000+

Mark and Rene Reid Yarnell have built a thirty thousand person downline as independent distributors for Nu Skin International. They have also received the American Dream Award from the Howard Ruff Company and have published two books and numerous audio tapes on the subject of network marketing. The couple currently resides in Reno, Nevada.

Mark writes, "It was my belief that one person can make a difference in this world that led me into the seminary in 1976, and subsequently into a decade of service as a Christian minister. After ten frustrating years in that field, I finally determined that in America wealth tends to be an adult's 'report card' and I exited the ministry to begin a new career in MLM."

Mark found his ability to make a difference was greatly enhanced by his association with MLM, rather than the other way around. His advice to anyone wanting to succeed in life is to set goals bigger than you are. "By creating goals bigger than ourselves, such as succeeding at MLM in order to fund a project for street people, we are setting in motion some very quantifiable principles."

Mark and Rene have proof that what they believe is true. "When we create a goal bigger than ourselves as a basis for an MLM activity, there is a tendency to work more diligently because others less fortunate are dependent on the outcome. In 1972, it took me four months to raise five thousand dollars in order to start my own company. In 1991, it took me less than four days to raise $185,000 for the lady in Michigan who needed a bone marrow transplant operation."

In January 1992, Rene and Mark took a two-week tour of New Zealand that turned into an adventure trip. They created a corporation which will take thirty people a month on breakthrough adventures for the purpose of overcoming their fears while bungee jumping, glacier climbing, and white water rafting. Not surprisingly, a good portion of each adventure will be spent helping the participants create altruistic goals as a necessary prelude to substantial wealth. ■

EACH YEAR BIGGER THAN THE YEAR BEFORE

Spotlight is on: Dayle and Jeannine Maloney

Company: Nutrition For Life

When Joined: 1985

Level of Achievement: Triple Diamond Executive

Size of Organization: 15,000+

Dayle Maloney first became involved with network marketing in 1983. Since then, he has increased his earnings each year. Yet to look at Dayle's comfortable lifestyle today, one would never guess the trials and misfortunes he has overcome.

Struck down by polio at the age of 18, Dayle was told he would never walk again. Determined not to succumb to this crippling disease, Dayle lay in his hospital bed formulating the first of many business ventures.

Within a year, Dayle became the youngest person ever to own a Dairy Queen franchise. From there, he went on to become a feature writer for an established midwest newspaper. Next, he set sales records in the recreational vehicle industry, owned his own RV dealership and travelled the country doing motivational speaking. Eventually he found his niche in network marketing.

But before Dayle could begin earning his millions, he would have to endure the fear and humiliation of a horrendous $350,000 debt. No one can say success came easy to Dayle.

Today, as a Triple Diamond Executive in Nutrition For Life, Dayle possesses important knowledge about choosing a winning company. "For anyone looking to earn a solid income in network marketing, they must pay close attention to the marketing plan *and* the product line," Dayle explains. "I have witnessed at least a half-dozen marketing program enhancements, introduced by company principles, all designed to benefit the distributors. Our product line is ideal because, number one, they are consumable products, and number two, people buy them because they want to, not because they have to."

Continuing, Dayle stressed, "Look for a firm with innovative ideas, one that will keep pace with the times and not be afraid to step out where others won't."

In 1985, Dayle's yearly income in commissions and bonuses totalled $53,568. By 1988 that figure rose to $240,224. In 1991, his income passed the $600,000 mark, and his estimated earnings for 1993 exceed $700,000.

Dayle fully expects to bring home a cool million in 1994. "This kind of steadily increasing success can be yours, too. Just choose your company carefully, then never, NEVER give up. ∎

VALUE BASED LEADERSHIP WORKS

Spotlight is on: Linda Reese Young & Dr. Jay Clark

Company: Oxyfresh USA, Inc.

When Joined: 1986

Level of Achievement: Regional Directors

Size of Organization: Not Available

In late 1986, when Linda Reese Young joined Jay Clark's dental practice, a patient introduced them to Oxyfresh products. The results were so positive that they started recommending Oxyfresh to all their patients. After nine months of success, they decided to go to a company sponsored seminar and learn more about the business opportunity Oxyfresh offered. That move changed their lives.

Linda recounts, "We learned about a company that deals 20 percent with product and 80 percent with people. The philosophy of Oxyfresh is to affect one person at a time in a positive way."

Now Jay and Linda work their networking business full-time. They are one of ten Regional Directors for the company and as Linda says, "We have the financial freedom to do what we want, live where we like, and pursue a life we respect."

Jay adds, "The quality of life can be measured by the quality of the relationships you have with other people. To test that out, remember back to the most wonderful experiences you've had in your life. There's someone you've shared them with.

"What prevents most of us from having a truly abundant life is all the stuff that's in the way: having to struggle with money, working two or three jobs, etc. People who are free can live richer, more abundant lives. I've never experienced or known about in any way a more powerful vehicle to achieve the kind of freedom where richly rewarding relationships can grow than in network marketing.

"It is often said, 'it's always too soon to quit in this business.' This is where good sponsoring comes in. Linda and I agree to accept accountability for the success of the people we sponsor into our business. One of the first things we do is help them establish realistic earnings expectations and develop a plan for when and how they will achieve them."

Linda stresses, "We believe in value based leadership. That means not living a life of 'shoulds' and unconditional acceptance free of judgments, assessments, and arbitrary opinions."

From Jay, "We've added two important features to our strategy. You have to refine listening skills and then put fun into the equation." ∎

LOOK FOR RISK AND EVALUATE POTENTIAL

Spotlight is on: Bob Waller

Company: Quorum International

When Joined: 1989

Level of Achievement: National Marketing Director

Size of Organization: Not Available

Bob Waller is a recent convert to network marketing. He spent sixteen years in banking, including seven years as president and chief executive officer of two banks that he started. His formal education includes a degree in marketing and a Masters degree in banking and finance. "So you see, my training was in the area of risk analysis of business entities, which gave me strong insight into the reasons that businesses either fail or succeed," says Bob when he reflects on his career move.

"After being introduced to MLM through the use of the product and seeing the tremendous market potential of the environmental products industry, I applied my strict guidelines of business success factors to an in-depth look at the company. The areas I reviewed included the history of the company, management, market share, competition and penetration in the marketplace, product quality, manufacturing capabilities, financial condition, marketing strategy, and the company's compensation plan."

After being satisfied with the results of his study, Bob remembers his first visit to the company plant, where he met Jay Martin, the President. "What I found was one of the best run and most financially sound companies that I had ever seen." His advice for those looking at multi-level opportunities is basic. "An investment decision involves only two basic criteria: risk and potential. After my logical look at MLM, I could see that the real risk was my desire and commitment to achieve financial independence."

Bob joined MLM in January and in eleven months had reached the National Marketing Director level. "I was able to earn as much in my first year as in my best years in banking, which was over six figures."

His final comments are equally to the point. "If you truly have a desire to own your own business without all the risks and overhead expenses usually involved and a way to have financial independence with the flexibility to start part-time, take an objective look at a company that can provide all that!"

Bob has been happily married twenty-four years and has three sons: twelve, sixteen, and twenty. Are they future multi-level marketers? Probably! ■

I'LL NEVER FORGET THAT FIRST NEW CAR

Spotlight is on: Margarita Gerritsen

Company: Shaklee U.S., Inc.

When Joined: 1972

Level of Achievement: Lifetime Master Coordinator

Size of Organization: 150 Sales Leaders

Margarita Gerritsen now lives in a beautiful home in Monterrey Park, California, but it wasn't always that way. In 1972, she was clearing cafeteria tables part-time, her children were not eating properly (one was in poor health), and her husband was in and out of jail. During her two-hour bus ride, she never dreamed of going into business for herself, much less being rich.

One day a co-worker told Margarita about Shaklee vitamins that might improve her child's health. Sensing that Margarita couldn't afford them, she gave her some. "You know, I make quite a bit of extra money selling Shaklee. There's a way for you to make some, too" her friend said.

Margarita's response was typical. "Who, me? I'm too shy, I don't know how to talk to people and I've never sold anything."

But she did it. She summoned up the courage to start knocking on doors in her neighborhood, and she soon had a group of clients and others like herself that she brought into the company. One month later she quit her job, and the following month Margarita's sales reached six thousand dollars. Within twelve months she qualified for her first bonus car. A year later she bought her first house. Reflecting on her hard times, Margarita says, "I remember how we were evicted repeatedly because we couldn't pay the rent. I'll never forget the hardships and the humiliation I suffered from being poor and from being on welfare."

In 1991, her nineteenth year, Margarita earned $332,000 and has earned eight cars since that first Maverick, including the Lexus she now drives. She pursues her active business with the help of a male secretary and a housekeeper, while her son handles her real estate investments. Speaking of that first car, she says, "It symbolizes the rise from squalor to success. I'll never forget the smell of that brand-new car." ■

PRESIDENT OF FUN

Spotlight is on: Ann and David Feinstein

Company: Sunrider International

When Joined: 1986

Level of Achievement: Master Directors

Size of Organization: 3,800

Six years ago, Ann and David made a collage treasure map depicting where they wanted to go together in life. Then they made sure every move fit into that scheme.

"It's a dream come true to find a business to which we could commit our hearts. What started in 1987 as a part-time effort sharing Sunrider's Philosophy of Regeneration, which combines health, fitness, and beauty products with friends, family, and business associates, has grown into a multi-national network of 3,800 distributors in the U.S., Israel, and Europe. We felt so good we couldn't keep our mouths shut," says Ann.

The business began evenings in their New York City studio apartment and weekends at the dining room table in New Jersey. "I knew we had to set the time aside to begin networking or it would have never gotten started," says Ann. With David's cooperation and support, eighteen months later, Sunrider became Ann's full-time pursuit.

"Building our Sunrider business has given me the chance to utilize the many sides of my personality and talents: my personal thirst for health, nutrition, and fitness. Having succeeded in the big pressure corporate world, I found myself becoming a prisoner of a forty story office building, working more than sixty-five hours a week building someone else's wealth. I came to realize there had to be a better life than that."

David supports Ann and their leadership team by teaching MLM bookkeeping, accounting and taxation seminars, and handles an integral part of the business by planning, scheduling, and organizing the meeting/seminars and potluck gatherings.

Recently, the Feinsteins served on Sunrider's Executive Advisory Board, were key in Sunrider's entry into Israel, and helped obtain Kosher certification for many of Sunrider's foods.

Ann proclaims, "Now I have a plaque on my desk that says: Ann R. Feinstein President of Fun!"

With David's office and the new Sunrider Center in the penthouse and their apartment a few floors below, they now work, travel, and play together. "This is our definition of a home-based business in New York City." ■

SHOW GOOD ETHICS AND LEADERSHIP

Spotlight is on: Jan D'Agostino

Company: Uni-Vite (Vi-Tality Products)

When Joined: 1988

Level of Achievement: Executive Director

Size of Organization: 1,216

Jan D'Agostino of Spokane, Washington, is a full-time Executive Director with UniVite, USA, marketers of the Micro-Diet and other nutritional products. This is Jan's first experience in network marketing and she's been with UniVite for four and a half years. Before that, she spent fifteen years as a bartender and has also owned a beauty salon. Jan currently earns just over $100,000 annually.

Jan believes multi-level marketing is the greatest opportunity in the history of the world. "I'm involved in network marketing because I didn't have to go to college and get a degree to have the income I'm having now. And, it's a no-risk business. It sure beats the $55,000 I had to invest in my beauty salon just to open the doors. What's more, it's fun.

"When I first started, I didn't understand multi-level well enough to explain it clearly to my family and friends. Then I made it my business to educate myself. I attended many training seminars, and I've probably read every book there is on multi-level and heard every tape five or more times. I needed to establish a comfort zone for myself with people because many other people and companies had tarnished the reputation of the business. Once I learned the truth for myself, I could get that across to other people. I truly, absolutely believe in my industry, my company, my product, and myself. That is my number one key to success."

When she talks about her current techniques for bringing others into UniVite, Jan says, "I not only sponsor, I teach. Sponsor and teach; sponsor and teach; sponsor and teach. I'm always there for my people. However strange or unexpected their questions may be, they are their questions and I'm there to answer them.

"I show good ethics, good leadership. I stand with my people and help them grow. And, I probably, no, I actually put them before me. When they get their dreams and their success, mine just happens.

"You cannot succeed in this business if you aren't honest. You can't do it. Network marketing rewards you for having honesty, integrity, and caring. And, you don't have to crawl over people to get to the top, either." ■

PRIDE IS HARD TO HIDE

Spotlight is on: Ed and Sue Williams

Company: Watkins

When Joined: 1980

Level of Achievement: Triple Diamond Gold Master

Size of Organization: 3,133

Ed and Sue Williams joined Watkins because they fell in love with the products. After attending Watkins 1981 convention, they decided to get serious and work the Watkins business. Ed and Sue say, "It was just about the best decision we ever made."

By 1984, they were able to purchase their dream home with an in-ground swimming pool and a new mini-van—all with cash. They add, "This is something that we just could not have done on Ed's former salary of thirty-five thousand dollars as a food service salesman." After just three years with Watkins, Ed and Sue had achieved financial independence. This year, they earned six times his former salary.

Ed and Sue have thoroughly enjoyed Watkins all expense paid vacations to Hawaii, London, the Bahamas, Portugal, Africa, and Spain—totalling over seventeen exciting free vacations since getting serious about Watkins in 1981.

When discussing successful selling, Ed and Sue say, "A product presentation without a demonstration is merely a conversation." They teach that in order to sell Watkins products, a good sales person must believe in as well as use the products. He or she must know both the features and benefits of each product. With the consistent quality in the Watkins entire product line, that's not hard to do. They say, "Be proud of that consistent quality. Watkins pride is truly hard to hide."

When it comes to motivating their downline, Ed and Sue firmly believe in a quote from Zig Ziglar, "You can have everything in life you want if you help enough other people get what they want."

This means promoting a team spirit: helping with that first party or helping with that first sponsorship, being available to answer questions, phoning key people on a regular basis and helping them organize their meetings, and recognizing and rewarding those who have done an outstanding job selling, sponsoring, and training.

Ed and Sue say, "What a company! The best!"

■

SELECTED COMPANIES UNDER FIVE YEARS OLD

The following thirteen companies represent a small sampling of the one to two thousand multi-level marketing start-ups estimated to have appeared since 1988.

In order to be included here, the editors looked at companies founded since 1988. Industry experts were polled for their recommendations. This list is certainly not extensive, and exclusion of any company does not implies that a company is deficient

The purpose of this section is to give the reader a quick overview of these fledgling companies. Anyone interested in any of the companies listed here can contact the company directly for samples and literature, or request more information by circling the appropriate number on the Reader Service page, and Upline Financial Press will provide clearinghouse services at no charge.

In each case, a short History lists the founders or officers and year founded. The Type of Plan refers to the marketing plan or compensation package offered. This could be Matrix, Unilevel or Stairstep/Breakaway, as described in the Glossary for MLM Terms. Association Membership can be either MLMIA or DSA, or both. The Initial Investment gives the fee that is required to become a distributor, and does not apply in all cases. The Product Line is a thumbnail sketch of the goods and services currently being marketed.

Finally, due to the tendency of multi-level companies to expand quickly, information about Foreign Markets could change rapidly.

A•DORA

P.O. BOX 528, BELLEVILLE, IL 62222-0528
618-236-2728 VOICE
618-236-2826 FAX

History *Founded in 1991 by Jim Rompel, President.*

Type of Plan *Unilevel*

Association Membership *N/A*

Initial Investment *N/A*

Product Line *Facial fluid that is designed to replace a range of products including moisturizers, beauty creams, sunscreens, anti-aging creams, and make-up bases.*

Foreign Markets *N/A*

BODY WISE INTERNATIONAL, INC.

6350 PALOMAR OAKS CT., SUITE A, CARLSBAD, CA 92009

619-438-8977 VOICE
619-438-9033 FAX

History *Founded in 1989 by Thomas T. Tierney and Ray W. Grimm, Jr.*

Type of Plan *Stairstep Breakaway*

Association Membership *MLMIA*

Initial Investment *$29.95*

Product Line *Nutritional systems designed for weight management, addressing cholesterol concerns, enhancing energy potential, and promoting general good health.*

Foreign Markets *N/A*

E. EXCEL INTERNATIONAL, INC.

1530 NORTH MOUNTAIN SPRINGS PARKWAY, SPRINGVILLE, UT 84663

801-489-4588 VOICE
801-489-4489 FAX

History *Founded in 1989 by Dr. Jau-Fei Chen, a scientist dedicated to nutritional immunology.*

Type of Plan *Stairstep Breakaway*

Association Membership *N/A*

Initial Investment *N/A*

Product Line *Herbal food products esspecially designed to strengthen the immune system. E. Excel also manufactures a line of personal care, skin, and hair maintenance products, along with a line exclusively for healthcare professionals.*

Foreign Markets *Canada, Australia, New Zealand, Thailand, Taiwan, France, Japan, Korea, and Malaysia*

ENHANCED LIVING INTERNATIONAL

1122 SOUTH 900 EAST, PROVO, UT 84606

801-375-4420 VOICE

801-375-4443 FAX

History *Subdivision of Trysan Research, Inc., founded in 1989 to develop and market purification equipment.*

Type of Plan *Stairstep Breakaway*

Association Membership *N/A*

Initial Investment *$24.95*

Product Line *Water purification, nutritional supplements, and extended shelf life dehydrated foods designed to enhance food values.*

Foreign Markets *Canada*

ENVIRO-TECH INTERNATIONAL

6600 WEST CHARLESTON, SUITE 125, LAS VEGAS, NV 89102

702-870-7878 VOICE

702-870-5899 FAX

History *Founded in 1991.*

Type of Plan *Modified Stairstep/Breakaway*

Association Membership *MLMIA*

Initial Investment *$34.95*

Product Line *Dri-Wash N Guard is a waterless car wash and protective glaze that can be applied to metal, glass, chrome, formica, and painted surfaces.*

Foreign Markets *Canada, Mexico*

FIRST FITNESS INTERNATIONAL, INC.

15944 MIDWAY ROAD, DALLAS, TX 75244

214-715-2900
214-715-2925 FAX

Independent
Distributor

History *Founded in 1989 by Lee Causey, President and Nigel Branson, Executive Vice President.*

Type of Plan *Stairstep Breakaway on Retail*

Association Membership *MLMIA*

Initial Investment *$29.00 Starter Kit*

Product Line *Health, beauty, and nutritional products including Lee Causey's Nutritional Cakes, Slim N Up, Fit to a Tea, Vital Green, Trimbolic, Iron Lady, First Relief, Delta State, Theracine, Bionic Tonic Megafit Tabs, and Biomega 2000.*

Foreign Markets *N/A*

MXM ESSENTIAL FORMULAS, INC.

2785 MITCHELL DRIVE, WALNUT CREEK, CA 94598

510-937-0300 VOICE
510-906-8600 FAX

History *Founded in 1992 by Andlinger & Co.*

Type of Plan *Stairstep Breakaway*

Association Membership *DSA*

Initial Investment *N/A*

Product Line *A full line of nutritional supplements including vitamins, fiber drinks, and an antioxidant complex, and personal care products for the skin and hair and a*

Foreign Markets *N/A*

NATURAL WORLD INCORPORATED

GLENBROOK INDUSTRIAL PARK, 652 GLENBROOK ROAD, STAMFORD, CT 06906

203-356-0000 VOICE

203-961-8646 FAX

History *Founded in 1991 by Austin O. Furst, Jr. and Janice K. De Long with the goal of developing and distributing naturally based personal care and household products.*

Type of Plan *Stairstep Breakaway*

Association Membership *DMA, DSA, and Humane Society*

Initial Investment *$19.95*

Product Line *Full line of household, nutritional, and personal care products designed to be environmentally safe.*

Foreign Markets *Targeted for 1994*

NATUS CORPORATION

4445 WEST 77TH STREET, MINNEAPOLIS, MN 55435

612-835-4626 VOICE

History *Founded in 1989 by Kate Billings.*

Type of Plan *Stairstep Breakaway*

Association Membership *N/A*

Initial Investment *$24.95*

Product Line *Aroma therapy products based on 100 percent natural essential oils made from flowers, trees, herbs, and plants such as Botanical Glycerin Bar, Touch of Jasmine Body Oil, Ylang Ylang Body Pampering Emulsion, and Intensive Sports Oil.*

Foreign Markets *N/A*

OMNITRITION

P.O. BOX 11640, CARROLLTON, TX 75008
214-446-1024 VOICE

History *Founded in 1989 by Roger Daley and Jim Fobair with over 40,000 distributors and $100 million in sales.*

Type of Plan *Stairstep*

Association Membership *DSA, MLMIA*

Initial Investment *N/A*

Product Line *Nutritional, dietary drinks and cookies, vitamins, herbal teas, and personal care products.*

Foreign Markets *Canada and Mexico*

OUR SECRET CREATIONS, INC.

155 NORTH SAN VICENTE BLVD., BEVERLY HILLS, CA 90211
213-852-4896 VOICE

History *Founded by Anita and Brian Reichenberg in 1982 and went MLM in 1990.*

Type of Plan *Stairstep Breakaway*

Association Membership *MLMIA*

Initial Investment *N/A*

Product Line *Hand-cut and polished, flawless zirconia in blue-white and colors representing all gemstones, jewelry, and Total Image Program of European anti-aging products under Kevis patent for hair, nails, and skin.*

Foreign Markets *N/A*

Outback Secrets International

6518 LBJ Freeway, Suite 105, Dallas, TX 75240

214-770-0077 Voice

History *Founded February 1993; product first available June 1993; well capitalized, Outback Secrets entered the Canadian market 124 days after it was founded in the U.S.*

Type of Plan *Unilevel*

Association Membership *N/A*

Initial Investment *$35 U.S.; $55 Canada*

Product Line *100% pure Emu Oil; Koala Komfort Back Cushion; Emu Oil Facial Cream; Emu Oil After Shave Moisturizer; Emu Oil Hand and Body Lotion; Tea Tree (melaleuca tree) Oil Antiseptic; Pet Care Antiseptic Cream*

Foreign Markets *Canada*

Quorum International

8777 East Via de Ventura, Suite 188, Scottsdale, AZ 85258

602-951-5885 Voice

History *Founded in 1991 by Doug Ridley, President.*

Type of Plan *Stairstep Breakaway*

Association Membership *N/A*

Initial Investment *$45.00 Starter Kit*

Product Line *Home, auto, and personal security devices, including the Immobilizer which disconnects vital auto electrical systems, Elert Personal Portable Alarm, Brace Door Protector, and PAAL personal attack alarm.*

Foreign Markets *Canada*

BOOKS, TAPES, VIDEOS AND ORGANIZATIONS

Following is a list of books, newsletters, newspapers, audio tapes, videos, and seminars which can help you in both choosing a multi-level marketing company to work with, and in becoming successful with an opportunity once you have made a selection. Some business-oriented books of a more general nature are included because, though they are not specifically oriented towards network marketing, large numbers of network marketers have found them to be an invaluable aid to building their business.

Due to space limitations, the following list is a sample from the total material available, and telephone numbers and addresses aren't included. Some of the material listed can be found in your local book store, but, since some of the material may be more difficult to find, Upline Financial Press, Inc. has compiled a more extensive list, including telephone numbers and addresses. If you would like a free copy of the full list, circle number 20 on the Reader Service page or write c/o Upline Financial Press, 8 Church Street, Suite 109, Montclair, NJ 07042. There is no charge for this service.

NEWSLETTERS AND MAGAZINES
Downline News, 6x, 18 pgs, newsletter
FreEnterpri$e, 12x, 150 pgs, magazine
Market Wave, 10x, 12 pgs, newsletter
Money Maker's Monthly, 12x, 60 pgs, tabloid
Netword Hotline, 10x, 8 pages, newsletter
Opportunity Connection, 6x, 100 pgs, magazine
Upline, 12x, 32 pgs, journal (No connection to
    Upline Financial Press)

BOOKS
Debbie Ballard
    How to Succeed in Your Own Network
        Marketing Business
Mario Brossi and Joseph Marino
    Multilevel Marketing: A Legal Primer
Dale Carnegie
    How to Win Friends and Influence People
George Clason
The Richest Man in Babylon
Joseph W. Coon
    The $even Secrets to Success in Network
        Marketing

Stephen R. Covey
    The 7 Habits of Highly Effective People
Don Failla
    How to Build a Large Successful MLM
        Organization
Mark Fisher
    The Instant Millionaire
John Milton Fogg
    The Greatest Networker in the World
Michael Gerber
    The E Myth
Barbara Sher and Annie Gottlieb
    Teamworks!
Napoleon Hill
    Think and Grow Rich
James Hume
    The Sir Winston Method
John Kalench
    Being the Best You Can Be in MLM
    How to Start, Run, and Stay in
        Business
    The Greatest Opportunity in the History of
        the World
Liz Kearney and Michale Bandley
    MLM Is Big Business
Gregory and Patricia Kishel
    Build Your Own Network Sales Business
    How to Start, Run, and Stay in Business
Peter B. Kyne
    The Go-Getter
Maxwell Maltz, M.D.
    Psycho-Cybernetics
Og Mandino
    The Greatest Salesman in the World
    The Greatest Success in the World
    Mission: Success
Beverly Nadler
    Congratulations... You Lost Your Job!
Robert Natiuk
    The Power of Inner Marketing
John Niednagle
    Success in M.L.M.
Dr. Norman Vincent Peale
    The Power of Positive Thinking
Price Pritchett, Ph.D.
    You^2
Paul Zane Pilzer
    Unlimited Wealth

Jan White-Ruhe
  Pour Yourself a Cup of Ambition
Tom ("Big Al) Schrieter
  Big Al Tells All
  Big Al's Turbo MLM
  How to Build MLM Leaders for Fun & Profit
David J. Schwartz, Ph.D.
  The Magic of Thinking Big
Gini Graham Scott, Ph.D.
  Get Rich Through Multi-Level Selling
  Success in Multi-Level Marketing
  Building a Winning Sales Team
D. Jack Smith
  MLM Laws in All 50 States
David Stewart
  Network Marketing—Action Guide for
    Success
  The Network Marketers Guide To Success
    (with Jeffrey Babener)
Randy Ward
  Winning the Greatest Game of All
Dennis Windsor
  Financially Free
Dexter Yager
  Everything I Know at the Top I Learned at
    the Bottom
  Millionaire Mentality
  Don't Let Anyone Steal Your Dream
Mark Yarnell
  Should You Quit Before You're Fired?
  Power Multi-Level Marketing (with
    Kevin McCommon)

AUDIO AND VIDEO TAPES

John Kalench
  Your Fast Track to MLM Success (V)
James B. Lawrence, CPA
  Tax Advantages for the Self Employed (V)
Network Productions
  Network Marketing—Turning Dreams Into
    Reality (V)
Tom "Big Al" Schreiter
  Live In London (A)
Randy Stoltz and Greg Stewart
  Network Marketing Vs. Pyramids
David Stewart
  Network Marketing in Action (V)
Success In Action
  Network Marketing in Action (V)
Bob Waller
  The Giant Awakens (V)
Randy Ward
  T.N.T.—Total Network Training (A)

Doris Woods
  Here's Doris..."No Hype, Just How!" (A)
Mark Yarnell
  Time Poverty: The Great American Epidemic
  The Battle for Success (both A)
Bob Waller
  The Giant Awakens (V)

PROGRAMS

Burke Hedges and the INTI Staff
  The Networking Dynamics Program
John Kalench and Millionaires in Motion
  The Master Prospector Kit
  The Start of Something Big

TRADE ORGANIZATIONS, CONSULTANTS, ATTORNEYS, AND INFORMATION SOURCES

TRADE ASSOCIATIONS

Direct Selling Association (DSA)
Multi-Level Marketing International
  Association (MLMIA)

CONSULTANTS AND PLAN EXPERTS

Business Underwriters International
  Harvey Jai Austin
Len Clements
Creative Communications and Research
  Gini Graham Scott, Ph.D.
International Multi-Level Consultants, Inc.
  Debbi A. Ballard
Millionaires in Motion
  J. Kalench, T. Williams, J. Michael Palka
MLM International
  Joe Hardwick
Network Marketing Investigative Services
  Corey Augenstein
Sheffield Resource Group
  Michael L. Sheffield
Success in Action
  David Stewart

ATTORNEYS

Babener and Orcutt
  Jeffrey A. Babener
D. Jack Smith

INFORMATION SOURCES

Food and Drug Administration
Freedom of Information Act
Dun & Bradstreet
Standard & Poors

INDEX

INDEX

SURVEY AND NOMINATION BALLOT

MAKING A GOOD THING BETTER

When we first visualized this book it was with two groups in mind. First, the millions of men and women who are or will be involved with Network or Multi-level Marketing. With the explosive growth MLM is experiencing, and is poised to continue experiencing, the public needs an objective reference-quality resource that can be turned to for help and advice. People will have varying needs—some people want to study MLM before considering an offer to get involved, others want to learn more about this "new fangled thing" a loved-one is doing, still others will already be out building successful networking businesses and simply want an outside body of information to share with downlines and prospects.

Name:_____
Street:_____
City:_____
State/Zip:_____,_____
Phone:(_____)_____

SURVEY SECTION
(please use separate piece of paper if necessary):

What I liked best about the book:

What I liked least about the book:

NOMINATION SECTION
(please use a separate piece of paper if necessary)

I nominate the following individual or couple for a Spotlight On Success profile:
Nominee's name:_____
Nominee's MLM company:_____
Years in MLM:_____ Approximate size of nominee's organization:_____

Reason Nominated:

I nominate the following MLM *company, or individual networker, for the following award (Please, only one nomination per response for both the corporate and individual awards. Explanations of each award are on pages166-167):*

CORPORATE AWARD NOMINATION:
Name of company nominated:_____
Years in business:_____
Nomination for (check one) __Environmental Responsibility __Community Service__Outstanding Newcomer
Reason for nomination:

INDIVIDUAL AWARD NOMINATION:
Name of individual or couple nominated:_____ Nominee's MLM Company:_____
Nomination for (check one):__Lifetime Achievement__Leadership__Free Enterprise
Reason for nomination:

PLEASE FEEL FREE TO MAKE PHOTOCOPIES OF THIS PAGE!

Mail completed to: Upline Financial Press, Inc., 8 Church Street, Suite 109, Montclair, NJ 07042